PRACTICAL CALCULUS
FOR
HOME STUDY

SIR ISAAC NEWTON (1642–1727)

(From Newton's Principia, Third Edition, 1726)

Nature and Nature's laws lay hid in night:
God said, "Let Newton be!" and all was light.
Alexander Pope.

I don't know what I may seem to the world, but, as to myself, I seem
to have been only as a boy playing on the seashore, and diverting myself in now and then finding a smoother pebble or a prettier shell than
ordinary, whilst the great ocean of truth lay all undiscovered before me.
Sir Isaac Newton.

PRACTICAL CALCULUS

FOR

HOME STUDY

BY

CLAUDE IRWIN PALMER

Late Professor of Mathematics and Dean of Students
Armour Institute of Technology

FIRST EDITION
FIFTEENTH IMPRESSION

McGRAW-HILL BOOK COMPANY, INC.

NEW YORK AND LONDON

THE MAPLE PRESS COMPANY, YORK, PA.

PREFACE

During the many years in which the author has been in close contact in his classes and through his books with men desirous of gaining facility in applying the principles of mathematics, requests have constantly come to him for a simple, practical treatment of the ideas considered in the calculus. Many men without college training have need for a working knowledge of the calculus and its practical applications, but there has been no book available that could give them the essentials of the subject without the assistance of an instructor.

This book aims to meet that need. It aims to give the man with limited mathematical training the ability to make use of the calculus as he needs it in his work.

To this end the explanations are detailed and complete. The fundamental questions of the calculus are repeated again and again so that they may be thoroughly impressed upon the mind of the student, and many illustrations and analogies are included to assist the student in grasping the essentials of the subject. The text avoids involved mathematical terminology and phraseology wherever possible.

In the treatment of different problems the differential is used much more than is usual because it enables the student to visualize problems more easily. Many examples which involve the writing of differential equations of scientific and engineering problems are included.

An important feature of the book is the fact that it brings out as early as possible the many helpful uses of the calculus.

While the emphasis in this treatment of the calculus is upon the practical applications of its principles—while the explanations are as non-technical as possible—the accuracy of precise mathematical methods has not been sacrificed. The development of the subject as here presented may be *non*-mathematical but it is not *un*-mathematical. For this reason, and because of the large number of solutions given, the engineer who is occasionally applying the calculus he learned in college will find the book valuable as a reference and review book. And the man with limited mathematical training, it is hoped, will secure from it a thorough understanding of what the calculus is, when to use it and how.

The author takes this opportunity to express his indebtedness to the many engineers who responded to his request for applications of the calculus, and to acknowledge the assistance of his colleagues, Professors W. C. Krathwohl and W. L. Miser, in revising the manuscript and reading the proof of the book.

C. I. PALMER.

ARMOUR INSTITUTE OF TECHNOLOGY,
    CHICAGO, ILL.,
      February, 1924.

A WORD TO THE STUDENT

"Do not imagine that mathematics is hard and crabbed, and repulsive to common sense. It is merely the etherealization of common sense."

LORD KELVIN.

Here as in my "Practical Mathematics" I am not talking to any particular class of men, but to engineers and all others who have any occasion to use calculus, and so desire an elementary knowledge of the subject. The language we use is chosen with the thought that it may be understood by such men. Of course technical mathematical terms cannot be avoided but the endeavor is not to use them when unnecessary.

The incentive to the writing of this text has come mainly from men who have studied the author's "Practical Mathematics" and who in numerous instances have urged a continuation of the work. Most of that was written with the constant encouragement of the student in the class room where questions and suggestions smoothed out many difficulties. This continuation of that work is written mainly to an absent audience but always with these former students in mind. It is therefore adapted to men with the preparation of those who have pursued the author's "Practical Mathematics" and others having sufficient mathematical training.

Since it is not possible for all concerned to meet in the class room where questions can be asked and explanations made, correspondence with the author is urged whenever it will tend to clear up obscure matters or will lead to bettering the presentation of the subject.[1] This will bring

[1] Correspondence of this nature may be addressed to Clark F. Palmer, 6440 Greenwood Ave., Chicago, Ill.

the writer and the reader into more personal and helpful relations. The author is aware that this is an unusual statement to make and will burden him with much correspondence, but the helpfulness to the reader who has no other means of getting assistance will make the extra labor worth while. Then, too, past experience has shown that the letters received from the reader are of great assistance to the writer in bettering future editions of the text. In other words, the desire is that we should all feel that we are working together to make this most useful branch of mathematics, the calculus, better understood and more readily applied by practical men.

These pages are, then, written for the practical man who, perhaps, has not had the advantage of even a high school training; but has, by home study and reading, gained a considerable knowledge of mathematical subjects. Such a man knows that a working knowledge of any subject in mathematics cannot be gained with ease. He knows from bitter experience that many months of hard work are necessary to master a great new piece of machinery in mathematics. To him it is unnecessary to say that each idea as it is presented must be thoroughly understood, and the manner of expressing these ideas in mathematical language must be mastered.

It is a fact that it is almost impossible to proceed very far into any branch of technical science without coming up against the calculus. In attempting to avoid calculus more time is often spent in solving a problem in some roundabout way than by fairly meeting it with the aid of calculus. It is true that correct results may often be derived by such methods, but they are time wasters. A man may travel from Chicago to New York by railroad or he may go afoot. He usually takes the train as it is quicker and more direct. The calculus is the quickest and most direct way of solving many problems. The man accustomed to making generalizations with its aid will not be content to use forms of special cases. When he has once mastered its fundamental principles, though he may not make direct use of them once a year, he has a decided advantage in the use of formulas from the fact that he understands the process of their derivation.

The great thing to be desired is for one to appreciate what calculus really is, to understand its fundamental principles, and to realize what a powerful tool it is in formulating the laws of nature. One should be able to read the books and papers in which the language of calculus is used, to understand the processes by which the formulas in common use are derived, and to use his mathematical knowledge in the solution of ordinary problems that may arise. Whether he will make use of his knowledge in his later work is another question. Certainly he cannot use knowledge that he has not gained. If a tool becomes dull and rusty with disuse it can be sharpened and polished in case of need.

One should not allow himself to be lured on merely because a subject is represented as easy; but he should assure himself that every problem that he attacks, whether it be easy or difficult, has a useful purpose, in that it will contribute in some measure to the perfecting of his mathematical equipment. The subject of calculus cannot be made *easy* but it can be made *plain*.

The tiresomeness of studying alone is accentuated in the case of calculus. Hours of perplexity over some obscure point could be avoided if a few words of help were obtainable. The greatest source of difficulty for the student, whether he is studying alone or with a teacher, is his lack of preparation for the work. A large proportion of the time that the average college student gives to the calculus is really spent in reviewing his previous mathematics. The student studying alone soon finds that he must have a better knowledge of logarithms than he gained from his previous study, that his algebra must be reviewed, that he must have a thorough understanding of fractional and negative exponents, and be as familiar with trigonometric formulas and functions as with the multiplication table.

It will often happen in certain places that the author is not understood, and the question is what is to be done. The natural tendency of the student, and especially of one studying alone, is not to hurry away from a difficult passage. The personal pride that does not like to acknowledge defeat, and the strong will that cannot endure to give up, both urge to continued effort; but often it is better to withdraw the thought from the subject for a time, and endeavor to determine wherein the difficulty lies. The mind may be fatigued due to long application or the preliminary matter may not have been read with sufficient care. After rereading the passages leading up to the subject causing the trouble one can often return to the pursuit and gain the desired end. To emphasize this the following quotation is given from the preface of Chrystal's "Algebra."

"Every mathematical book that is worth reading must be read 'backwards and forwards,' if I may use the expression. I would modify Lagrange's advice a little and say, 'Go on, but often return to strengthen your faith.' When you come on a hard or dreary passage, pass it over; and come back to it after you have seen its importance or found the need of it further on."

CONTENTS

CHAPTER V

CURVES AND THEIR EQUATIONS

CHAPTER VI

PROBLEMS IN MAXIMA AND MINIMA

CHAPTER VII

CHANGES IN QUANTITIES. DIFFERENTIALS

CHAPTER VIII

RATE OF CHANGE. SPEED, VELOCITY, ACCELERATION

CHAPTER IX

INTEGRATION

CHAPTER X

TRIGONOMETRIC FUNCTIONS

CHAPTER XI

LOGARITHMIC AND EXPONENTIAL FUNCTIONS

CHAPTER XII

THREE IMPORTANT TYPES OF FUNCTIONS

CHAPTER XIII

CURVATURE, TANGENTS, NORMALS

CHAPTER XVI

ARC LENGTHS. AREAS OF SURFACES

CHAPTER XVII

VOLUMES

CHAPTER XVIII

FUNCTIONS OF SEVERAL VARIABLES. PARTIAL DIFFERENTIATION

CHAPTER XIX

Double and Triple Integration. Surfaces, Volumes

CHAPTER XX

Center of Gravity. Moment of Inertia

CHAPTER XXI

Further Applications of Integration

CHAPTER XXII

Series. Taylor's Theorem

CHAPTER XXIII

ANALYTIC GEOMETRY

PRACTICAL CALCULUS
FOR HOME STUDY

CHAPTER I

FUNDAMENTAL IDEAS

1. It is a recognized fact in all walks of life, and it is certainly thoroughly ingrained in mathematical science, that every real advance goes hand in hand with the invention of sharper tools and simpler methods. The tools of calculus are surprisingly effective and the methods are very efficient, but familiarity with the tools and ability in using the calculus cannot be gained by listening to talks on its wonders or reading about its applications. A general survey, however, helps one to appreciate the subject. Then, if he realizes that each individual must build for himself his own mathematical machinery in order to be able to use it effectively, he is ready to proceed.

Every boy knows that he cannot learn to skate by sitting on the bank and watching the others skate; but he can learn some things about how he should handle himself to be a successful skater. Then, too, the performance of a skilful skater may be interesting to him and make him more determined to master the art of skating. Here it may be of interest and to some degree instructive, to consider a simple problem where calculus is used in the solution. Such a problem can readily be selected in chemistry, electricity, mechanics, or from any one of many sources. Let us select one that can be easily understood by anyone and discuss it at some length.

Illustrative example. Suppose a ladder 40 ft. in length rests with one end on the ground and the other against a building. We will suppose that the ground is level and that the wall of the building is perpendicular to the ground. It is required to find the rate at which the upper end of the ladder will descend along the wall if the lower end of the ladder is pulled out along the ground at the rate of 2 ft. a second.

You may say that this is not a practical problem; but, at least, we will all agree that it is a more or less interesting question. Now, how can the question be answered and what tools shall we use? Let us first think over the relations of the numbers involved in the problem. We can easily visualize the ladder resting against the building and so do not need to draw a figure. In the picture we have in mind we see a right-angled triangle having the ladder as hypotenuse, the ground as base, and the building as altitude. We can connect with the picture the following numbers:

(1) The length of the ladder, the hypotenuse, is 40 ft. and is a constant value.

(2) The distance the foot of the ladder is from the building, the base, is a variable as the ladder is moved. It may be represented by x.

(3) The distance from the ground to the top of the ladder, the altitude, is a variable. It may be represented by y.

(4) The rate at which the foot of the ladder is moved is 2 ft. a second and is constant.

(5) The rate at which the top of the ladder is moving down is evidently a variable, and it is this that we wish to find.

In thinking the question over with the picture in mind we probably feel quite certain that the top of the ladder is moving down slowly when the foot of the ladder is near the wall, and gradually moves faster and faster as the foot of the ladder is moved at a uniform rate further from the wall. If this is so, let us find the rate at which the top is moving down just at the instant when the foot of the ladder is 10 ft. from the wall, also when it is 20 ft. from the wall, and when it is 30 ft.

In any such problem we first express the number of which the rate of change is to be found in terms of the other numbers. This gives

$$y = \sqrt{40^2 - x^2}.$$

At this point in the solution the machinery of calculus must be used, and while the step is as easy as multiplication, it may seem a mystery. Nothing is omitted in the work here, and the process is as simple as writing when one learns how to do it.

$$\frac{dy}{dx} = \frac{-2x}{2\sqrt{40^2 - x^2}} = -\frac{x}{\sqrt{40^2 - x^2}}.$$

The symbol $\frac{dy}{dx}$ represents the relation between the rate of change of y and the rate of change of x, and we may read it "the relative rate of change of y to x." That is, if y changes one-half as fast as x, then $\frac{dy}{dx} = \frac{1}{2}$; if three times as fast, $\frac{dy}{dx} = 3$.

To find the value of $\frac{dy}{dx}$ for any particular value of x, all we have to do is to put that value of x in the place of x in the expression $-\frac{x}{\sqrt{40^2 - x^2}}$.

When $x = 10$, $\frac{dy}{dx} = -\frac{10}{\sqrt{40^2 - 10^2}} = -\frac{10}{\sqrt{1500}} = -0.2582$.

The minus sign means that y is decreasing in length as x is increasing; and, since the decimal is about $\frac{1}{4}$, y is decreasing about one-fourth as rapidly as x is increasing, or at a rate of about $\frac{1}{2}$ ft. a second. More nearly, the rate at which y is decreasing or the rate at which the top of the ladder is moving down at the instant when the foot of the ladder is 10 ft. from the building is

$$0.2582 \times 2 \text{ ft. a second} = 0.5164 \text{ ft. a second.}$$

To answer the question when the foot of the ladder is 20 ft. from the building, we substitute 20 for x; and when the foot of the ladder is 30 ft. from the building, we substitute 30 for x.

When $x = 20$,

$$\frac{dy}{dx} = -\frac{20}{\sqrt{40^2 - 20^2}} = -\frac{20}{\sqrt{1200}} = -0.57735.$$

Then the top of the ladder is moving down at the rate of
$$0.57735 \times 2 \text{ ft. a second} = 1.1547 \text{ ft. a second.}$$

When $x = 30$,

$$\frac{dy}{dx} = -\frac{30}{\sqrt{40^2 - 30^2}} = -\frac{30}{\sqrt{700}} = -1.134.$$

Then the top of the ladder is moving down at the rate of

$$1.134 \times 2 \text{ ft. a second} = 2.268 \text{ ft. a second.}$$

In a similar manner the rate at which the top of the ladder would be moving as the foot of the ladder was moved further and further away could be computed. It would be found to move more and more rapidly until the instant when the foot of the ladder was 40 ft. from the building, when the relations we dealt with in the triangle would cease to exist, and the fraction $\dfrac{x}{\sqrt{40^2 - x^2}}$ would have zero in its denominator, which is the algebraic way of telling us that everything is called off.

In following through the discussion of the preceding problem the reader has not gained any ability to use calculus. That can only come from systematically developing the machinery of calculus, and this will require the most careful study for months.

Numerous examples of the applications of calculus are found in succeeding lists of exercises, but the main effort in this text is to develop the methods of calculus so that they can be applied in whatever field one may be working. In applying mathematics we should always keep in mind two things: first, one must be thoroughly familiar with what he is working; and second, he must be able to use the necessary mathematics.

The following problems could as readily be discussed as the ladder problem and are given here to show somewhat the class of problems considered in calculus:

A wheel is rolling along a straight track. What are the horizontal and vertical velocities of a point on the wheel when in any position with reference to the track?

A circular path around a garden is lighted by an arc light placed over the center of the garden. What is the height of the light above the ground to give the greatest illumination on the path?

What are the dimensions of a beam of rectangular cross section of greatest strength that can be cut from a given log?

A certain number of electric cells are used to give a current in a telegraph wire of known resistance. How shall they be connected to give the greatest current?

Find the work done by a gas expanding in a cylinder with a movable piston.

Find the work done in pumping out a cistern in the form of a frustum of a cone.

Areas and volumes of various shapes can be readily found though they are of forms that cannot be handled by ordinary geometry.

A torpedo shot under water has a speed of 75 ft. a second at the instant its compressed air is exhausted. Its retardation due to friction of the water is 4 ft. per second per second. How far will it move before coming to rest?

Find the total pressure on a vertical bulkhead of given dimensions at a given distance below the surface of the water.

2. Change is everywhere in nature and is manifest on every hand. We see it in growth and decay and in the movement of the heavenly bodies, and it is of the greatest interest to everyone from earliest infancy. Mathematics may or may not have anything to do with these changes. If a thing that is being measured changes in magnitude the number expressing the measure will change, that is, it is a *variable*. If we are to apply mathematics to such quantities and take note of the changes, we must have a scheme for handling variable numbers.

From the earliest times great difficulty was encountered when these variable quantities were considered in a mathematical way. Because of this difficulty it has always been customary to deal with a quantity as if it did not change when it was not absolutely necessary to take the change into consideration. For instance, the rate of a train in going from one station to another is a variable, but in many problems the average rate can be used, and this is a constant. Again a person's age is a constantly increasing quantity, but for convenience we call it a constant for periods of a year each. On the other hand, it may be of the utmost importance for one to be able to deal mathematically with the variation in the rate at which a body falls, or with the rate of change of the current in an electric circuit, or with the rate at which a chemical reaction is taking place.

In the more elementary branches of mathematics the numbers usually dealt with are considered as constants, that is they do not change in value; but the quantities with which we have to deal in life activities are, for the most part, in a state of change and often have to be dealt with as variables. In scientific work and engineering one is concerned very largely with quantities which vary. Here also the manner of variation is a consideration of primary importance. It is necessary then to have mathematical machinery to consider problems involving quantities that vary. The endeavor to invent such machinery went on for centuries and finally resulted in the invention of the calculus by Newton and Leibniz.

Up to this point we have made a general survey of the subject. In the next article a more formal statement is made about the content of calculus, after which we proceed with the development of the subject. The solitary student can master this only with great care in his study and by constantly reviewing whenever it is necessary.

3. Differential and integral calculus.—The subject of calculus is divided into two parts known as **differential calculus** and **integral calculus.** One of these is the inverse of the other.

Differential calculus is concerned with the rate of change of any quantity which changes or varies. In an intelligent discussion of any such question involving the finding or using the rate of change of a quantity, the ideas of differential calculus are involved. As a mathematical subject, differential calculus expresses these ideas in mathematical symbols and manipulates them in a definite and precise fashion. That is, the machinery of differential calculus handles these facts in a manner that is a great saving of time and mental energy.

Integral calculus deals with questions that are the inverse of those considered in differential calculus. That is, the fundamental question in integral calculus is: Given the rate of change of a quantity and the value of the quantity at some certain instant, to find the value of the quantity at any instant.

The machinery of calculus was developed during the latter half of the seventeenth century by Newton and Leibniz. They are said to have invented the calculus. By this it is meant that they invented the symbolic treatment of the ideas involved. But the fundamental ideas of calculus were as common before their time as after.

It is in the calculus that we find the greatest development of mathematical analysis and its applications in almost every field of science and engineering. Here, as is always the case in the study of mathematics, it is necessary to understand clearly *what* is under consideration and *how* it is represented in mathematical symbols.

4. Preparation for the study of calculus.—For the intelligent study of calculus one cannot know too well the more elementary subjects in mathematics. In writing this text the author has presupposed a knowledge of algebra, geometry, trigonometry, and analytic geometry. In order, however, to help those who are weak in these subjects or have not studied certain topics, frequent references[1] are given, and explanations made of operations that are likely to be unfamiliar. As a further assistance, some of the fundamental ideas of analytic geometry are given in **Chapter XXIII.** The reader who *knows* the subjects treated in the author's "Practical Mathematics" should be able to understand this text.

[1] Because of the very wide distribution of the author's "Practical Mathematics" among practical men, references are given as **P. M. I, II, III,** or **IV** when referring to the author's "Practical Mathematics" in Four Parts, Third Edition; and **H. S.** when referring to his "Practical Mathematics for Home Study," Second Edition.

5. Constants and variables.—From the statements of the previous articles it is seen that it is necessary to divide the numbers considered into two classes which are called constants and variables. (**P. M. II, Art. 114; H. S., Art. 314.**)

A **constant** is a number that retains the same value. Constants may be divided into two classes: First, those that always have the same value; and, second, those which have the same value in one problem or discussion, but may have another value in a different problem or discussion.

Examples of the first class are the numbers represented by the numerals, by π used to represent the ratio of the circumference to the diameter of a circle, and by e the base of the natural logarithms. (**P. M. IV, Art. 18; H. S., Art. 354.**)

Constants of the second class are numbers represented by letters in formulas where the same letter has a definite value during a discussion. In using the formula $A = \pi r^2$ in finding the area of a particular circle, both A and r are constant, while in dealing with a different circle, they will take different constant values.

A **variable** is a number that may take an indefinite number of values in the same problem or discussion.

If s stands for the distance a moving train is from a station it has left, then s represents a variable and takes all possible values from zero to the value it has when the train makes the next stop.

If p represents the price of a stock, then p may have many values during a month. Here, however, p will not take all the intervening values between the highest and lowest, but will change by jumps of a greater or less amount.

In the curve of the equation $3x + 4y = 12$, which is plotted in Fig. 1, and is a straight line, the values of both x

and y vary as we pass along the curve from left to right.
(**P. M. II. Art. 125; H. S., Art. 326.**)   Here both x and y
take all possible values both positive and negative.

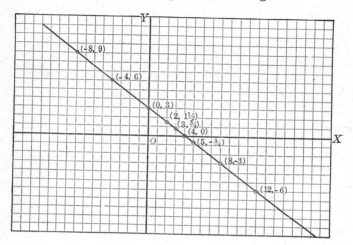

Fig. 1.

In these definitions and illustrations of the constant and
the variable, we have spoken of the number itself as the
constant or the variable.   Many writers, however, speak of
the *symbol* as the constant or the variable, and it will be
frequently so used in this text

EXERCISES

1. Think of ten problems that arise from conditions in real life.
How many of these involve variables?

2. A circular sheet of steel is being increased in size by increasing
its temperature.   Its area is given by the formula $A = \pi r^2$.   Which
are variables and which constants in the formula?

3. The distance that a body near the surface of the earth falls is
given by the formula $s = \frac{1}{2}gt^2$.   Which are variables and which constants in the formula?

4. The weight that a beam supported at both ends and weighted in
the middle will support is given by the formula $W = k\dfrac{bd^2}{l}$.   Which of
these numbers are variables?   (**P. M. II, Art. 119; H. S., Art. 320.**)

6. Functions.—When variables are dealt with it seems quite necessary to think of their relations to each other, that is, it is necessary to consider how a change in one affects another. This influence that variables have upon each other is an extremely important idea in life and must be expressed in a mathematical fashion if we are to deal with such matters in mathematics.

Suppose that the variables being considered are the number of hours that a man works and the total amount that he receives. Then evidently the amount that he receives depends upon the number of hours he works. If he receives $1.50 an hr., and A and h are respectively the total number of dollars he receives and the number of hours he works, then

$$A = 1.50h.$$

Here we say that A is a function of h.

Definition. When two variables are so related that for every value of one there is a corresponding value of the other, one variable is said to be a **function** of the other.

In the formula $s = \frac{1}{2}gt^2$, where s is the distance a body near the earth's surface will fall in time t seconds, and g is the constant acceleration due to gravity, s is evidently a function of t.

When we do not wish to express the exact relation between the variables, or when it is not known, the relation is written in a general form as follows:

(1) Using A and h with meanings already given, $A = f(h)$ means that A depends upon the value of h. It is read "A equals a function of h," or "A equals the f-function of h."

(2) If s is the distance that a train runs in t hours, then $s = f(t)$. This is true whether or not the rate is constant. If a variable rate r is also thought of, then $s = f(r, t)$. This is read "s equals a function of r and t."

Other letters besides f are used in writing functions. Thus, $y = F(x)$, read "y equals capital F-function of x." $y = g(x)$, $s = \varphi(y)$, etc.

Different letters are used to represent the functions when different relations exist between the variables. The same letter is used when the same relation exists though the variables are different. This will be explained more fully later.

The student should note that $f(x)$ does not mean f times x. In fact, f does not represent a number. Further, a student studying by himself should always be careful to read mathematical expressions of all kinds *exactly as they should be read*. He does not have the advantage of class drill with his fellow students and can very easily form bad habits in reading and writing the language of mathematics. This may greatly handicap him in all his future work in mathematics. Remember that *clear thinking can occur only when one has an exact language that is accurately expressed*.

7. Independent and dependent variables.—A variable that depends upon another for its value is called a **dependent variable.** The variable that it depends upon is called an **independent variable.**

It is evident that the dependent variable is a function of the independent variable. Frequently when two variables are related either may be taken as the independent variable and the other as the dependent.

Thus, if A and r represent the area and the radius, respectively, of a circle, A may be thought of as depending upon r, or r may be thought of as depending upon A. That is, if r be changed at pleasure a corresponding change will occur in A; or, if A be changed at pleasure, a corresponding change will take place in r.

In the former case $A = f(r)$, in the latter case $r = F(A)$. The exact functions that show these relations are

(1) $A = \pi r^2$,

(2) $r = \sqrt{A \div \pi}$.

It is evident that a variable may depend upon two or more independent variables. Thus, the area A of a triangle depends upon both the base b and the altitude h. That is, $A = f(b, h)$, and the exact relation is $A = \frac{1}{2}bh$. Here a change in either b or h, or in both b and h will produce a corresponding change in A.

8. Explicit and implicit functions.—When the equation is $y = f(x)$, that is, when the equation expresses y explicitly in tems of x, y is an **explicit function** of x.

Thus, in $y = 3x^2 + x$, y is an explicit function of x.

If two variables are involved in an equation in such a manner that it is necessary to solve the equation in order to express either explicitly in terms of the other, then either variable is said to be an **implicit function** of the other.

Thus, in $x^2 + y^2 = a^2$, y is an implicit function of x and x is an implicit function of y. If this equation is solved for y, $y = \pm \sqrt{a^2 - x^2}$, in which y is an explicit function of x. If solved for x, $x = \pm \sqrt{a^2 - y^2}$, in which x is an explicit function of y.

Such functions as $y = \pm\sqrt{a^2 - x^2}$, where for each value of the independent variable there are two values of the dependent variable, are called **double valued functions.** When for each value of the independent variable there is just one value of the dependent variable the function is said to be **single valued.**

Implicit functions involving x and y may be written $f(x, y)$, $F(x, y)$, $\varphi(x, y)$, etc.

In the same discussion or problem, the same functional symbol is used to represent the same function, that is, the same relation between the numbers.

Thus, if $\quad f(x) = 2x^2 + 3x + 1,$

then $\qquad\quad f(a) = 2a^2 + 3a + 1,$

and $\qquad\quad f(3) = 2 \cdot 3^2 + 3 \cdot 3 + 1 = 28.$

If $\qquad f(x, y) = 3x^2 + 4xy - y,$

then $\qquad f(2, 3) = 3 \cdot 2^2 + 4 \cdot 2 \cdot 3 - 3 = 33,$

and $\qquad f(y, x) = 3y^2 + 4xy - x.$

If $\qquad\quad \varphi(x) = \sin^2 x + \cos^2 x,$

then $\quad \varphi(30°) = \sin^2 30° + \cos^2 30° = (\tfrac{1}{2})^2 + (\tfrac{1}{2}\sqrt{3})^2 = 1,$

and $\quad \varphi(90°) = \sin^2 90° + \cos^2 90° = 1^2 + 0^2 = 1.$

EXERCISES

1. Write ten relations between variables and express each dependent variable as a function of the independent variable or variables.

2. Think of several related variables where you do not know the exact relations. In each case select the dependent variable and write as a function of the independent variables.

Suggestion. The amount that a stalk of corn will grow in 24 hr. depends upon the soil, temperature, moisture, sunshine, size of the stalk, etc.

3. Express the volume of a sphere as a function of its radius. As a function of its diameter.

4. Express the area of a right circular cylinder as a function of its radius and altitude.

5. Express the area of a square as a function of its diagonal. Express its diagonal as a function of its area.

6. Express the weight that a beam, supported at both ends and weighted in the middle, will support. Use the notation of exercise 4, p. 10. By solving the equation express each of b, d, and l in terms of the other letters.

7. Express the circumference of a circle as a function of the area of the circle.

Suggestion. Let C = the length of the circumference, r = radius, and A = area of circle.

Then $\qquad\qquad C = 2\pi r, \text{ and } r = \sqrt{\dfrac{A}{\pi}}.$

$\therefore \qquad\qquad C = 2\pi\sqrt{\dfrac{A}{\pi}} = 2\sqrt{A\pi}.$

8. Express the surface of a sphere as a function of the volume of the sphere.

9. Express the horsepower of an electric power machine as a function of the electromotive force and the current. (**P. M. II, Art. 89; H. S., Art. 288.**)

10. Express the resistance of a conductor of electricity as a function of its length and diameter if circular in cross section.

11. Given $x^2 + y^2 = 25$, solve for both x and y in terms of the other and express each as an explicit function of the other.

12. If $\varphi(x) = \sin x$, find $\varphi(0°)$, $\varphi(45°)$, $\varphi(240°)$, $\varphi(\sin^{-1} 1)$, $\varphi(\cos^{-1} \frac{1}{2})$, $\varphi(\tan^{-1} 1)$.

13. If $f(x) = x^3 + 3x^2 - 2x - 4$, find $f(0)$, $f(3)$, $f(-4)$.

14. If $f(x) = \log_{10} x$, find $f(100)$, $f(47.62)$, $f(0.012)$.

15. If $F(x) = \sqrt{x^2 + 1}$, find $F(0)$, $F(-3)$, $F(4\sqrt{3})$.

16. If $f(x, y) = 3x^2y + 4xy^2 - 2y^3$, find $f(-x, y)$, $f(x, -y)$, $f(-x, -y)$.

17. If $f(y) = 3^y$, find $f(x)$ and $f(x + y)$. Also prove that $f(x) \cdot f(y) = f(x + y)$.

18. If $f(x) = \sin x$ and $F(x) = \cos x$, prove that
$$f(x + y) = f(x) \cdot F(y) + F(x) \cdot f(y). \quad \text{(P. M., IV, Art. 85; H. S., Art. 424.)}$$

19. If $y = \sin x$, express x explicitly in terms of y. If $y = 2^x$, express x explicitly in terms of y.

9. Functions, variables, increments.—*Example* 1. If a suspended coiled wire spring has a weight attached to its lower end, the spring will be stretched. The amount of stretching will depend upon the weight, the greater the weight the greater the elongation. The elongation is then a function of the weight. If the weight is not so great that the elastic limit of the spring is reached, the elongation varies directly as the weight. The law connecting the variables is then stated by the linear[1] equation

$$y = kx,$$

where y is the elongation, x the weight, and k a constant. That is, y is a function of x, and a change in the variable x produces a corresponding change in y.

A change in the weight is called an **increment** of the weight, or an increment of x, and is represented by the symbol Δx (read "increment of x" or "delta x"). A corresponding change in the elongation is called an increment of the elonga-

---

[1] A **linear equation** is an equation of the first degree. Such an equation as the above plots into a straight line, hence the name.

tion, or an increment of y, and is represented by Δy.   The letter, Δ, is the Greek letter delta.

Here x represents the independent variable and y the dependent variable.   It is evident that for every Δx there is a Δy.   Their relation may be shown as follows:

For any particular value of x as x_1, $y_1 = kx_1$.   (1)

If $x = x_1 + \Delta x$, $y_1 + \Delta y = k(x_1 + \Delta x)$.   (2)

Subtracting (1) from (2), $\Delta y = k\Delta x$.

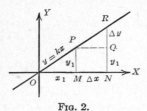

FIG. 2.

That is, Δy varies directly as Δx, and is independent of the value of x.   This is shown graphically in Fig. 2.   The locus of $y = kx$ is a straight line with slope[1] k. P is a point on this straight line with coördinates (x_1, y_1).

$MN = PQ = \Delta x$, and $QR = \Delta y$.

No matter what the magnitude of Δx,

$$\Delta y = \Delta x \tan QPR = k\Delta x.$$

Example 2.   The distance s that a heavy body near the earth's surface falls from rest in time t is given by the formula $s = \frac{1}{2}gt^2$.

If $t = t_1$, $s_1 = \frac{1}{2}gt_1^2$.   (1)

If $t = t_1 + \Delta t$, $s_1 + \Delta s = \frac{1}{2}g(t_1 + \Delta t)^2$.   (2)

Subtracting (1) from (2), $\Delta s = \frac{1}{2}g(2t_1\Delta t + \Delta t^2)$.

That is, the value of Δs depends upon both t and Δt. This is shown graphically in Fig. 3.

---

[1] The slope of a line is the tangent of the angle it makes with the positive x-axis.

The locus of $s = \frac{1}{2}gt^2$ is a parabola. The point P has coördinates (t_1, s_1), and Δt and Δs are as shown in the figure. It is evident from the figure that Δs depends upon both t and Δt, that is, the increment Δs is different for each value of t though Δt is kept the same, and it also varies with Δt when t is kept constant.

Numerical illustration. In example 2, suppose that $t_1 = 2$, that is, the instant under consideration is 2 seconds after the body begins to fall. Find the value of Δs when $\Delta t = \frac{1}{4}$. Use $g = 32$.

Solution. If $t = t_1 = 2$,

$$s_1 = \frac{1}{2} \times 32 \times 2^2 = 64.$$

This means that the body has fallen 64 ft. at the end of 2 sec.

If $t = t_1 + \Delta t = 2 + \frac{1}{4}$,

$$s_1 + \Delta s = \frac{1}{2} \times 32 \times (2\frac{1}{4})^2 = 81.$$

Subtracting, $\qquad \Delta s = 17.$

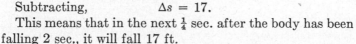

Fig. 3.

This means that in the next $\frac{1}{4}$ sec. after the body has been falling 2 sec., it will fall 17 ft.

It is evident that if $t_1 = 3$ and $\Delta t = \frac{1}{4}$, a different value of Δs will be found; also the value of Δs will be different if $t_1 = 2$ and $\Delta t = \frac{1}{3}$. Find that these values of Δs are respectively 25 and $23\frac{1}{9}$.

EXERCISES

1. If $y = 10x$ and x_1 is any particular value of x, find Δy when x_1 takes the increment Δx. Find Δy when $x_1 = 4$ and $\Delta x = 2$. Find Δy for any other value of x_1 and $\Delta x = 2$. Do the values of Δy change as x changes? Plot so as to show all these values graphically.

2. If a rectangle has an altitude that is constantly 4 in., and the base is changing, find the change in the area when the base changes $\frac{1}{2}$ in. If the area is A and the base is x, what is ΔA when $\Delta x = \frac{1}{2}$? Does ΔA vary with x?

3. If $y = 2x^2 + 1$ and $x = 2$, find Δy when $\Delta x = 0.5$. Find Δy when $\Delta x = 0.01$. Plot.

4. Express the area A of a square as a function of its side x. Find ΔA for $x_1 = 6$ and $\Delta x = 1$. Illustrate by means of a square.

This is illustrated in Fig. 4. The increment of the area ΔA is represented by the two rectangles and the small square. If the dimensions are in inches, the change in the area is 13 sq. in.

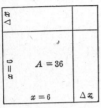

FIG. 4.

5. Express the area A of a circle as a function of its radius r. Find ΔA for $r = 10$ and $\Delta r = 0.5$. Illustrate by means of a circle.

6. If $y = \sin x$, find Δy when $x_1 = 30°$ and $\Delta x = 1°$. When $\Delta x = 1'$. When $\Delta x = 10''$. Under what conditions is Δy the tabular difference in a table of natural sines?

Note. In determining the value of Δy from the table of natural functions by interpolating only approximate values are found.

7. If $y = \sin x$, find Δy when $x_1 = 42°10'$ and $\Delta x = 1'$. When $\Delta x = 30''$.

8. If $y = \sin x$, find Δy when $x_1 = \frac{1}{4}\pi$ and $\Delta x = \frac{1}{8}\pi$.

9. If $y = \log_{10} x$, find Δy when $x_1 = 78.5$ and $\Delta x = 0.01$. When would Δy be the tabular difference if **Table VII** is used?

10. If $y = \dfrac{1}{x+1}$, show that $\Delta y = \dfrac{-\Delta x}{(x_1+1)(x_1+\Delta x + 1)}$.

11. If $y = \sqrt{a^2 - x^2}$, show that $\dfrac{\Delta y}{\Delta x} = -\dfrac{2x_1 + \Delta x}{2y_1 + \Delta y}$.

Solution. Given $y = \sqrt{a^2 - x^2}$.

Let $x = x_1$, $\qquad\qquad y_1 = \sqrt{a^2 - x_1^2}$.

Let $x = x_1 + \Delta x$, $\qquad y_1 + \Delta y = \sqrt{a^2 - (x_1 + \Delta x)^2}$.

Subtracting, $\qquad\qquad \Delta y = \sqrt{a^2 - (x_1 + \Delta x)^2} - \sqrt{a^2 - x_1^2}$.

Multiplying and dividing by $\quad \sqrt{a^2 - (x_1 + \Delta x)^2} + \sqrt{a^2 - x_1^2}$,

$$\Delta y = \frac{a^2 - (x_1 + \Delta x)^2 - (a^2 - x_1^2)}{\sqrt{a^2 - (x_1 + \Delta x)^2} + \sqrt{a^2 - x_1^2}}$$

$$= -\frac{2x_1\Delta x + \Delta x^2}{y_1 + \Delta y + y_1}.$$

$$\therefore \quad \frac{\Delta y}{\Delta x} = -\frac{2x_1 + \Delta x}{2y_1 + \Delta y}.$$

12. If $y = \dfrac{1}{x+1}$, find $\dfrac{\Delta y}{\Delta x}$ when $x_1 = 1$ and $\Delta x = 0.01$.

13. If a train goes m miles in t hours, what is the meaning of $\dfrac{m}{t}$, and of $\dfrac{\Delta m}{\Delta t}$?

14. If $s = 16t^2$ and $t_1 = 2$, find Δs and $\dfrac{\Delta s}{\Delta t}$ when $\Delta t = 1$; when $\Delta t = 0.1$; when $\Delta t = 0.01$; when $\Delta t = 0.001$. What value does $\dfrac{\Delta s}{\Delta t}$ seem to be approaching as Δt becomes smaller?

15. If $y = x^3$ and $x_1 = 1$, find Δy and $\dfrac{\Delta y}{\Delta x}$ when $\Delta x = 10$; when $\Delta x = 1$; when $\Delta x = 0.1$; when $\Delta x = 0.01$; when $\Delta x = 0.001$. What value does $\dfrac{\Delta y}{\Delta x}$ approach as Δx becomes small? What then is the slope of the tangent line at the point where $x = 1$ of the curve of $y = x^3$? Plot.

CHAPTER II

LIMITS

10. Illustrations and definitions.—Considerable use is made of limits in elementary geometry, trigonometry, and algebra; but much greater use is necessary in the study of calculus. The following are simple illustrations of limits:

(1) The variable which takes the successive values 1.3, 1.33, 1.333, 1.3333, · · · has as a limit $1\frac{1}{3}$. That is, the more figures there are taken, the more nearly the number approaches $1\frac{1}{3}$.

(2) The $\sqrt{2}$ is the limit of the successive values 1.4, 1.41, 1.414, 1.4142, · · ·. The diagonal of a unit square is the limit of the line lengths represented by this series of numbers.

(3) If a point starts at the end A of the line AB, Fig. 5, and during the first second, moves half the length of the line to C; during the next second, half the remaining distance to D; continuing in this way to move half the remaining distance during each successive second, then the distance that the point is from A is a variable of which AB is the limit.

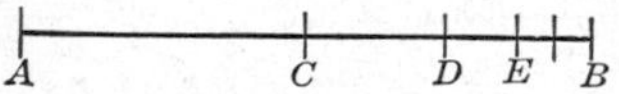

Fig. 5.

(4) If $y = \dfrac{12}{x + 2}$ and x is a variable approaching 2 as a limit, then evidently y is a variable approaching 3 as a limit.

Definitions. When a variable changes in such a manner that its successive values approach a constant so nearly

20

that the difference between the constant and the variable *becomes* and *remains* less, in absolute value, than any assigned positive number, however small, the constant is the **limit of the variable.**

The variable is said to *approach a constant as a limit.*

If the variable is represented by x and the constant by a, then the statement "x approaches a as a limit" is written thus, $x \rightarrow a$.

The form $\displaystyle\lim_{x \to a} [f(x)] = A$ is read "the limit of $f(x)$ as x approaches a as a limit is A."

When a variable changes in such a manner that it becomes and remains greater than any assigned positive number, however great, it is said to **increase without limit** or to **become infinite.**

The notation to represent this is $x \rightarrow \infty$, which is read "x increases without limit" or "x becomes infinite."

The form $\displaystyle\lim_{x \to \infty} [f(x)] = A$ is read "the limit of $f(x)$ as x becomes infinite is A."

When a variable changes in such a manner that it becomes and remains less than any assigned negative number, however great in absolute value, it is said to **decrease without limit** or to **become infinite negatively.**

The notation to represent this is $x \rightarrow -\infty$.

11. Limits of functions.—It is well to state here that it is not always easy to find the limit of a function. In fact, it is often difficult and requires the greatest ingenuity. In dealing with problems of limits in this text no elaborate methods can be developed. The student will then have to rely to a great extent upon his good sense and general knowledge. The following examples should be studied with the greatest care with the view of thoroughly appreciating the meaning of a limit, as well as seeing how one may arrive at the limit in a few simple cases.

Example 1.   What is $\displaystyle\lim_{x\to0}\left[\dfrac{2+x}{3-x}\right]$?

Here it is readily seen that as x approaches 0 as a limit
$$\frac{2+x}{3-x} \to \frac{2}{3}.$$

In such a case the limit can be found by letting x **equal** its limit, but this is not the manner it should be thought out.   The real meaning of the question is to find the value toward which $\dfrac{2+x}{3-x}$ tends as x takes a succession of values that approach 0.   For instance, let x take the series of values $1, \frac{1}{2}, \frac{1}{4}, \frac{1}{8}, \cdots$, and compute the corresponding values of $\dfrac{2+x}{3-x}$.   They are $\frac{3}{2}, 1, \frac{9}{11}, \frac{17}{23}, \frac{33}{47}, \frac{65}{95}, \frac{129}{191}, \cdots$.   And it is seen that this series is approaching more and more closely to $\frac{2}{3}$.

Example 2.   What is $\displaystyle\lim_{x\to0}\left[\dfrac{3}{x}\right]$?

Here, evidently, as x approaches 0 from the positive side, $\dfrac{3}{x}$ becomes and remains larger than any large positive number, that is, it increases without limit.

Then $\displaystyle\lim_{x\to0}\left[\dfrac{3}{x}\right] = \infty$.

If x approaches 0 from the negative side, the successive values of $\dfrac{3}{x}$ are negative, and then $\dfrac{3}{x}$ decreases without limit.

Example 3.   What is $\displaystyle\lim_{\theta\to\frac{1}{2}\pi}\left[\tan\,\theta\right]$?

Here, evidently, $\tan\,\theta$ increases without limit as θ approaches $\frac{1}{2}\pi$ from values of θ smaller than $\frac{1}{2}\pi$ and decreases without limit as θ approaches $\frac{1}{2}\pi$ from larger values.   It is evident, then, that $\tan\,\frac{1}{2}\pi$ has no numerical value.

Example 4.   What is $\displaystyle\lim_{x\to\infty} \dfrac{x^3 + x^2 + 1}{4x^3 + x - 3}\Big]$?

Here as x becomes very large it might seem that the fraction would approach no value because both numerator and denominator would increase without limit.   If, however, both numerator and denominator are divided by x^3

$$\frac{x^3 + x^2 + 1}{4x^3 + x - 3} = \frac{1 + \dfrac{1}{x} + \dfrac{1}{x^3}}{4 + \dfrac{1}{x^2} - \dfrac{3}{x^3}}.$$

Then as x becomes very large each of the fractions, $\dfrac{1}{x}, \dfrac{1}{x^3}, \dfrac{1}{x^2}$, and $\dfrac{3}{x^3}$ becomes very small and approaches 0 as a limit; and the value of the fraction approaches $\frac{1}{4}$ as a limit.

$$\therefore \lim_{x\to\infty}\left[\frac{x^3 + x^2 + 1}{4x^3 + x - 3}\right] = \tfrac{1}{4}.$$

Example 5.   What is $\displaystyle\lim_{x\to0}\left[\frac{\sin x}{x}\right]$, where x is in radians?

If $x = 0$, $\sin x = 0$ and $\dfrac{\sin x}{x}$ becomes $\dfrac{0}{0}$, which is meaningless.

If values of x near 0 are taken, the value of $\dfrac{\sin x}{x}$ will be found to approach 1 as a limit.   This will be dealt with in a different manner later.   (See **Art. 70.**)

EXERCISES

Carefully consider the following exercises and arrive at the limits given.

1. $\displaystyle\lim_{x\to0}\left[\frac{3 - 2x}{4 + x}\right] = \frac{3}{4}.$

2. $\displaystyle\lim_{\theta\to\frac{1}{2}\pi}[\sec \theta] = \infty.$

3. $\displaystyle\lim_{x\to\infty}\left[\frac{3x^2 + 2x - 1}{x^2 - x + 1}\right] = 3.$

4. $\displaystyle\lim_{x\to0}\left[\frac{\sin x}{x + 1}\right] = 0.$

5. $\displaystyle\lim_{x\to1}\left[\frac{3x^2 - 2x + 2}{x^2 - 2x + 1}\right] = \infty$

6. $\displaystyle\lim_{x\to\frac{1}{2}\pi}\left[\frac{x}{\tan x}\right] = 0.$

7. $\displaystyle\lim_{x\to\infty}\left[\frac{x^3 + 1}{2x^2 + 1}\right] = \infty$

8. $\displaystyle\lim_{x\to0}\left[\frac{\cos x}{x}\right] = \infty.$

12. Elementary theorems of limits.—The following theorems will be found useful in dealing with limits. They are given here without proof.

(1) If two variables that approach limits are equal for all their successive values, their limits are equal.

(2) The limit of the sum of a constant and a variable that approaches a limit is the sum of the constant and the limit of the variable.

(3) The limit of the product of a constant and a variable that approaches a limit is the product of the constant and the limit of the variable.

(4) If each of a finite number of variables approaches a limit, the limit of their sum is the sum of their respective limits.

(5) If each of a finite number of variables approaches a limit, the limit of their product is the product of their respective limits.

(6) If each of two variables approaches a limit, the limit of their quotient is the quotient of their limits, *except when the limit of the divisor is zero.*

If the limit of the divisor is zero, the limit of the quotient may have a definite finite value or the quotient may become infinite, but it is not determined by finding the *quotient of the limits* of the two variables. The calculus determines such limits as these exceptional cases.

$$R = \frac{\pi L}{A} = 10.4 X$$

$$R \, f(L, A)$$

Account Name	REPORT OF D
	Inches

-1212

Account Name	REPORT OF DA	
	Inches	

-1212

Account Name	REPORT OF D/ Inches	

-1212

		REPORT OF D.
Account Name		**Inches**

-1212

CHAPTER III

DERIVATIVES

13. The reader is again reminded that we are endeavoring to express in mathematical language the ideas and relations that occur in real life. Here the particular idea that is to be expressed mathematically is the relation between the rates of changes of related variables. Since variables can be related in a great variety of ways, various illustrations might be given. Before studying the mathematical treatment in the next article the following illustration should be thought through carefully.

In Fig. 6, suppose a point P is moving along the curve in the direction of the arrow. It is then moving upward and toward the right. At any position on the curve, we may think of the relation between its rate of movement upward and its rate of movement toward the right. For instance, at P_1 the point is moving upward about twice as rapidly as it is moving toward the right. As the point continues to move along the curve from P_1, it rises less rapidly compared with its motion

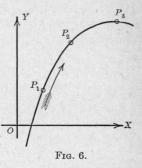

Fig. 6.

toward the right. When it is at P_2 it is rising about as rapidly as it is moving toward the right; and when at P_3 it is not moving upward at all.

The ratio of the upward rate of motion to the rate toward the right is 2 at P_1, 1 at P_2, and 0 at P_3.

25

Evidently between P_1 and P_3 may be found a position where the ratio of the upward rate to the rate toward the right has any value desired between 2 and 0.

Further, notice that the direction the point is moving is always in *the direction of the tangent line to the curve* for any

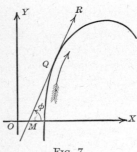

FIG. 7.

position of the point.   For instance, when the moving point is at Q, Fig. 7, it is moving in the direction of the tangent MR. It is also an important fact that *the ratio of the upward rate to the rate toward the right is equal to the tangent of the angle φ which the tangent line makes with the x-axis.*

Since the tangent of φ is the slope of the tangent line, this ratio equals the slope of the tangent line.

What is meant by the direction a point is moving at any instant when passing along a curve must be clearly understood.   It will help if one thinks of the direction an automobile is headed at any instant when moving on a curved road.   That is, in what direction would the automobile move if at any instant it should continue to move in the direction it is headed at that instant.

The direction along a curve at any instant is exactly determined by the derivative, which will now be discussed.

14. The derivative of a function.—The fundamental conception of differential calculus, and one that is of the greatest importance in mathematics, is the derivative of a function.   If y is a function of x, and if the notation for increments as previously given is used, the **derivative** is defined as the limit approached by the quotient $\dfrac{\Delta y}{\Delta x}$ as Δx approaches zero.

If the curve, Fig. 8, represents the function $y = f(x)$, the quotient $\dfrac{\Delta y}{\Delta x}$ is the slope of the secant line P_1P.

Now if P_1 remains fixed and Δx approaches zero as a limit, the point P moves along the curve approaching P_1 as a limit, and the secant P_1P turns about P_1 toward the limiting position QR, defined to be the **tangent to the curve** at the point P_1. Hence *the slope of the tangent is precisely the quantity called the derivative.*

It is evident that the value of the derivative depends upon the position of P_1 on the curve.

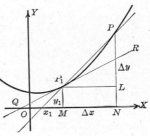

Fig. 8.

What has been said leads to the following definition: The **slope of a curve** at any point is the slope of the tangent to the curve at that point. That is, the direction of the curve at any point is the same as the direction of the line tangent to the curve at that point.

The notation for the derivative is $\dfrac{dy}{dx}$, read "the derivative of y with respect to x." By definition

$$\frac{dy}{dx} = \lim_{\Delta x \to 0}\left[\frac{\Delta y}{\Delta x}\right].$$

Of course the independent variable and the function may be represented by other letters. Thus $\dfrac{du}{dt} = \lim\limits_{\Delta t \to 0}\left[\dfrac{\Delta u}{\Delta t}\right]$.

The notation $\dfrac{dy}{dx}\Big|_{x=x_1}$ is used to indicate the value of $\dfrac{dy}{dx}$ for the particular value x_1 of x.

Example. Given $y = x^2$, find $\dfrac{dy}{dx}\Big|_{x=2}$, and thus find the slope of the tangent to the parabola $y = x^2$ at the point (2, 4).   Plot

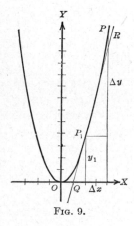

FIG. 9.

Solution.   (1) Given $y = x^2$.

(2) When $x = 2$,
$$y = 4.$$

(3) If x takes an increment Δx,
$$y + \Delta y = (2 + \Delta x)^2$$
$$= 4 + 4\Delta x + \Delta x^2.$$

(4) Subtracting (2) from (3),
$$\Delta y = 4\Delta x + \Delta x^2.$$

(5) Dividing by Δx,
$$\frac{\Delta y}{\Delta x} = 4 + \Delta x.$$

(6) Letting $\Delta x \rightarrow 0$,
$$\frac{dy}{dx}\Big|_{x=2} = 4.$$

Hence the slope of the tangent to the parabola $y = x^2$ at the point (2, 4) is 4.

The plotting is shown in Fig. 9.

EXERCISES

1. Given $s = 16t^2$, find $\dfrac{ds}{dt}\Big|_{t=2}$.   In exercise 14, page 19, the question was asked as to the value that $\dfrac{\Delta s}{\Delta t}$ seemed to be approaching as Δt became smaller, that is, as $\Delta t \rightarrow 0$.   Is $\dfrac{ds}{dt}\Big|_{t=2}$ this value?

2. Given $y = x^3$, find $\dfrac{dy}{dx}\Big|_{x=1}$.   Is this the value that $\dfrac{\Delta y}{\Delta x}$ seemed to approach in exercise 15, page 19?

3. If a point is moving along the curve of exercise 2, how many times as rapidly as it is moving toward the right is it rising when $x = 1$?   When $x = 4$?   When $x = 0$?   When $x = -2$?   Plot the curve and see if your results seem reasonable.

4. As in exercise 3, what is the value of x when the point is rising 27 times as rapidly as it is moving toward the right?   When 2 times as rapidly?   When 3000 times as rapidly?

Suggestion. Find $\dfrac{dy}{dx}$ for any value of x, put it equal to 27 and solve the equation for x..

5. Given $y = 2x^2 - 6$, find $\dfrac{dy}{dx}$ when $x = 3$. When $x = \sqrt{3}$. When $x = -\sqrt{3}$. Plot and find whether the curve is rising or falling in passing toward the right for each of these values of x.

TANGENTS AND NORMALS

15. Inclination and slope of a line.—In analytic geometry the **inclination** of a line is defined to be the angle it makes with the positive part of the x-axis; and the **slope** of a line is defined to be the tangent of the inclination. That is, if φ is the inclination and m is the slope of a line then

$$m = \tan \varphi.$$

The slope of a line through two points is readily found as follows: In Fig. 10, let $P_1(x_1, y_1)$ and $P_2(x_2, y_2)$ be two definite points on the line P_1P_2. Draw P_1Q parallel to OX, and QP_2 parallel to OY.

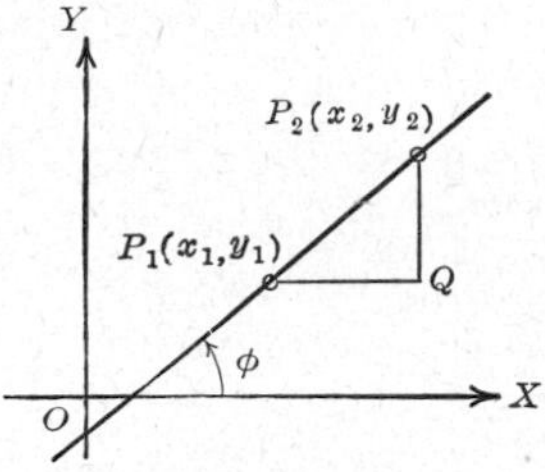

Fig. 10.

Then   angle $QP_1P_2 = \varphi$.

But $\tan QP_1P_2 = \dfrac{QP_2}{P_1Q} = \dfrac{y_2 - y_1}{x_2 - x_1}$.

$\therefore\ m = \tan \varphi = \dfrac{y_2 - y_1}{x_2 - x_1}$.

16. Equation of a straight line when the slope and a point on the line are known.—Since a straight line is completely determined when a point on the line and the direction of the line are known, these facts can be used in writing the equation of a line.

Let (x_1, y_1) be a definite point on the line and (x, y) be any other point on the line, also let m be the slope of the line, then the equation of the line is

$$\frac{y - y_1}{x - x_1} = m,$$

which may be written

[1] $$y - y_1 = m(x - x_1).$$

This is called the **point slope form** of the equation of a straight line.

Example. Find the equation of a line making an angle of 60° with the x-axis and passing through the point $(3, 5)$.

Here $x_1 = 3$, $y_1 = 5$, and $m = \tan 60° = \sqrt{3}$.

Hence the equation of the line is

$$y - 5 = \sqrt{3}(x - 3),$$ By [1].

or $$\sqrt{3}x - y + 5 - 3\sqrt{3} = 0.$$

17. Tangents and normals to curves.—In **Art. 15**, it is shown that the derivative can be used to find the slope of a line tangent to a curve. It follows from this and [1] that the equation of the tangent to the curve $y = f(x)$ at the point (x_1, y_1) is

[2] $$y - y_1 = \frac{dy}{dx}\bigg|_{x=x_1} (x - x_1).$$

Definition. The **normal to a curve** at any point of that curve is the line perpendicular to the tangent to the curve at that point.

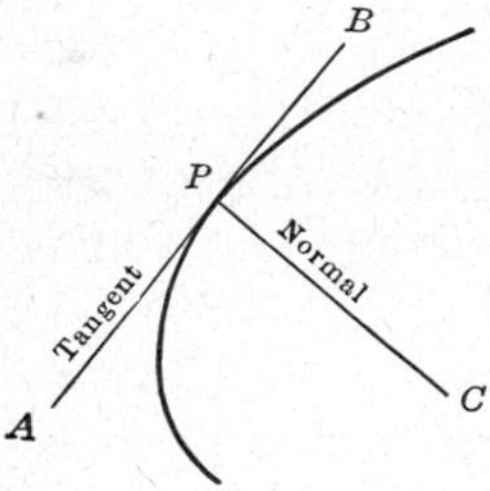

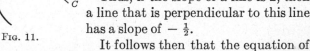

Now it is shown in analytic geometry that if two lines are perpendicular to each other, the slope of either is the negative reciprocal of the slope of the other.

Thus, if the slope of a line is 2, then a line that is perpendicular to this line has a slope of $-\frac{1}{2}$.

Fig. 11.

It follows then that the equation of the normal to a curve $y = f(x)$ at the point (x_1, y_1) is

[3] $$y - y_1 = -\frac{1}{\dfrac{dy}{dx}\bigg|_{x=x_1}} (x - x_1).$$

Example 1. Find the equations of the tangent and the normal to the curve $y = x^2$ at the point where $x = 2$.

Solution. First find $\dfrac{dy}{dx}\Big|_{x=2} = 4$ as in the solution of the example **Art. 15.**

If (x_1, y_1) is the point of tangency, $x_1 = 2$, and y_1 can be found by putting 2 for x in the equation of the curve. This gives $y_1 = 2^2 = 4$.

Then the equation of the tangent is

$$y - 4 = 4(x - 2), \qquad \text{By [2].}$$
or
$$4x - y - 4 = 0.$$

The equation of the normal is

$$y - 4 = -\tfrac{1}{4}(x - 2), \qquad \text{By [3].}$$
or
$$x + 4y - 18 = 0.$$

In Fig. 9, QR is the tangent. The normal is perpendicular to QR at P_1.

This method for finding the equations of the tangents and normals is the neatest and best that the machinery of mathematics gives. It also shows an important use of the derivative.

Example 2. Find the equations of the tangent and normal to the ellipse $4x^2 + 9y^2 = 36$ at the point (x_1, y_1). Also find these equations when $x_1 = 2$. Plot.

Solution. (1) Given $4x^2 + 9y^2 = 36$.

(2) Let $x = x_1$ and $y = y_1$. $4x_1^2 + 9y_1^2 = 36$.

If x takes the increment Δx, y will have the increment Δy, and

(3) $4(x_1 + \Delta x)^2 + 9(y_1 + \Delta y)^2 = 36,$
or $\quad 4x_1^2 + 8x_1\Delta x + 4\Delta x^2 + 9y_1^2 + 18y_1\Delta y + 9\Delta y^2 = 36$

(4) Subtracting (2) from (3),

$$8x_1\Delta x + 4\Delta x^2 + 18y_1\Delta y + 9\Delta y^2 = 0.$$

(5) Transposing and arranging, $\dfrac{\Delta y}{\Delta x} = -\dfrac{8x_1 + 4\Delta x}{18y_1 + 9\Delta y}$.

Passing to the limits and noting that $\Delta y \rightarrow 0$ as $\Delta x \rightarrow 0$,

$$\frac{dy}{dx}\bigg|_{x=x_1} = -\frac{4x_1}{9y_1}.$$

Substituting in [2], the equation of the tangent is

$$y - y_1 = -\frac{4x_1}{9y_1}(x - x_1),$$

or $\qquad 4x_1x + 9y_1y = 4x_1{}^2 + 9y_1{}^2.$

Since by (2) $4x_1{}^2 + 9y_1{}^2 = 36$ the equation of the tangent
is

$$4x_1x + 9y_1y = 36.$$

Similarly the equation of the normal is

$$y - y_1 = \frac{9y_1}{4x_1}(x - x_1).$$

When $x = 2$, $y = \pm \frac{2}{3}\sqrt{5}$.

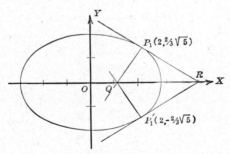

Fɪɢ. 12.

Substituting these values for x_1 and y_1 in the equation of
the tangent, the equation of the tangent at the point
$(2, \frac{2}{3}\sqrt{5})$ is

$$4{\cdot}2x + 9{\cdot}\tfrac{2}{3}\sqrt{5}y = 36,$$

or $\qquad\qquad 4x + 3\sqrt{5}y = 18.$

And the equation of the tangent at the point $(2, -\frac{2}{3}\sqrt{5})$ is

$$4{\cdot}2x + 9(-\tfrac{2}{3}\sqrt{5})y = 36,$$

or

$$4x - 3\sqrt{5}y = 18.$$

Likewise the equations of the normals are, at the point $(2, \frac{2}{3}\sqrt{5})$,

$$9\sqrt{5}x - 12y = 10\sqrt{5};$$

and at the point $(2, -\frac{2}{3}\sqrt{5})$,

$$9\sqrt{5}x + 12y = 10\sqrt{5}.$$

The plotting is shown in Fig. 12.

EXERCISES

Write the equations of the lines through the given points and having the given slopes or inclinations.

1. Point $(2, 3)$, slope 1.

2. Point $(-2, 7)$, slope 2.

3. Point $(3, 2)$, slope -2.

4. Point $(-4, -1)$, slope $-\frac{1}{3}$.

5. Point $(-1, 5)$, slope $\frac{4}{5}$.

6. Point $(3, 4)$, inclination $45°$.

7. Point $(-2, -1)$, inclination $120°$.

8. Point $(4, -2)$, inclination $30°$.

9. Find the slope of the tangent and the normal to $y = 4x^2$ at the point where $x = 0.5$.

10. Given $y = x^2 + 2$, find $\dfrac{dy}{dx}\Big|_{x=1}$ and write the equations of the tangent and normal at this point.   Check the result by plotting.

11. Find the equations of the tangent and normal to the curve $y = 3x^2 - 1$ at the point where $x = 2$.

CHAPTER IV

DIFFERENTIATION OF ALGEBRAIC FUNCTIONS

18. Differentiation by rules.—The process of finding the derivative of a function is called **differentiation.**

The method used in the preceding articles in finding the derivative is called the **fundamental method** since it is based directly upon the definition of a derivative. The derivative of any function can be found by this method, but the work can be greatly shortened by using rules or formulas which can be established by fundamental methods or otherwise. The rules needed in differentiating algebraic functions will be considered first, and later those necessary to differentiate trigonometric, exponential, and logarithmic functions.

In the formulas, x, y, u, and v denote variables, which, of course, may be functions of variables, and a, c, and n denote constants.

19. The derivative when f(x) is x.—Since the equation $y = x$ represents a straight line with slope equal to 1, and by **Art. 15,** $\dfrac{dy}{dx}$ is the slope of the curve at any point, it follows that

[4] $$\frac{dx}{dx} = 1.$$

In general, *the derivative of a variable with respect to itself is unity.*

34

20. The derivative when f(x) is c.—Since $y = c$ is the equation of a straight line with slope equal to 0, it follows that

[5] $$\frac{dc}{dx} = 0.$$

In general, *the derivative of a constant is zero.*

21. The derivative of the sum of functions.—Given $y = u + v$, where u and v are functions of x, and let Δy, Δu, and Δv be the increments of y, u, and v, respectively, corresponding to the increment Δx.

Let $x = x_1$, then $\qquad\qquad y_1 = u_1 + v_1.$
Let $x = x_1 + \Delta x$, then $y_1 + \Delta y = u_1 + \Delta u + v_1 + \Delta v.$
Subtracting, $\qquad\qquad \Delta y = \Delta u + \Delta v.$

Dividing by Δx, $\qquad\qquad \dfrac{\Delta y}{\Delta x} = \dfrac{\Delta u}{\Delta x} + \dfrac{\Delta v}{\Delta x}.$

Let $\Delta x \to 0$, then $\qquad \dfrac{dy}{dx}\Big|_{x=x_1} = \dfrac{du}{dx}\Big|_{x=x_1} + \dfrac{dv}{dx}\Big|_{x=x_1}.$

It is evident that any number of functions can be treated in a similar manner, then

[6] $$\frac{d(u + v + w + \cdots)}{dx} = \frac{du}{dx} + \frac{dv}{dx} + \frac{dw}{dx} + \cdots$$

Or, *the derivative of the sum of any number of functions is equal to the sum of their derivatives.*

Example. If $y = x^3 + 3x^2 - 4x + 3$,

$$\frac{dy}{dx} = \frac{d(x^3)}{dx} + \frac{d(3x^2)}{dx} - \frac{d(4x)}{dx} + \frac{d(3)}{dx}.$$

22. The Derivative of the product of two functions.—With the notation as in the previous article, given $y = uv$.

Let $x = x_1$, then $\qquad\qquad y_1 = u_1v_1.$
Let $x = x_1 + \Delta x$, then $y_1 + \Delta y = (u_1 + \Delta u)(v_1 + \Delta v).$
Subtracting, $\qquad\qquad \Delta y = u_1\Delta v + v_1\Delta u + \Delta u \cdot \Delta v.$

Dividing by Δx, $\qquad \dfrac{\Delta y}{\Delta x} = u_1\dfrac{\Delta v}{\Delta x} + v_1\dfrac{\Delta u}{\Delta x} + \Delta u\,\dfrac{\Delta v}{\Delta x}.$

Let $\Delta x \to 0$ and notice that $\Delta u \dfrac{\Delta v}{\Delta x}$ also approaches zero as a limit,

then $\qquad \dfrac{dy}{dx}\Big|_{x=x_1} = u_1 \dfrac{dv}{dx}\Big|_{x=x_1} + v_1 \dfrac{du}{dx}\Big|_{x=x_1}$

[7] $\qquad\qquad \therefore \dfrac{d(uv)}{dx} = u\dfrac{dv}{dx} + v\dfrac{du}{dx}.$

Or, *the derivative of the product of two functions is equal to the first times the derivative of the second plus the second times the derivative of the first.*

Example. If $y = (x - 2)(x^2 + 1)$,

$$\frac{dy}{dx} = (x - 2)\frac{d(x^2 + 1)}{dx} + (x^2 + 1)\frac{d(x - 2)}{dx}.$$

23. The derivative of the product of a constant and a function.—Given $y = cu$, where c is a constant. By the previous article

$$\frac{dy}{dx} = c\frac{du}{dx} + u\frac{dc}{dx}.$$

But $\qquad\qquad \dfrac{dc}{dx} = 0.$ $\qquad\qquad$ By [5].

[8] $\qquad\qquad \therefore \dfrac{d(cu)}{dx} = c\dfrac{du}{dx}.$

Or, *the derivative of the product of a constant and a function is equal to the constant times the derivative of the function.*

Examples. If $y = 4(x - 2)$, $\quad \dfrac{dy}{dx} = 4\dfrac{d(x - 2)}{dx}.$

If $y = \dfrac{u}{a}$, $\qquad\qquad\qquad \dfrac{dy}{dx} = \dfrac{1}{a}\dfrac{du}{dx}.$

24. The derivative of the quotient of two functions.—
Given $\qquad\qquad\qquad y = \dfrac{u}{v}.$

Let $x = x_1$, then $\qquad\qquad y_1 = \dfrac{u_1}{v_1}.$

Let $x = x_1 + \Delta x$, then $\quad y_1 + \Delta y = \dfrac{u_1 + \Delta u}{v_1 + \Delta v}$.

Subtracting, $\Delta y = \dfrac{u_1 + \Delta u}{v_1 + \Delta v} - \dfrac{u_1}{v_1} = \dfrac{v_1 \Delta u - u_1 \Delta v}{v_1(v_1 + \Delta v)}$.

Dividing by Δx, $\qquad \dfrac{\Delta y}{\Delta x} = \dfrac{v_1 \dfrac{\Delta u}{\Delta x} - u_1 \dfrac{\Delta v}{\Delta x}}{v_1(v_1 + \Delta v)}$.

Let $\Delta x \to 0$, then $\dfrac{dy}{dx}\Big|_{x=x_1} = \dfrac{v_1 \dfrac{du}{dx}\Big|_{x=x_1} - u_1 \dfrac{dv}{dx}\Big|_{x=x_1}}{v_1{}^2}$.

[9] $\qquad \therefore \dfrac{d\left(\dfrac{u}{v}\right)}{dx} = \dfrac{v\dfrac{du}{dx} - u\dfrac{dv}{dx}}{v^2}$.

Or, *the derivative of the quotient of two functions is equal to the denominator times the derivative of the numerator minus the numerator times the derivative of the denominator, all divided by the square of the denominator.*

Example. If $y = \dfrac{x-1}{2x}$,

$$\dfrac{dy}{dx} = \dfrac{2x\dfrac{d(x-1)}{dx} - (x-1)\dfrac{d(2x)}{dx}}{4x^2}.$$

25. The derivative of the power of a function.—Given $y = u^n$.

(a) *When n is a positive integer.*
Writing as a product $y = u \cdot u^{n-1}$.

Then $\dfrac{dy}{dx} = u^{n-1}\dfrac{du}{dx} + u\dfrac{d(u^{n-1})}{dx}$. $\hspace{2em}$ By [7]

Writing u^{n-1} as the product $u \cdot u^{n-2}$,

$$\dfrac{dy}{dx} = u^{n-1}\dfrac{du}{dx} + u\left[u^{n-2}\dfrac{du}{dx} + u\dfrac{d(u^{n-2})}{dx}\right]$$

$$= 2u^{n-1}\dfrac{du}{dx} + u^2\dfrac{d(u^{n-2})}{dx}.$$

When this process is performed n times the last term will contain $\dfrac{d(u^{n-n})}{dx}$, which is zero by [5].

[10] $$\therefore \frac{d(u^n)}{dx} = nu^{n-1}\frac{du}{dx}.$$

(b) *When n is a fraction, $\dfrac{p}{q}$, where p and q are positive integers.*

Given $$y = u^{\frac{p}{q}}$$

Raising both sides of the equation to the qth power,

$$y^q = u^p.$$

Then $$qy^{q-1}\frac{dy}{dx} = pu^{p-1}\frac{du}{dx}. \qquad \text{By (a) of this article.}$$

Solving for $\dfrac{dy}{dx}$, $\dfrac{dy}{dx} = \dfrac{pu^{p-1}}{qy^{q-1}}\dfrac{du}{dx}$

$$= \frac{pu^{p-1}}{qu^{\frac{p}{q}(q-1)}}\frac{du}{dx} = \frac{p}{q}u^{\frac{p}{q}-1}\frac{du}{dx}.$$

$$\therefore \frac{d\left(u^{\frac{p}{q}}\right)}{dx} = \frac{p}{q}u^{\frac{p}{q}-1}\frac{du}{dx}.$$

(c) *When n is negative, either integral or fractional,*
Let $n = -m$.

Then $y = u^{-m} = \dfrac{1}{u^m}.$

Clearing of fractions, $yu^m = 1$

Then $myu^{m-1}\dfrac{du}{dx} + u^m\dfrac{dy}{dx} = 0.$ \qquad By [7], [10], [5].

Solving for $\dfrac{dy}{dx}$, $\dfrac{dy}{dx} = -\dfrac{myu^{m-1}}{u^m}\dfrac{du}{dx}$

$$= -myu^{-1}\frac{du}{dx} = -mu^{-m-1}\frac{du}{dx}.$$

$$\therefore \frac{d(u^{-m})}{dx} = -mu^{-m-1}\frac{du}{dx}.$$

Therefore formula [**10**] is established when the exponent is a positive or negative integer or fraction. It is expressed in the following rule:

The derivative of a function affected by a constant exponent n is equal to n times the function affected by the exponent n − 1, times the derivative of the function.

Examples. If $y = (x^2 + x + 1)^4$,

$$\frac{dy}{dx} = 4(x^2 + x + 1)^3 \frac{d(x^2 + x + 1)}{dx}.$$

If $y = (x + 1)^{\frac{1}{2}}$, $\dfrac{dy}{dx} = \frac{1}{2}(x + 1)^{-\frac{1}{2}} \dfrac{d(x + 1)}{dx}.$

If $y = (x^2 - 1)^{-3}$, $\dfrac{dy}{dx} = -3(x^2 - 1)^{-4} \dfrac{d(x^2 - 1)}{dx}.$

26. Summary of formulas for algebraic functions.— The formulas here summarized enable one to differentiate algebraic functions.

[4] $\dfrac{dx}{dx} = 1.$

[5] $\dfrac{dc}{dx} = 0.$

[6] $\dfrac{d(u + v + w + \cdots)}{dx} = \dfrac{du}{dx} + \dfrac{dv}{dx} + \dfrac{dw}{dx} + \cdots$

[7] $\dfrac{d(uv)}{dx} = u\dfrac{dv}{dx} + v\dfrac{du}{dx}.$

[8] $\dfrac{d(cu)}{dx} = c\dfrac{du}{dx}.$

[9] $\dfrac{d\left(\dfrac{u}{v}\right)}{dx} = \dfrac{v\dfrac{du}{dx} - u\dfrac{dv}{dx}}{v^2}.$

[10] $\dfrac{d(u^n)}{dx} = nu^{n-1}\dfrac{du}{dx}.$

These formulas must be learned perfectly before one can proceed with the examples which follow. Multiplying without knowing the multiplication tables is easy compared with differentiating without knowing these formulas. If the formulas and rules of differentiation are well learned, their application is one of the easiest processes in mathematics.

Examples of differentiation.—

Example 1.   Given $y = 7x^3$, find $\dfrac{dy}{dx}$.

$$\frac{dy}{dx} = \frac{d(7x^3)}{dx} = 7\frac{d(x^3)}{dx} = 7 \cdot 3x^2\frac{dx}{dx} = 21x^2.$$

By [**8**], [**10**], [**4**].

Example 2.   Given $y = x^3 + 2x^2 - 5x + 6$, find $\dfrac{dy}{dx}$.

$$\frac{dy}{dx} = \frac{d(x^3)}{dx} + \frac{d(2x^2)}{dx} - \frac{d(5x)}{dx} + \frac{d(6)}{dx}$$

By [**6**].

$$= 3x^2 + 4x - 5.$$

By [**10**], [**8**], [**5**], and [**4**].

Example 3.   Given $y = (x^2 + 2x)(3x - 2)$, find $\dfrac{dy}{dx}$.

$$\frac{dy}{dx} = (x^2 + 2x)\frac{d(3x - 2)}{dx} + (3x - 2)\frac{d(x^2 + 2x)}{dx}$$

By [**7**].

$$= (x^2 + 2x)3 + (3x - 2)(2x + 2) = 9x^2 + 8x - 4.$$

By [**4**], [**5**], [**6**], [**8**], [**10**].

Example 4.   Given $y = \dfrac{x^2 + 2}{3x - 1}$, find $\dfrac{dy}{dx}$.

$$\frac{dy}{dx} = \frac{(3x - 1)\dfrac{d(x^2 + 2)}{dx} - (x^2 + 2)\dfrac{d(3x - 1)}{dx}}{(3x - 1)^2}$$

By [**9**].

$$= \frac{(3x - 1)2x - (x^2 + 2)3}{(3x - 1)^2} = \frac{3x^2 - 2x - 6}{(3x - 1)^2}.$$

Example 5.   Given $y = \sqrt[3]{x^2 + 3x}$, find $\dfrac{dy}{dx}$.

$$\frac{dy}{dx} = \frac{d\sqrt[3]{x^2 + 3x}}{dx} = \frac{d(x^2 + 3x)^{\frac{1}{3}}}{dx}$$

$$= \tfrac{1}{3}(x^2 + 3x)^{-\frac{2}{3}}\frac{d(x^2 + 3x)}{dx}$$

$$= \tfrac{1}{3}(x^2 + 3x)^{-\frac{2}{3}}(2x + 3) = \frac{2x + 3}{3\sqrt[3]{(x^2 + 3x)^2}}.$$

EXERCISES

In the following find the derivative of the function with respect to the independent variable.

1. $y = 3x^2$.
2. $y = 5x^4$.
3. $y = 7x^{\frac{3}{2}}$.
4. $y = ax^{\frac{3}{2}}$.
5. $y = \frac{3}{4}x^{\frac{3}{2}}$.

6. $y = 4\sqrt{x}$.
7. $y = 3\sqrt[3]{x}$.
8. $y = \sqrt[5]{x^3}$.
9. $y = 3x^{-\frac{3}{2}}$.
10. $y = -4x^{\frac{3}{2}}$.

11. $y = -17\sqrt{x^3}$.
12. $y = -2\sqrt[5]{x^4}$.
13. $s = \frac{1}{2}gt^2$.
14. $s = 4t^{\frac{3}{2}}$.
15. $s = \frac{1}{2}t^{\frac{3}{2}}$.

16. $y = x^4 + 3x^2 + 2$.
17. $y = 3x^2 - 2x + 6$.
18. $y = x^3 - x^{\frac{3}{2}} + 3x$.
19. $y = x^{\frac{3}{2}} - x^{-\frac{1}{2}} + 4$.
20. $y = x^{\frac{1}{2}} - 3x^{-3} + 2$.

21. $y = (2x + 1)^3 - 3$.
22. $y = (3x^2 + 2)^4 - 2x$.
23. $y = (2x + 3)^{\frac{3}{2}} - 3x$.
24. $y = \sqrt{2x^2 - 7x}$.
25. $y = \sqrt[3]{x^2 + 7x - 2}$.

26. $y = \dfrac{1}{x^2}$.
27. $y = \dfrac{1}{x^3}$.
28. $y = \dfrac{3}{2x^2}$.

29. $y = \dfrac{2}{x + 1}$.
30. $y = \dfrac{1}{\sqrt{x + 1}}$.
31. $y = \dfrac{5}{(x^2 - 1)^2}$.

32. $y = \dfrac{x - 1}{x + 1}$.
33. $y = \dfrac{x + 2}{x - 3}$.
34. $y = \dfrac{x}{x^2 + 1}$.

35. $y = 3x^7 - 4x^6 + 3x^4 - 3$.
36. $y = \sqrt{x + 1} - \sqrt{x - 1}$.
37. $y = \sqrt{3x^3 + 7x^2 - 3x + 2}$.
38. $y = \sqrt{ax^2 + bx + c} - \sqrt{x + d}$.
39. $y = x^2(x^3 + 5)^{\frac{3}{2}}$.
40. $y = \dfrac{2x - 1}{(x - 1)^2}$.
41. $y = \sqrt{\dfrac{x - 1}{x + 1}}$.
42. $y = \dfrac{x}{\sqrt{x^2 - a^2}}$.
43. $s = \sqrt{t + 1} + \sqrt[3]{2t - 3}$.
44. $s = t^{\frac{1}{2}} + 2t^{-\frac{1}{2}} + 3t^4$.

45. $y = (x^2 + 1)(x^3 - 2x + 1)$.
46. $y = (x + a)^n(x - b)^m$.
47. $y = (x + 1)^5(2x - 1)^3$.
48. $y = \dfrac{2x^2 - 1}{(x - 1)^2}$.
49. $s = \dfrac{t^n}{(1 + t)^n}$.
50. $s = \sqrt{\dfrac{t^2 - 1}{t^2 + 1}}$.

51. Find the slope of the tangent line to the curve $y = x^3$ at the point where $x = 0$. At the point where $x = 1$. Where $x = 2$.

52. In exercise 51, what is the slope of the curve at each of the points? How many times faster is y increasing than x at each of the points?

53. If a point is moving from the origin along the curve $y = 2x^2$ in the first quadrant, what is the relative rate of increase of x and y when $x = 1, 2$, and 4, respectively?

54. Find the equations of the tangent and the normal to the curve $y = x^3 + 4x^2 + x - 6$ at the point $(0, -6)$. At the point $(2, 20)$.

55. In the curve of exercise 54, where is the tangent line parallel to the x-axis?

Suggestion. When the tangent line is parallel to the x-axis its slope is zero and hence $\dfrac{dy}{dx} = 0$.

56. Find the equations of the tangent and the normal to the curve $y = x + \dfrac{1}{x}$ at the point (x_1, y_1).

57. Find the point on the curve $y = x^3 + 3x^2 - 4x - 12$ at which the tangent has a slope of -7. What is the equation of the tangent at this point? Plot the curve.

58. The heat H, required to raise a unit weight of water from $0°C$. to a temperature t, is given by the formula

$$H = t + 0.00002t^2 + 0.0000003t^3.$$

Find $\dfrac{dH}{dt}$ and compute the value of $\dfrac{dH}{dt}$ where $t° = 35°C$.

27. Differentiation of implicit functions.—In the previous exercises, the dependent variable in each was expressed as an explicit function of the independent variable. Often it is either not convenient or not possible to express one variable as an explicit function of the other. In such a case the usual rules for finding the derivative can be applied and the desired derivative found as an implicit function of the variables involved. The method can be best illustrated by examples.

Example 1. Given $x^2 + y^2 = 25$, find $\dfrac{dy}{dx}$ as an implicit function of x and y.

Since y is a function of x, the left-hand member is the sum of two functions of x.

Differentiating, $2x + 2y\dfrac{dy}{dx} = 0$.

$$\therefore \frac{dy}{dx} = -\frac{x}{y}.$$

If y is expressed as an explicit function of x before finding the derivative, the work is not so simple. The work is then as follows:

Solving for y, $y = \pm\sqrt{25 - x^2}$.

$$\frac{dy}{dx} = \frac{-2x}{\pm 2\sqrt{25 - x^2}} = -\frac{x}{\pm\sqrt{25 - x^2}}.$$

Example 2.   Given $x^2y^3 = 25$, find $\dfrac{dy}{dx}$ and $\dfrac{dx}{dy}$ each as an implicit function of x and y.

Solution.   Since x^2y^3 is the product of two functions, x^2 and y^3, we have:

For $\dfrac{dy}{dx}$, $x^2\dfrac{d(y^3)}{dx} + y^3\dfrac{d(x^2)}{dx} = \dfrac{d(25)}{dx}$,   By [**7**].

or $3x^2y^2\dfrac{dy}{dx} + 2xy^3 = 0$.   By [**10**], [**5**]

Solving for $\dfrac{dy}{dx}$, $\dfrac{dy}{dx} = -\dfrac{2xy^3}{3x^2y^2} = -\dfrac{2y}{3x}$.

For $\dfrac{dx}{dy}$, $x^2\dfrac{d(y^3)}{dy} + y^3\dfrac{d(x^2)}{dy} = \dfrac{d(25)}{dy}$,   By[**7**].

or $3x^2y^2 + 2xy^3\dfrac{dx}{dy} = 0$.   By [**10**], [**5**]

Solving for $\dfrac{dx}{dy}$, $\dfrac{dx}{dy} = -\dfrac{3x^2y^2}{2xy^3} = -\dfrac{3x}{2y}$.

Example 3.   Find the equation of the tangent line to the curve $x^5 - y^5 + x^3 - y = 0$ at the point $(1,1)$.

Solution.   Differentiating, $5x^4 - 5y^4\dfrac{dy}{dx} + 3x^2 - \dfrac{dy}{dx} = 0$.

Solving for $\dfrac{dy}{dx}$, $\dfrac{dy}{dx} = \dfrac{5x^4 + 3x^2}{5y^4 + 1}$.

When $x = 1$ and $y = 1$, $\dfrac{dy}{dx} = \frac{4}{3}$.

Then the slope of the tangent at (1,1) is $\frac{4}{3}$.

Hence the equation of the tangent is $y - 1 = \frac{4}{3}(x - 1)$,

or $$4x - 3y - 1 = 0.$$

EXERCISES

In the following find the derivatives as implicit functions.

1. $x^3 + y^3 = a^3$, find $\dfrac{dy}{dx}$.

2. $y^3 + y = x^3 + x$, find $\dfrac{dy}{dx}$.

3. $\dfrac{x^2}{a^2} + \dfrac{y^2}{b^2} = 1$, find $\dfrac{dy}{dx}$.

4. $pv = c$, find $\dfrac{dp}{dv}$ and $\dfrac{dv}{dp}$.

5. $x^4 - 4x^2y^2 + y^3 = 0$, find $\dfrac{dy}{dx}$ and $\dfrac{dx}{dy}$.

6. $x^{\frac{4}{3}} + y^{\frac{4}{3}} = a^{\frac{4}{3}}$, find $\dfrac{dy}{dx}$ and $\dfrac{dx}{dy}$.

7. $x^{\frac{3}{2}} + y^{\frac{3}{2}} = a^{\frac{3}{2}}$, find $\dfrac{dy}{dx}$.

8. $(x + y)^{\frac{1}{2}} + (x - y)^{\frac{1}{2}} = a$, find $\dfrac{dy}{dx}$.

9. $\left(p + \dfrac{a}{v^2}\right)(v - b) = k$, find $\dfrac{dp}{dv}$ and $\dfrac{dv}{dp}$.

10. Find the slope of the circle $x^2 + y^2 = 25$ where $x = 2$, (a) when the point is in the first quadrant, and (b) when the point is in the fourth quadrant.

11. Find the equations of the tangent and normal to the circle $x^2 + y^2 = r^2$ at the point (x_1, y_1).

Solution. Given $x^2 + y^2 = r^2$.

Differentiating, $2x + 2y\dfrac{dy}{dx} = 0$, or $\dfrac{dy}{dx} = -\dfrac{x}{y}$.

$\therefore \dfrac{dy}{dx}\Big|_{x = x_1} = -\dfrac{x_1}{y_1} =$ slope of tangent line.

Then equation of tangent is $y - y_1 = -\dfrac{x_1}{y_1}(x - x_1)$.

Simplifying, $\qquad\qquad x_1x + y_1y = r^2.$

Equation of normal is $\qquad x_1y - y_1x = 0.$

The equation of the normal shows that the normal at any point of a circle passes through the center of the circle.

12. Find the equations of the tangent and the normal to the circle $x^2 + y^2 = 25$ at the point $(3, 4)$.

13. Find the equations of the tangent and the normal to the circle $x^2 + y^2 - 4x + 6y - 24 = 0$ at the point $(1, 3)$.

14. Find the equations of the tangent and normal to the ellipse $16x^2 + 25y^2 = 144$ at the point in the first quadrant where $x = 2$.

15. Find the equations of the tangent and normal to the parabola $x^{\frac{1}{2}} + y^{\frac{1}{2}} = a^{\frac{1}{2}}$ at the point (x_1, y_1).

CHAPTER V

CURVES AND THEIR EQUATIONS

28. It is well known that in the sciences, in engineering, and in many lines of business a curve is used to represent relations between quantities, that is, to represent functional relations. Curves showing the rise and fall in the prices of stocks and bonds, of food, of fuel, the increase or decrease in population, and for many other purposes, are frequently found in newspapers and magazines. Measurements taken in laboratory experiments are plotted and curves are traced from which may be read interesting and instructive facts concerning the relations of the quantities involved.

Usually such curves as those mentioned cannot be represented exactly by an equation; but a study of curves and their equations enables one to learn facts concerning related quantities that would otherwise be obscure. The mathematical machinery for such a study can readily become very complicated, and it requires the closest attention to details for one to master it. One should endeavor to visualize the ideas and methods at each step, and memorize the important facts.

29. The curve or locus of an equation.—*Definition.* The **curve** or **locus** of an equation is the curve that contains all the points whose coördinates satisfy the equation; and conversely, the coördinates of all points on the curve must satisfy the equation.

Methods for plotting the curve of an equation are discussed in **P. M. II, Chapt. XVI; IV, Arts. 78–83;**

H. S. Arts., 323–327, 417–422. These methods depend upon finding points and connecting them by a smooth curve. We are now to find out how to learn some facts about the curve of an equation from the equation itself. This information in turn can be applied to quantities whose relations are given by the equations. In this way it can be turned to practical value.

This study will be taken up under two main headings, *first*, those facts that can be learned without the calculus, and, *second*, those facts that can be learned with the help of the calculus.

The properties of the curve of an equation that can be studied to good advantage without the calculus will be taken up under three headings as follows:

(1) *The intercepts of the curve.*
(2) *The symmetry of the curve.*
(3) *The extent of the curve.*

Such a study of an equation is called a **discussion of the equation**.

FACTS ABOUT CURVES WITHOUT AID OF CALCULUS

30. Intercepts.—The **x-intercepts** of a curve are the abscissas of the points where the curve intersects, or meets, the x-axis. The **y-intercepts** are the ordinates of the points where the curve intersects, or meets, the y-axis. Together the x-intercepts and the y-intercepts are called the **intercepts of the curve**.

Evidently, the x-intercepts are found by putting $y = 0$ in the equation and solving for x. Likewise the y-intercepts are found by putting $x = 0$ and solving for y.

It follows that, if an equation contains no constant term, the curve passes through the origin.

Example.   Find the intercepts for the equation
$$16x^2 + 25y^2 = 400.$$
Putting $y = 0$, $16x^2 = 400$, or $x = \pm 5$.
Putting $x = 0$, $25y^2 = 400$, or $y = \pm 4$.
∴ the x-intercepts are $+5$ and -5, and the y-intercepts are $+4$ and -4.

EXERCISES

Find the intercepts for the following equations:

1. $3x - 5y = 15$.

2. $2x - 3y = 0$.

3. $x^2 + y^2 = 25$.

4. $4x^2 + y^2 = 64$.

5. $4x^2 + y^2 - 8x - 2y + 1 = 0$.

6. $5x^2y - 15x + 4y = 0$.

7. $y = \dfrac{x(x-2)}{(x+2)(x-1)}$.

8. $y = (x+2)(x-1)(x-3)$.

9. $xy = 6$.

10. $y = \sin x$.

11. $y = \cos x$.

12. $y = \sin^{-1} x$.

31. Symmetry, geometrical properties.—Two points are said to be **symmetrical with respect to a given point** when the given point bisects the line joining the two points.   The given point is called the **center of symmetry.**

Two points are said to be **symmetrical with respect to a given line** when the given line is the perpendicular bisector of the line joining the two points. The given line is called the **axis of symmetry.**

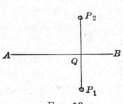

FIG. 13.

Thus, in Fig. 13, if Q bisects P_1P_2 P_1 and P_2 are symmetrical with respect to Q. Also, if AB is the perpendicular bisector of P_1P_2, P_1 and P_2 are symmetrical with respect to AB.

If the points of a curve can be arranged in pairs which are symmetrical with respect to a line or point, then the curve itself is said to be **symmetrical** with respect to the line or point.

Thus, in Fig. 14, the curve is symmetrical with respect to each of the coördinate axes and with respect to the origin. Tell why.

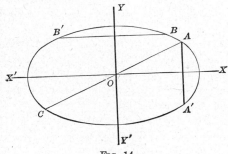

Fig. 14.

EXERCISES

1. Has a square a center of symmetry? Has a rectangle? A circle? A parallelogram? A regular hexagon?

2. How many axes of symmetry has each of the figures of exercise 1?

3. In rectangular coördinates give the point that with each of the following is symmetrical with respect to the x-axis: (2, 4), (−2, 5), (−4, −2), (6, −8), (x, y). With respect to the y-axis. With respect to the origin.

32. Symmetry, algebraic properties.—In the preceding article symmetry has been considered from the side of geometry. It remains to determine how symmetry can be seen by an inspection of the equation.

If a curve is symmetrical with respect to the x-axis, it follows that every point (x, y) on the curve has a corresponding point $(x, -y)$ on the curve. Then the coördinates of the point $(x, -y)$ must satisfy the equation; that is, if $-y$ is substituted for y, the equation reduces to the original form. It is evident that this occurs in an algebraic equation *when only even powers of y appear in the equation.*

Likewise the curve is symmetrical with respect to the y-axis if, when $-x$ is substituted for x, the equation reduces to the original form. This occurs in an algebraic equation *when only even powers of x appear in the equation.*

Since the pair of points (x, y) and $(-x, -y)$ are symmetrical with respect to the origin, it follows that if, when $-x$ is substituted for x and $-y$ for y, the equation reduces to its original form, the curve is symmetrical with respect to the origin. It is evident that this occurs in an algebraic equation *if each term is of even degree, or if each term is of odd degree, in x and y.* In applying this test a constant term is considered as of even degree.

It also follows that if a curve is symmetrical to both coördinate axes it is symmetrical with respect to the origin.

Example. Test the equation $x^2y + y^2 - 3x^2 + 6 = 0$ for the symmetry of the curve.

Putting $-x$ for x, $(-x)^2y + y^2 - 3(-x)^2 + 6 = 0$.

Simplifying, $x^2y + y^2 - 3x^2 + 6 = 0$,

which is exactly the same form as the original. Hence the curve of the equation is symmetrical with respect to the y-axis.

Putting $-y$ for y, $x^2(-y) + (-y)^2 - 3x^2 + 6 = 0$.

Simplifying, $-x^2y + y^2 - 3x^2 + 6 = 0$,

which cannot be put into the same form as the original equation. Hence the curve of the equation is not symmetrical with respect to the x-axis.

EXERCISES

State for which of the following equations the curves are symmetrical with respect to the x-axis, the y-axis, and the origin.

1. $3x + y + 1 = 0$
2. $x^2 + y^2 = 36$.
3. $x^2 - y^2 = 16$.
4. $3x^2 + 2y^2 = 12$.
5. $x^2 + y^2 + 4x = 16$.
6. $y = \sin x$.
7. $y = \cos x$.
8. $x^2y^2 = 16$.
9. $x^3 + y = 6$.
10. $x^2 + 2xy + y^2 = 9$.
11. $y^2 = (x + 1)(x - 2)$.
12. $x^2y^2 + 4x^4 = 16$.
13. $x^2 + 4x + 2y + 3 = 0$.
14. $x^3 - x = y$.

33. Extent.—Under this heading we endeavor to find how the curve lies with reference to the coördinate axes by finding, first, for what values of either variable there are no points on the curve; and, second, for what values of either variable the curve extends to infinity.

To do this the equation is solved for each variable in terms of the other. First, if a radical of even index involves a

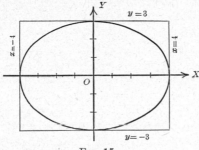

Fig. 15.

variable, certain values of that variable may give imaginary values for the other variable, in which case there are no points on the curve. If no radicals of even index are involved, there will be at least, one real value of either variable for a real value of the other. In which case there are points on the curve for every value of either variable.

An imaginary number usually appears as the square root of a negative number.

Second, if the solution for either variable gives rise to a fraction having the other variable in the denominator, then certain finite values of the second variable may make the first infinite. If no such fraction occurs both variables may become infinite at the same time.

Example. Investigate $9x^2 + 16y^2 = 144$ as to extent.

Solving for x, $\qquad\qquad x = \pm \tfrac{4}{3} \sqrt{9 - y^2}.$

Solving for y, $\qquad\qquad y = \pm \tfrac{3}{4} \sqrt{16 - x^2}.$

Therefore x is imaginary when $9 - y^2 < 0$, that is, when $y < -3$, or when $y > +3$.

And y is imaginary when $16 - x^2 < 0$, that is, when $x < -4$, or when $x > +4$.

This means that the curve is confined to the portion of the plane in which the abscissas do not exceed 4 in absolute value, and the ordinates do not exceed 3 in absolute value. That is, the curve does not extend outside of a rectangle bounded by the lines

$$x = 4, \ x = -4, \ y = 3, \text{ and } y = -3.$$

34. What is gained by the discussion of an equation.— If one is to plot an equation, much time is often saved by a discussion of the equation. The intercepts give the points where the curve intersects, or touches, the coördinate axes. If any symmetry is discovered it makes it unnecessary to plot so many points. For instance, if it is found that the curve is symmetrical with respect to the x-axis, but not the y-axis, it is necessary to plot points in the first and second quadrants only, and then locate points symmetrical to these in the third and fourth quadrants.

If the curve is found to be symmetrical with respect to both coördinate axes, the work of plotting is lessened still more; for then it is necessary to find points in the first quadrant only. The points in the other quadrants can be located by taking points in each so that they will be symmetrically placed to those in the first quadrant.

Then, too, the discussion assists by telling where not to look for points, and by giving some idea as to the general shape of the curve.

Thus, in the curve of the equation $9x^2 + 16y^2 = 144$ used in the example of **Art. 33,** one would not try to find points where x is greater than 4 or less than -4.

Example. Discuss the equation $x^3 - ax - y = 0$ and plot the curve.

Discussion. *Intercepts.* Let $x = 0$, then $y = 0$.

Let $y = 0$, then $x^3 - ax = 0$.

Solving this for x, $x = 0$ or $\pm\sqrt{a}$.

Hence the y-intercept is 0, and the x-intercepts are 0 and $\pm\sqrt{a}$.

Symmetry. Since all terms are of odd degree in x and y, the curve is symmetrical with respect to the origin.

Extent. Solving for y, $y = x^3 - ax$.

The letter a represents an arbitrary constant and may have any value assigned to it. But, in assigning a value, do not choose one that would cause a term to disappear. For the purposes of this discussion it is given the value 4.

Since no even root is involved, either variable has a real value for any value of the other.

Since large positive values of x make $x^3 - ax$ large and positive, for such values of x, y increases as x increases.

Likewise, for numerically large negative values of x, y decreases as x decreases.

Plotting. T a b u l a t i n g coördinates for positive values of x, the curve can be located in the first and fourth quadrants and, by symmetry, in the second and third quadrants, and is as shown in Fig. 16. The arbitrary

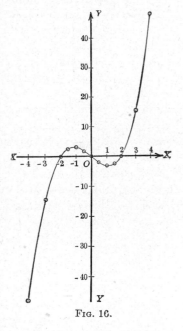

Fig. 16.

value assigned to a is 4, and the unit on the y-axis is one-fifth of that on the x-axis.

x	0	$\frac{1}{2}$	1	$1\frac{1}{2}$	2	3	4
y	0	$-1\frac{7}{8}$	-3	$-2\frac{5}{8}$	0	15	48

EXERCISES

Discuss each of the following equations and plot their curves.

1. $x^2 + y^2 = 64$.

2. $x^2 - y^2 = 64$.

3. $4x^2 + 9y^2 = 36$.

4. $4x^2 - 9y^2 = 36$.

5. $y^2 = 8x$.

6. $x^2 = 8y$.

7. $x^2 = 8y - 6$.

8. $x^2 + y^2 - 4x - 20 = 0$.

9. $xy = 15$.

10. $y^2 = (x - 2)(x + 1)(x + 3)$.

11. $y^2 = (x - 1)^2 (x - 2)$.

12. $y(x - 1) = 1$.

13. $y = x^3$.

14. $9x^3 = y^2$

FACTS ABOUT CURVES BY THE AID OF CALCULUS

35. So far in this work some properties of curves have been determined without the help of calculus. By means of the derivative other properties of the curve and its function may be discussed. Some of these will now be given. For the present the discussion will be confined to equations (1) whose curves have no break, at least in the part of the curve considered; and (2) where for each value of the independent variable there is but one point on the curve. Such curves, as well as the functions giving rise to them, are said to be **continuous** and **single-valued**.

A sine curve (**P. M. IV, Art. 78; H. S. Art. 417**) is a single valued curve since for any value of x there is but one value of y.

A circle is not single valued since for a value of x there may be two values of y. For instance, in the circle $x^2 + y^2 = 25$, $y = \pm\sqrt{25 - x^2}$, and when $x = 4$, $y = \pm 3$. Such a curve is called **double valued.** The circle may be regarded as made up of two single-valued curves. One of these is the upper half of the circle and the other the lower half. When the circle has the equation $x^2 + y^2 = 25$, the upper half has the equation $y = +\sqrt{25 - x^2}$, and the lower half has the equation $y = -\sqrt{25 - x^2}$.

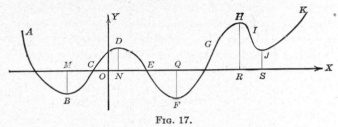

Fig. 17.

36. Some properties of a curve and its function.—If the curve, Fig. 17, is thought of as traced by a moving point passing from left to right, the following properties may be noted:

(1) The curve is *falling* from A to B, from D to F, and from H to J; and the corresponding function is *decreasing.*

(2) The curve is *rising* from B to D, from F to H, and from J to K; and the corresponding function is *increasing.*

(3) If the curve rises to a certain position and then falls, such a position is called a **maximum point** of the curve. D and H are such points. The ordinate, that is, the value of the function, at such a point is called a **maximum ordinate** or a **maximum value of the function.**

(4) If the curve falls to a certain position and then rises, such a position is called a **minimum point** of the curve. B, F, and J are such points. The ordinate, that is, the

value of the function, at such a point is called a **minimum ordinate** or a **minimum value of the function.**

(5) The curve is *concave upward* between A and C, E and G, and I and K. It is *concave downward* between C and E, and G and I.

(6) Points C, E, G, and I where the concavity changes, are called **points of inflection.**

Curves may have other peculiarities, but these will not be considered here.

37. Curves rising or falling, functions increasing or decreasing.—Since by definition, **Art. 14,** the slope of a curve at any point is the same as the slope of the tangent at that point, it follows that when the slope is positive the curve is rising, and when the slope is negative the curve is falling. This is, of course, when passing from left to right.

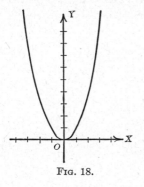

Fig. 18.

Stated with reference to the function this becomes the following very useful principle:

When the derivative of a function is positive, the function increases as the independent variable increases; when the derivative is negative, the function decreases as the independent variable increases.

It also follows that the ratio of the change of the function at any point to that of the variable is equal to the value of the derivative of the function with respect to the variable, for that point.

Example 1. For what values of x is the curve $y = x^2$ rising and for what values falling?

Solution. Given $y = x^2$.

Then $$\frac{dy}{dx} = 2x.$$

Now $2x$ is positive when x is positive, and negative when x is negative. Hence the curve is rising when $x > 0$, and falling when $x < 0$.

The curve is as shown in Fig. 18.

Example 2. For what values of x is the function $y = \frac{1}{2}x^3$ increasing and for what values is it decreasing?

Solution. Given $\quad y = \frac{1}{2}x^3$.

Then $\qquad \dfrac{dy}{dx} = \frac{3}{2}x^2$.

But x^2 cannot be negative for any value of x. Hence $\dfrac{dy}{dx}$ is never negative and the function is never decreasing. Is the function always increasing? Is it increasing when $x = 0$?

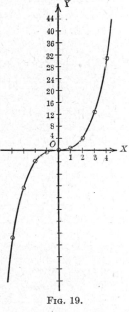

Fig. 19.

The curve is as shown in Fig. 19.

Example 3. For what value of x is the curve of the equation $y = \frac{1}{3}x^3 - \frac{1}{2}x^2 - 6x$ rising and for what values falling? For what values of x is y increasing 6 times as fast as x?

Solution. Given $y = \frac{1}{3}x^3 - \frac{1}{2}x^2 - 6x$.

Then $\qquad \dfrac{dy}{dx} = x^2 - x - 6$.

Factoring, $\qquad \dfrac{dy}{dx} = (x + 2)(x - 3)$.

Then $\dfrac{dy}{dx}$ is positive when $x < -2$ and when $x > 3$, and negative when $-2 < x < 3$.

Hence the curve is rising when $x < -2$ and when $x > 3$, and falling when $-2 < x < 3$.

The values of x for which y is increasing 6 times as fast as x can be found by putting $x^2 - x - 6 = 6$, and solving for x.

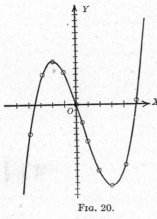

FIG. 20.

This gives $x = 4$ or -3.

The curve is as shown in Fig. 20.

EXERCISES

1. Draw a curve in the first quadrant such that the derivative of its function is always positive. Such that the derivative of its function is always negative.

2. Draw a line such that the derivative of its function is always equal to 0. Always equal to 1. Always equal to 3. Always equal to -1.

3. Draw a circle with its center at the origin. For what portions of the circle is the curve rising? For what portions falling? When is the derivative of the function representing this circle positive? When negative? When zero?

Passing from left to right, for what values of x are the loci of the following equations rising and for what values falling?

4. $y = 3x - 6$.

5. $y = 4x^2 + 16x - 7$.

6. $y = \sqrt{4x}$.

7. $y^3 = 8x^2$.

8. $y = x^3 + 3$.

9. $xy = 15$.

10. $y = x^2 - 9x$.

11. $y = x^3 - x^2 - 2x$.

12. $y = x^3 - 2x^2 + x - 3$.

13. $y(1 + x^2) = x$.

14. $y(x^2 - 1)^2 = x^3$.

15. $6y = 2x^3 - 3x^2 - 12x - 6$.

16. $y = x^4 - 6x^2 + 8x + 6$.

17. $y = (x^2 - 1)^4$.

18. In exercise 11, how many times as rapidly as x is y increasing when $x = 10$? When $x = 3$? When $x = -1$? When $x = 0$?

19. In exercise 12, for what values of x is y increasing 7 times as rapidly as x? For what values of x is y decreasing 4 times as rapidly as x is increasing?

38. Maximum and minimum.—The subject of maximum and minimum has many practical applications, and this phase of the work will be given in the next chapter. Here we will consider curves and their functions.

From the definitions of **Art. 36,** it is clear that if a curve is plotted in rectangular coördinates, the curve is *rising* at nearby points on the left of a maximum point, and *falling* at nearby points on the right. For a minimum point the curve is *falling* for nearby points on the left and *rising* on the right. The student can readily state this with reference to the function.

It is evident that for an ordinary maximum point or an ordinary minimum point like those shown in Fig. 17, the tangent line is parallel to the x-axis, that is, its slope is zero.

It follows that these points can be determined from the function as follows:

(1) Equate $\frac{dy}{dx}$ to zero and solve for x.

(2) Determine whether $\frac{dy}{dx}$ is positive or negative for nearby points on the left and right.

(3) A point where $\frac{dy}{dx} = 0$ is a maximum point if $\frac{dy}{dx} > 0$ for nearby points on the left and $\frac{dy}{dx} < 0$ for nearby points on the right.

(4) A point where $\frac{dy}{dx} = 0$ is a mini-mum point if $\frac{dy}{dx} < 0$ for nearby points on the left and $\frac{dy}{dx} > 0$ for nearby points on the right.

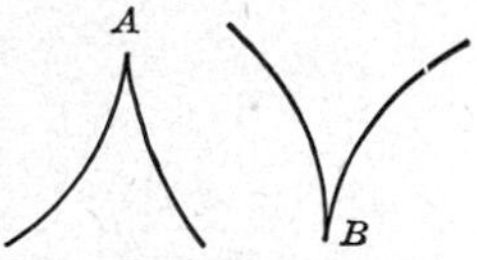

Fig. 21.

It is distinctly understood that these tests determine only such points as are illustrated in Fig. 17. For cusp maximum and minimum points as shown in Fig. 21, the tangent is perpendicular to the x-axis and hence $\dfrac{dy}{dx} = \infty$.

Example.   Determine the maximum and minimum points of the function $y = x^3 - 3x^2 + 4$ and plot the curve.

Solution.   Given $y = x^3 - 3x^2 + 4$.

$$\frac{dy}{dx} = 3x^2 - 6x = 3x(x - 2).$$

$$\therefore \frac{dy}{dx} = 0 \text{ for } x = 0, \text{ and } x = 2.$$

When $x < 0$ but near 0, $\dfrac{dy}{dx} > 0$ and the curve is rising.

When $x > 0$ but near 0, $\dfrac{dy}{dx} < 0$ and the curve is falling.

$\therefore$ the curve has a maximum point when $x = 0$.

When $x < 2$ but near 2, $\dfrac{dy}{dx} < 0$ and the curve is falling.

When $x > 2$ but near 2, $\dfrac{dy}{dx} > 0$ and the curve is rising.

$\therefore$ the curve has a minimum point when $x = 2$.

Plotting.   When $x = 0$, $y = 4$. $\therefore$ (0, 4) is a maximum point.

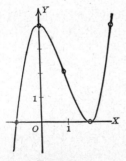

When $x = 2$, $y = 0$. $\therefore$ (2, 0) is a minimum point.

Factoring, $y = (x+1)(x-2)(x-2)$. $\therefore$ the x-intercepts are -1, 2, and 2.

A few other points will make the plotting fairly accurate.   See Fig. 22.

Fig. 22.

x	1	3	4	-2
y	2	4	20	-16

EXERCISES

Determine the maximum and minimum points of the following curves and plot.

1. $y = x^2$.

2. $2y = x^2 - 4x + 6$.

3. $y = 6x - x^2 + 4$.

4. $4x^2 + 9y^2 = 36$.

Suggestion. This is a double valued function for

$$y = \pm \tfrac{2}{3} \sqrt{9 - x^2}.$$

When using the positive value a maximum point will be found, and a minimum when using the negative value.

5. $y = (x+4)(x-2)(x-4)$.

6. $16y = x^2 - 32x$.

7. $y = x^3 - 7x^2 + 36$.

8. $y = x^4 - 4x^3$.

9. By finding the maximum point of the curve, find the coördinates of the vertex of the parabola
$2x^2 - 18x + 15y - 21 = 0$.

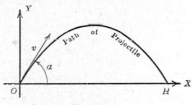

Fig. 23.

10. If the resistance of the air is not taken into account, the path of a projectile may be considered to be a parabola. If it starts at the origin with a velocity of v feet per second at an angle of α with the horizontal, Fig. 23, the equation of the path is

$$y = \tan \alpha \cdot x - \frac{g}{2v^2 \cos^2 \alpha} x^2.$$

(*a*) Find the maximum value of the function and thus find a formula for finding the height to which a projectile rises. (**P. M. IV, p. 71; H. S., p. 493.**)

(*b*) By taking twice the abscissa of the maximum point find the range of the projectile.

Suggestion. Note that α, v, and g are constants.

Differentiating, $\dfrac{dy}{dx} = \tan \alpha - \dfrac{g}{v^2 \cos^2 \alpha} x$.

39. Concavity and points of inflection.—It is evident from an inspection of a curve that is *concave upward* that the tangent line turns *counter-clockwise* in passing along a curve from left to right that is, the slope of the tangent *increases*.

Likewise, if the curve is *concave downward*, the tangent line turns *clockwise*, that is, the slope of the tangent is *decreasing*.

Thus, in Fig. 24, the tangent line turns counter-clockwise in passing from A to D, and the slope increases from a negative value at A to a positive value at D.

FIG. 24.   FIG. 25.

Likewise, in Fig. 25, the tangent turns clockwise in passing from A to D, and the slope decreases from a positive value at A to a negative value at D.

It remains to determine how the concavity of a curve can be determined from its function.

Since the derivative of a function of x is itself a function of x, it is evident that the derivative of this first derivative may be found.   It is called the **second derivative** of y with respect to x.

If $y = f(x)$, the second derivative is $\dfrac{d}{dx}\left(\dfrac{dy}{dx}\right)$ and is represented by the symbol $\dfrac{d^2y}{dx^2}$.

Thus, if
$$y = x^3 - 6x^2 + 12x - 3,$$
$$\frac{dy}{dx} = 3x^2 - 12x + 12,$$
and
$$\frac{d^2y}{dx^2} = 6x - 12.$$

From the foregoing, it is evident that when $\dfrac{d^2y}{dx^2}$ is positive, $\dfrac{dy}{dx}$ is increasing; and when $\dfrac{d^2y}{dx^2}$ is negative, $\dfrac{dy}{dx}$ is decreasing.

Or, if $y = f(x)$ is the equation of a curve, the slope of the tangent is increasing when passing from left to right and the curve is concave upward for the values of x that make $\dfrac{d^2y}{dx^2}$ *positive*.

Likewise, the curve is concave downward when $\dfrac{d^2y}{dx^2}$ is *negative*.

From (6) of **Art. 36,** it is evident that a point of inflection is a point on a curve at which the concavity changes from upward to downward or *vice versa*. A point of inflection can be determined by finding the values of x for which $\dfrac{d^2y}{dx^2}$ changes sign, providing the function is finite for that value of x.

Example. Investigate $y = x^3 - 3x^2 + x + 2$ for concavity and points of inflection.

Solution. Given $y = x^3 - 3x^2 + x + 2$.

$$\frac{dy}{dx} = 3x^2 - 6x + 1.$$
$$\frac{d^2y}{dx^2} = 6x - 6 = 6(x - 1).$$

Since when $x < 1$, $6(x - 1)$ is negative; and when $x > 1$, $6(x - 1)$ is positive, the curve is concave downward at the left of $x = 1$, and concave upward at the right of $x = 1$. Therefore, it has a point of inflection at the point $(1, 1)$.

EXERCISES

In exercises 1–10 investigate for concavity and points of inflection.

1. $y = x^3$.
2. $y = x^4$.
3. $y = x^5$.
4. $y = 3x - x^3$.
5. $y = x^4 - 6x^2$.
6. $y = (x + 2)(x - 2)(x - 3)$.
7. $y = 3x^4 - 4x^3 - 1$.
8. $y = x^3 - 4x^2 + 4x - 1$.
9. $y = x^4 - 2x^2 + 40$.
10. $y = 3x^4 - 16x^3 - 6x^2 + 48x + 17$.

11. In the example, Art. **39**, find the slope of the tangent to the curve at the point of inflection, find the maximum and minimum points, and plot the curve.

12. In the example referred to in exercise 11, if the curve is being traced by a point moving from left to right, for what values of x does y increase at the same rate as x? How rapidly is the curve rising when $x = 3$ if x is increasing at the rate of 2 in. a second?

13. Investigate the greatest possible number of points of inflection of the curves of

(1) $y = ax^2 + bx + c,$
(2) $y = ax^3 + bx^2 + cx + d,$
(3) $y = ax^4 + bx^3 + cx^2 + dx + e.$

In exercises 14–19 plot the curves showing the values of y, $\dfrac{dy}{dx}$, and $\dfrac{d^2y}{dx^2}$, using the same set of axes for the three curves of each. What facts can be read from these curves?

14. $y = 4x^3.$　　　　　　　　**17.** $y = (x + 2)(x - 2)(x - 3).$

15. $y = 3x^4.$　　　　　　　　**18.** $y = x^3 - 12x + 7.$

16. $y = 3x - x^3.$　　　　　　**19.** $y = x^4 - 2x^2 - 8.$

40. Second test for ordinary maximum or minimum points.

—In dealing with functions where the second derivative can readily be found, the ordinary maximum or minimum points can often be more quickly determined by the help of the second derivative.

Since the curve is concave downward at an ordinary maximum point, the second derivative is *negative* if it is not zero.

Since the curve is concave upward at an ordinary minimum point, the second derivative is *positive* if it is not zero.

This gives the following method very frequently used for finding ordinary maximum or minimum points of a given curve $y = f(x)$:

(1) Find $\dfrac{dy}{dx}$ and $\dfrac{d^2y}{dx^2}.$

(2) Put $\frac{dy}{dx} = 0$, and solve for x.

(3) Substitute each of these values of x into $\frac{d^2y}{dx^2}$ and find its values.

(4) A value of x for which $\frac{dy}{dx} = 0$ and $\frac{d^2y}{dx^2}$ is negative gives a maximum value.

(5) A value of x for which $\frac{dy}{dx} = 0$ and $\frac{d^2y}{dx^2}$ is positive gives a minimum value.

If $\frac{d^2y}{dx^2} = 0$ for the values of x for which $\frac{dy}{dx} = 0$, this test does not apply and one should apply the test of **Art. 38**. That is, it should be distinctly understood that the test of this article is a *sufficient* condition but not a *necessary* one. By this we mean that if the test applies there is a maximum or a minimum point, but if it does not apply there still may be a maximum or a minimum point.

It must be remembered that the test based directly upon the definition of **Art. 38** is a sure test. That is, if a function *increases* to a certain value and then *decreases*, that value is a maximum; and, if a function *decreases* to a certain value and then *increases*, that value is a minimum.

Example. Determine the values of x for which

$$y = 2x^3 - 3x^2 - 36x + 10$$

has maximum or minimum values.

Solution. Given $y = 2x^3 - 3x^2 - 36x + 10$.

$$\frac{dy}{dx} = 6x^2 - 6x - 36.$$

$$\frac{d^2y}{dx^2} = 12x - 6.$$

Putting $\frac{dy}{dx} = 0,\ 6x^2 - 6x - 36 = 0.$

Solving for x, $\quad x = -2$ and $+3$.

Substituting these values in the second derivative,

$$\frac{d^2y}{dx^2}\bigg|_{x\,=\,-\,2} = 12(-2) - 6 = -30,$$

and

$$\frac{d^2y}{dx^2}\bigg|_{x\,=\,3} = 12\cdot3 - 6 = 30.$$

Hence the function has a maximum value when $x = -2$, and a minimum value when $x = 3$.

EXERCISE

Solve exercises 1–9 of Art. **38** by the methods of this article and compare the work with that done in the previous article.

41. Cusp maximum and minimum points.—So far the maximum and minimum points of the curve have been points where the tangent line was parallel to the x-axis, that is, points for which $\frac{dy}{dx} = 0$. While this is the ordinary kind of maximum and minimum points, it is not the only kind that occur.

The **cusp maximum** or **cusp minimum** points are finite points on the curve where the tangent line is perpendicular to the x-axis, that is, points for which $\frac{dy}{dx} = \infty$.

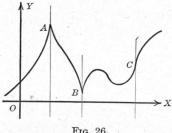

Fig. 26.

It should be noted that this is not a test for a maximum or a minimum point. It only locates a *possible* maximum or minimum point. The test is to determine whether (1) the curve rises to that point and then falls, or (2) falls to that point and then rises. If (1) is true, it is a maximum point. If (2) is true, it is a minimum point.

If neither (1) nor (2) is true, it is neither a maximum nor a minimum point.

In Fig. 26, for each of the points A, B, and C, $\dfrac{dy}{dx} = \infty$. Point A is a maximum point, point B is a minimum point, and point C is neither.

Example 1.   Test $y = \tfrac{15}{2}\,(x-2)^{\frac{2}{3}}$ for a maximum or a minimum value.

Differentiating, $\qquad \dfrac{dy}{dx} = \dfrac{5}{(x-2)^{\frac{1}{3}}}.$

If $\qquad \dfrac{dy}{dx} = \infty$, $x - 2 = 0$ and $x = 2$.

When $x < 2$, $\dfrac{5}{(x-2)^{\frac{1}{3}}} < 0$, since the cube root of a negative number gives a negative number, and hence the curve is falling.

When $x > 2$, $\dfrac{5}{(x-2)^{\frac{1}{3}}} > 0$, and hence the curve is rising.

Therefore there is a minimum value of the function when $x = 2$.

Example 2.   Test $y = 15(x-2)^{\frac{1}{3}}$ for maximum and minimum values.

Differentiating, $\dfrac{dy}{dx} = \dfrac{5}{(x-2)^{\frac{2}{3}}}.$

Then $\qquad \dfrac{dy}{dx} = \infty$ when $x = 2$.

When $x < 2$, $(x-2)^{\frac{2}{3}}$ is positive and $\dfrac{5}{(x-2)^{\frac{2}{3}}} > 0$.

When $x > 2$, $(x-2)^{\frac{2}{3}}$ is positive and $\dfrac{5}{(x-2)^{\frac{2}{3}}} > 0$.

Hence the curve is rising both before and after $x = 2$.

Therefore there is neither a maximum nor a minimum point at $x = 2$.

EXERCISES

Test the following curves for cusp maximum or minimum points:

1. $y = 4 + (x - 1)^{\frac{2}{3}}$.   **3.** $y = 8 - (x + 2)^{\frac{1}{2}}$.

2. $y = \dfrac{x}{x - 2}$.   **4.** $y = \dfrac{x^2}{x - 2}$.

Note. In exercise 4, the value of x for which $\dfrac{dy}{dx} = \infty$ does not give a finite point on the curve.

5. $x^{\frac{2}{3}} + y^{\frac{2}{3}} = a^{\frac{2}{3}}$.

Suggestion. In this exercise y is a double valued function of x. It is then necessary to consider the positive and negative values of y separately.

CHAPTER VI

PROBLEMS IN MAXIMA AND MINIMA

42. Questions involving maximum and minimum values are of frequent occurrence in actual problems. They arise in business, in manufacturing, and in engineering, when it is desired to make efficiency and output a maximum or to reduce the cost of labor and material to a minimum. For instance, the speed of a machine is to be found for which its efficiency is a maximum; or the voltage is to be determined which makes the cost of a transmission line a minimum; or that load on an induction motor which gives the highest power-factor is to be determined. Many specific examples will be found in the problems of this chapter.

43. Helpful theorems.—Often the labor in finding maximum and minimum values can be greatly shortened by making use of certain facts and theorems that are so evident as not to require proof.

(1) If c is a constant, any value of x which makes $f(x)$ a maximum, or a minimum, also makes $c + f(x)$ a maximum, or a minimum; and conversely.

(2) If c is a positive constant, any value of x which makes $f(x)$ a maximum, or a minimum, also makes $cf(x)$ a maximum, or a minimum; and conversely.

(3) If c is a negative constant, any value of x which makes $f(x)$ a maximum makes $cf(x)$ a minimum, and any value of x which makes $f(x)$ a minimum makes $cf(x)$ a maximum; and conversely.

(4) If n is a positive integer any value of x which makes $f(x)$ positive and a maximum, or a minimum, also makes $[f(x)]^n$ a maximum, or a minimum.

(5) Any value of x which makes $f(x)$ a maximum, or a minimum, and positive also makes $\log f(x)$ a maximum, or a minimum; and conversely.

(6) Any value of x which makes $f(x)$ finite, not zero, and a maximum makes $\dfrac{1}{f(x)}$ a minimum; and any value of x which makes $f(x)$ finite, not zero and a minimum makes $\dfrac{1}{f(x)}$ a maximum.

44. Suggestions in solving problems in maxima and minima.—The first steps in the solution are much the same as for a problem in algebra where equations are to be set up for solution.

First, study the problem to understand fully the relations between the variables involved. If the quantities involved are in a field that is not familiar to the student he should omit the problem.

Second, choose convenient letters to represent the variables, and represent the variable that is to be a maximum or a minimum as a function of the others. If there are altogether more than two variables, write other equations involving the variables so that all can be eliminated except two, one of which is the one that is to be a maximum or a minimum.

Third, proceed by the methods of the previous chapter for finding the maximum and minimum values.

45. Illustrative examples.—*Example* 1. Find the relative values of two positive variables such that their sum is a minimum when their product is a constant c.

Solution. Let x and y be the variables, and let s be their sum which is to be a minimum.

Then $\qquad s = x + y.$

But $\qquad xy = c$, or $y = \dfrac{c}{x}.$

Hence $\qquad s = x + \dfrac{c}{x}.$

Differentiation, $\dfrac{ds}{dx} = 1 - \dfrac{c}{x^2}.$

Putting $\qquad \dfrac{ds}{dx} = 0,\ 1 - \dfrac{c}{x^2} = 0.$

Solving, $\qquad x = \sqrt{c}.$

But $\qquad y = \dfrac{c}{x} = \sqrt{c}.$

$\therefore$ the two variables are equal.

That these values make s a minimum can be shown by finding

$$\frac{d^2s}{dx^2} = \frac{2c}{x^3},$$

which is positive, for $x = +\sqrt{c}.$

It may be noted that if $\dfrac{ds}{dx}$ becomes infinite, x approaches zero and s becomes infinite, and is not minimum.

The relation of the variables given in this example is one that often arises in practical problems. It may be stated as a theorem in the following form: When the product of two positive variables is a constant, their sum is a minimum when the variables are equal to each other.

Example 2. A container for storing gas is to be made in the form of a right circular cylinder open at the bottom where it rests in water. Find the most economical dimensions for the cylinder if it is made of sheet steel of the same thickness throughout.

Solution. This problem requires that the material or the surface of the container shall be a minimum for a given volume.

Let r be the radius and h the height of the cylinder, S the area of the surface, and V the volume which is a constant.

(1) Then $S = 2\pi rh + \pi r^2$.

(2) And $V = \pi r^2 h$, from which $h = \dfrac{V}{\pi r^2}$.

Substituting in (1), $S = \dfrac{2V}{r} + \pi r^2$.

Differentiating, $\dfrac{dS}{dr} = -\dfrac{2V}{r^2} + 2\pi r$,

and $\dfrac{d^2S}{dr^2} = \dfrac{4V}{r^3} + 2\pi$.

Putting $\dfrac{dS}{dr} = 0$, $-\dfrac{2V}{r^2} + 2\pi r = 0$.

Solving for r, $r = \sqrt[3]{\dfrac{V}{\pi}}$.

Substituting this value of r in $\dfrac{d^2S}{dr^2}$, gives a positive value.

Hence when $r = \sqrt[3]{\dfrac{V}{\pi}}$, S is a minimum.

Substituting this value of r in (2) gives $h = \sqrt[3]{\dfrac{V}{\pi}}$.

Therefore the tank should be made with its radius equal to its height.

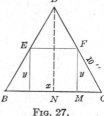

Fig. 27.

Example 3. Find the dimensions of the rectangle of greatest area that can be inscribed in an equilateral triangle each of whose sides is 10 in., provided that one of the sides of the rectangle is on a side of the triangle.

Solution. Let $x =$ the base and $y =$ the altitude of the rectangle as shown in Fig. 27. Also let $A =$ the area of the rectangle which is to be a maximum.

Then $A = xy$.

And $NC : ND = MC : MF$, because of similar triangles.

But $NC = 5$, $ND = 5\sqrt{3}$, $MC = \frac{1}{2}(10 - x)$, and $MF = y$.

Substituting these values in the proportion,
$$5 : 5\sqrt{3} = \frac{1}{2}(10 - x) : y.$$
Solving for y, $y = \frac{1}{2}\sqrt{3}(10 - x)$.

Substituting this in the first equation,
$$A = \frac{1}{2}\sqrt{3}(10x - x^2).$$

Differentiating, $\dfrac{dA}{dx} = \frac{1}{2}\sqrt{3}(10 - 2x)$,

and $$\frac{d^2A}{dx^2} = -\sqrt{3}.$$

Putting $\dfrac{dA}{dx} = 0$, $x = 5$, which makes A a maximum for $\dfrac{d^2A}{dx^2}$ is negative.

The corresponding value of y is $y = \frac{5}{2}\sqrt{3}$.

This shows that the base of the rectangle is half a side of the triangle, and its altitude is half the altitude of the triangle.

Example 4.   The intensity of illumination from a given source of light L
varies as the sine of the angle φ at which
the light rays strike the illuminated
surface, divided by the square of the
distance from the light.   Find the height of a light directly
over the center of a given circle so that it shall give a
maximum illumination to the circumference.

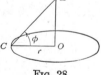

Fig. 28.

Solution.   In Fig. 28, let $OL = x$ be the height, $OC = r$,
and $I =$ illumination at C, any point on the circumference.

Then $$I = k\,\frac{\sin \varphi}{CL^2}.$$

But $$CL = \sqrt{x^2 + r^2}, \text{ and } \sin \varphi = \frac{x}{\sqrt{x^2 + r^2}}.$$

Substituting these values in the first equation,

$$I = k \frac{x}{(x^2 + r^2)^{\frac{3}{2}}}.$$

Differentiating, $\dfrac{dI}{dx} = k\dfrac{(x^2 + r^2)^{\frac{3}{2}} - 3x^2(x^2 + r^2)^{\frac{1}{2}}}{(x^2 + r^2)^3}$

$$= k\frac{r^2 - 2x^2}{(x^2 + r^2)^{\frac{5}{2}}}$$

But $\dfrac{dI}{dx} = 0$ when the numerator of this fraction equals 0.

$\therefore r^2 - 2x^2 = 0$, and $x = \frac{1}{2}r\sqrt{2}$.

It can easily be shown that this gives the value of I for a maximum.

Example 5.   A storage battery of n cells is to be connected in a series-parallel plan so as to give maximum power in a constant external resistance of R ohms.   Each cell has an e.m.f. of e volts and the internal resistance of each cell is r ohms.   How must the cells be connected?

Solution.   Let x = number of cells connected in parallel.

Then $\dfrac{n}{x}$ = number of cells in series.

The total internal resistance is then $\dfrac{n}{x}r \div x = \dfrac{nr}{x^2}$ ohms.

And the total resistance of the circuit is $\dfrac{nr}{x^2} + R$.

The e.m.f. acting in the circuit is $\dfrac{ne}{x}$ ohms since $\dfrac{n}{x}$ cells of e volts each are in series.

Then the current delivered is

$$i = \frac{ne}{x} \div \left(\frac{nr}{x^2} + R\right) = \frac{nex}{nr + Rx^2}.$$

Hence the power P which this current produces, in the resistance R is

$$P = Ri^2 = \frac{Rn^2e^2x^2}{(nr + Rx^2)^2}.$$

But P will become a maximum when $\dfrac{x^2}{(nr + Rx^2)^2}$ is a maximum. By **Art. 43** (2).

Put $P' = \dfrac{x^2}{(nr + Rx^2)^2}$ and find $\dfrac{dP'}{dx}$.

$$\frac{dP'}{dx} = \frac{(nr + Rx^2)^2 2x - 2x^2(nr + Rx^2)2Rx}{(nr + Rx^2)^4}$$

$$= \frac{2x(nr - Rx^2)}{(nr + Rx^2)^3}.$$

But $\dfrac{dP'}{dx} = 0$ when $2x(nr - Rx^2) = 0$, or $x = \sqrt{\dfrac{nr}{R}}$.

EXERCISES

1. Find the area of the greatest rectangle that can be bounded by a line 20 in. long.

2. A farmer owns land along a railroad which is fenced. Using this fence for one side of his field the farmer wishes to enclose a rectangle containing 80 acres. Find the least cost for building the fence at $2 a rod.

3. Divide 5 into two parts such that the square of one part times the cube of the other part shall be a maximum.

4. A square sheet of tin 18 in. on a side has a small square cut out of each corner so that the sides may be turned up to form an open box. Find the side of the small squares so that the box shall have maximum volume.

Suggestion. Let x = side of a small square in inches. Then volume = $x(18 - 2x)^2$.

5. A rectangular sheet of tin 16 in. by 30 in. is to have a square piece cut out of each corner so that the sides may be turned up to form an open box. Find a side of the squares so that the box shall have a maximum volume.

6. A tin vegetable can to contain 1 qt. is to be made in the form of a right-circular cylinder with closed ends. Find its dimensions when containing a minimum of material. Make no allowance for waste or seams.

7. A tank with a square base and open top is to hold 40 bbl. Find its dimensions if the area of its sides and bottom is a minimum.

8. Find the relative values of u^p and v^q such that $u^p + v^q$ is a minimum when $u^m v^n = c$, where p, q, m, n, and c are constants.

Suggestion. This exercise is the general case of example 1 and is much more difficult in the algebraic manipulation.

Let $$s = u^p + v^q.$$

By implicit differentiation,

(1) $$\frac{ds}{du} = pu^{p-1} + qv^{n-1}\frac{dv}{du}.$$

But $$u^m v^n = c.$$

Differentiating, $$mu^{m-1}v^n + nu^m v^{n-1}\frac{dv}{du} = 0.$$

Solving for $\frac{dv}{du}$, $$\frac{dv}{du} = -\frac{mu^{m-1}v^n}{nu^m v^{n-1}} = -\frac{mv}{nu}.$$

Substituting this value of $\frac{dv}{du}$ in (1),

$$\frac{ds}{du} = pu^{p-1} - qv^{q-1}\frac{mv}{nu}$$

$$= pu^{p-1} - \frac{mqv^q}{nu}.$$

Putting $\frac{ds}{du} = 0$, $\quad pu^{p-1} - \dfrac{mqv^q}{nu} = 0.$

Or $$pu^{p-1} = \frac{mqv^q}{nu}.$$

Dividing both members of this equation by pv^q and multiplying by u gives

$$\frac{u^p}{v^q} = \frac{mq}{np}.$$

This may be stated as a theorem as was done for example 1. It is a useful fact used in practical problems.

9. Find the relative values of u and v such that uv is a maximum when $u + v = c$, where c is a constant. Compare with example 1, and state as a theorem.

10. Find the relative values of u^p and v^q such that $u^p v^q$ is a maximum when $u^m + v^n = c$, where p, q, m, n, and c are constants. This is the general case of exercise 9.

11. The parcel post regulations limit the size of a package to such a size that the length plus the girth equals 6 ft. Find the dimensions and the volume of the largest cylindrical package that can be sent by parcel post.

Suggestion. Let x = diameter in feet, y = length in feet, and V = volume in cubic feet.

Then
$$V = \tfrac{1}{4}\pi x^2 y.$$
But
$$\pi x + y = 6, \text{ or } y = 6 - \pi x.$$
Then
$$V = \tfrac{1}{4}\pi x^2(6 - \pi x) = \tfrac{3}{2}\pi x^2 - \tfrac{1}{4}\pi^2 x^3.$$

Differentiating, $\dfrac{dV}{dx} = 3\pi x - \tfrac{3}{4}\pi^2 x^2.$

Putting $\dfrac{dV}{dx} = 0$ and solving for x, $x = \dfrac{4}{\pi}$ or 0.

Find $y = 2$ and $V = 2.55$.

12. As in exercise 11, find the dimensions and volume of the largest package in the form of a rectangular solid that can be sent by parcel post if the cross section perpendicular to the length is a square.

13. A man is in a row boat 5 mi. from the nearest point P of a straight shore line. He wishes to reach a point Q on the shore 6 mi. from P as quickly as possible. At what point should he reach the shore if he can row 2 mi. an hour and walk 4 mi. an hour?

14 Given that the strength of a beam of rectangular cross section varies as the product of its breadth by the square of its depth. Find the dimensions of the cross section of the strongest rectangular beam that can be cut from a cylindrical log whose diameter is $2a$. (**P. M. II, Art. 119; H. S., Art. 320.**)

Suggestion. Let s = strength, x = breadth, and y = depth of beam.

Then $s = kxy^2$.

Eliminate y by means of the relation $y^2 = 4a^2 - x^2$.

Hence $s = kx(4a^2 - x^2)$.

Differentiate and equate derivative to zero.

15. Show that the following construction gives dimensions agreeing with the previous exercise. The strongest rectangular beam that can be cut from a round log can be laid out on the end of the log as follows: Draw the diameter AB, Fig. 29, and trisect it at E and F. Draw perpendiculars to the diameter at E and F to meet the circumference

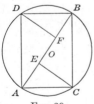

Fig. 29.

at C and D respectively. Then $ACBD$ is the required cross section of the beam.

16. Given that the stiffness of a beam of rectangular cross section varies as the product of its breadth by the cube of its depth. Find the dimensions of the cross section of the stiffest rectangular beam that can be cut from a cylindrical log whose diameter is $2a$.

17. Show that the following construction gives dimensions agreeing with the previous exercise.   The stiffest rectangular beam that can be

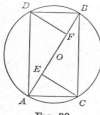

cut from a round log can be laid out on the end of the log as follows: Draw the diameter AB, Fig. 30, and divide it into four equal parts by the points E, O, and F.   Draw perpendiculars to the diameter at E and F to meet the circumference at C and D respectively.   Then $ACBD$ is the required cross section of the beam.

18. The lower corner of a leaf of a book n inches in width is folded over so as just to reach the inner edge of the page.   If the crease of the fold is to have a minimum length, find the

FIG. 30.

distance x from the lower corner to the lower end of the crease.

19. As in the previous exercise find x so that the area of the part folded over shall be a minimum.

20. A circular path around a plot of ground 100 ft. in diameter is to be illuminated by a single light placed at S, Fig. 31, above the center of the plot.   Find the height y for the best illumination   if   the   illumination   varies directly as $\dfrac{\sin \varphi}{s^2}$ for any point in the path.

21. The illumination on a plane surface by a luminous point is directly proportional to the cosine of the angle of incidence of the rays of light, and inversely as the square of its distance from the source of light.   Find

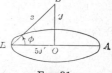

FIG. 31.

the height above the floor to place a light in order that a point on the floor at a horizontal distance a from the light shall receive the maximum illumination.   (The **angle of incidence** is the angle the ray of light makes with the perpendicular to the surface illuminated.)

22. Given that the work of propelling a steamer through the water varies as the cube of her speed.   Find the most economical rate an hour against a current running 6 mi. an hour.   Against a current running a miles an hour.

Suggestion. Let V = speed of the steamer in still water.

Then kV^3 = work per hour.

And $V - 6$ = speed against the current.

Hence $\dfrac{kV^3}{V-6}$ = work per mile of distance covered against current.

Find V to make this a minimum.

23. The cost of fuel consumed in propelling a steamer through the water varies as the cube of her speed, and is \$25 an hour when the speed is 10 mi. an hour. The other expenses are \$100 an hour. Find the most economical speed to run the steamer. Find the cost to run 100 mi. at the most economical speed. Find the cost to run 100 mi. at 10 mi. an hour. At 15 mi. an hour.

Suggestion. Let C = cost per hour for fuel, and V = speed per hour.

Then $C = kV^3$.

But $C = 25$ when $V = 10$.

Then $25 = k\cdot10^3$, or $k = \frac{1}{40}$.

The total cost T for going a distance s is

$$T = \frac{V^3}{40}\cdot\frac{s}{V} + 100\cdot\frac{s}{V}.$$

Here the variables are T and V.

24. A lever with the fulcrum at one end and the lifting force at the other end has a 1200-lb. weight hanging at a point 3 ft. from the fulcrum. If the lever weighs 12 lb. per foot, find its length so as to make the lifting force least. (**P. M. II, p. 112; H. S., p. 355.**)

25. A telegraph pole at a turn in the direction of the line is stayed by a guy wire 24 ft. long fastened to the pole and to a stake driven in the ground. How far from the foot of the pole should the stake be driven so that the moment about the foot of the pole shall be a maximum?

26. The power delivered to an external circuit by a 30-volt generator of internal resistance 2 ohms when the current is i amperes is $30i - 2i^2$ watts. For what current will this generator deliver the maximum power?

27. It is required to arrange n voltaic cells so as to obtain a maximum current through an external resistance R. The e.m.f. of each cell is e and its internal resistance is r. State as a rule.

Solution. Let x = number arranged in series.

Then $\dfrac{n}{x}$ = number arranged in parallel.

Hence ex = e.m.f. of battery.

And $\dfrac{rx^2}{n}$ = total internal resistance.

If I = current, $I = \dfrac{ex}{\dfrac{rx^2}{n} + R} = \dfrac{enx}{rx^2 + nR}$.

Differentiating, $\dfrac{dI}{dx} = \dfrac{(rx^2 + nR)en - enx \cdot 2rx}{(rx^2 + nR)^2}$

$$= \frac{en^2R - enrx^2}{(rx^2 + nR)^2}.$$

Putting $\dfrac{dI}{dx} = 0$, $en^2R - enrx^2 = 0$.

$\therefore R = \dfrac{rx^2}{n}$, which is the same as the internal resistance.

Hence the rule: For a suitable resistance, the maximum current R is obtained from a battery by arranging so that the internal resistance equals the external resistance.

28. In a transformer of constant impressed e.m.f., $E = 2300$ volts. The constant loss, that is, the loss that is independent of the output is $P = 500$ watts. The internal resistance is $r = 20$ ohms. At what current i is the efficiency of the transformer a maximum?

Solution.   Let F = efficiency.

Then $F = \dfrac{\text{output}}{\text{input}}$.

But   input $= 2300i$, and output $= 2300i - 500 - 20i^2$.

Hence $F = \dfrac{2300i - 500 - 20i^2}{2300i} = \dfrac{115i - 25 - i^2}{115i}$.

Differentiating, $\dfrac{dF}{di} = \dfrac{25 - i^2}{115i^2}$.

Putting $\dfrac{dF}{di} = 0$, $\dfrac{25 - i^2}{115i^2} = 0$ and $i = 5$.

$\therefore$ for maximum efficiency,

$$F = \frac{115 \times 5 - 25 - 5^2}{115 \times 5}$$

$$= 0.913 = 91.3 \text{ per cent.}$$

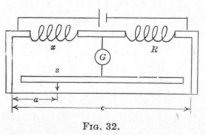

Fig. 32.

29. In measuring the resistance x with a slide-wire bridge, Fig. 32, the percentage of error due to any error in setting the slider, s, is inversely proportional to $ac - a^2$. Show that the best measurements can be made when the slider is near the center of the space c.

30. In a certain mine two formations of rock, one hard and one soft, are separated by a plane that is vertical.   From a point A on the dividing plane a horizontal tunnel is to be made to a point B in the hard rock.   To dig the tunnel it costs \$6 a linear foot in the soft rock and \$10 in the hard rock.   Find the most economical cost and the number of feet of tunnel in each rock if the length of the perpendicular from B to the dividing plane is 100 ft. and the foot of this perpendicular is 300 ft. from A.

31. An impulse turbine is driven by a jet of water or steam flowing at a rate of s_1 feet a second.   At what peripheral speed, s_2, is the output a maximum?

Suggestion.   Since the direction of the jet and the peripheral motion are in the same direction, the impulse force is proportional to the difference between their speeds.   .

Hence $k(s_1 - s_2) =$ impulse force.

But the power P is the impulse force times the speed.

Hence $\qquad P = k(s_1 - s_2)s_2 = k(s_1 s_2 - s_2{}^2)$.

Differentiating and noting that s_1 is a constant,

$$\frac{dP}{ds_2} = k(s_1 - 2s_2).$$

Putting $\dfrac{dP}{ds_2} = 0, \quad s_1 - 2s_2 = 0$, or $s_2 = \tfrac{1}{2}s_1$.

That is, the output is a maximum when the peripheral speed of the impulse wheel is one-half the velocity of the jet.

CHAPTER VII

CHANGES IN QUANTITIES. DIFFERENTIALS

46. Long before the machinery of the calculus was developed there were the ideas which the subject was to deal with. For generations these ideas were pressing forward and insisting upon recognition and expression in mathematical symbols. Clear and clean-cut ideas are absolutely essential before one attempts to put them into mathematical language. Symbolism without ideas is nothing but the dry bones of mathematics, and the rattling of bones is not very interesting or profitable to anyone, and least of all to the man of a practical turn of mind. The reader is then urged to consider very carefully the ideas connected with related changing quantities.

47. Changes in related variables.—The changes that take place in quantities which vary are often the subject of thought and give rise to many questions in every-day affairs. A change in one variable is frequently thought of as being connected in some manner with the change in another variable. When these changes are to be dealt with mathematically it is necessary first to express them in the symbols of mathematics.

Since a change in any quantity takes place in some period of time, it is very common to think of time as one of the variables. In such a case it is usual to consider time as the independent variable. Thus, the change in the position of a train requires some period of time. The change in the position of the train and the change in time during which the change in the position takes place, are spoken of as corresponding changes in the two variables.

Of course, it is not necessary that time should always be one of the variables. For instance, if a change in the length of a bar of steel is caused by a change of temperature, the two variables are length and temperature.

Another important idea frequently connected with changes is expressed by the word *uniform*. We say that a flywheel is revolving uniformly, or a train is moving uniformly. Just what is meant by this must be understood in a very exact sense before the idea can be expressed in the symbols of mathematics. In the two illustrations we mean that equal changes take place in equal intervals of time. That is, the flywheel makes just so many revolutions per minute during each minute; and the train is moving just so many feet per second for each second. It is said that the two variables in each illustration *change uniformly with respect to each other*. If the number of revolutions was not the same for each minute, or if the distance passed over by the train was not the same for each second, the changes would be *non-uniform with respect to each other*.

Uniform change is readily dealt with in the calculus, and it is a very common thing to speak of related changes as being uniform, for convenience in handling them mathematically. This is also done in common conversation when we say that an automobile is going 30 mi. an hour. What we mean is that, if the automobile should continue at a *uniform rate* for the next hour, it would travel 30 mi.

Consider the particular case of a train gaining speed after leaving a station. At some particular instant we say it is moving 30 ft. a second. If then the change in the time is one second, the corresponding uniform change in the distance the train is from the station is 30 ft. That is, if the change in distance *became* and *remained* uniform at the particular instant in question, the change would be 30 ft. in one second.   This is not the actual change in the distance, which might be 35 ft. during the next second.

There are then three ideas:

(1) *The change or increment of time.*

(2) *The actual change or increment in the distance.*

(3) *The change in the distance if that change had become and remained uniform.*

These ideas are considered in a definite mathematical fashion in the following articles.

48. Relations between increments.—When two variables are so related that the ratio of their corresponding increments is *constant*, either variable is said to **change uniformly with respect to the other.**

When the variables are related by an equation of the first degree, as $y = mx + b$, where $\Delta y = m\Delta x$, then $\dfrac{\Delta y}{\Delta x} = m$. That is, either variable changes *uniformly* with respect to the other.

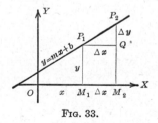

Fig. 33.

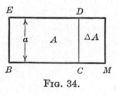

Fig. 34.

This is also evident from Fig. 33, in which $y = mx + b$ is the equation of the line P_1P_2 with slope m. P_1 is *any* point on this line and $\dfrac{\Delta y}{\Delta x} = m$.

In Fig. 34, $BCDE$ is a rectangle having a constant altitude a and a variable base x.   When x takes an increment Δx, the area A will take an increment $a \cdot \Delta x$, that is A and x change uniformly with respect to each other.

$$\therefore \Delta A = a\Delta x, \text{ or } \frac{\Delta A}{\Delta x} = a.$$

When two variables are so related that the ratio of their corresponding increments is variable, either variable is said to **change non-uniformly with respect to the other.**

If the variables s and t are related by the equation

$$s = \tfrac{1}{2}gt^2,$$

then $\Delta s = \tfrac{1}{2}g(2t\Delta t + \Delta t^2)$.   By **Art. 9,** example 2.

$$\therefore \frac{\Delta s}{\Delta t} = \tfrac{1}{2}g(2t + \Delta t).$$

Here $\dfrac{\Delta s}{\Delta t}$ is a variable for it varies with t, that is, different values of t give different values of $\dfrac{\Delta s}{\Delta t}$, and the change is *non-uniform.*

49. Differentials.—If two variables are so related that one is dependent and the other independent, then for corresponding values of the variables:

(1) The **differential of the independent variable** is the same as its increment.

(2) The **differential of the dependent variable** is what would be its increment, if at the corresponding values considered, its change *became* and *remained* uniform with respect to the independent variable.

The differential of a variable is denoted by writing d before it.

Thus, differential of x is denoted by dx.   Also dy, $d(x^3)$, $d(x^2 + 2x + 1)$, and $d\,f(x)$ denote the differentials of y, x^3, $x^2 + 2x + 1$, and $f(x)$, respectively.   It is to be noted that in no sense does dy mean d times y.

50. Illustrations.—It follows from the definitions that the differentials of variables which change uniformly with respect to each other are their corresponding increments.

(1) Thus, if $y = mx + b$, $dx = \Delta x$ and $dy = \Delta y$, for y changes uniformly with respect to x.

It should be noted that $dy = \Delta y$ when, and only when, the graph of $y = f(x)$ is a straight line.

(2) If the rectangle of constant altitude, Fig. 34, is increased in area by increasing the base by the length CM, the area is increased by the rectangle $CMND$. Here evidently the area A is a function of the base x. Since A and x change *uniformly* with respect to each other, $CM = dx$ and rectangle $CMND = dA$.

(3) At the instant when an automobile passes a certain point on the road it is moving at a rate of 20 mi. an hour. Here the two related variables are numbers showing time and distance. If the differential of the time t is taken as 1 hr., then the differential of the distances is 20 mi. That is, for a change of 1 hr. in the time the change in the distance would be 20 mi., provided the rate at which the automobile was moving became and remained uniform. In symbols this would be written: If $dt = 1$ hr., $ds = 20$ mi. For smaller changes one could readily write the corresponding differentials.

If $dt = 1$ min., $ds = \frac{1}{3}$ mi.

If $dt = 1$ sec., $ds = 29\frac{1}{3}$ ft.

(4) consider the curve $y = f(x)$ Fig. 35 as being traced by a point starting from the origin and moving to the right and upward. The direction that the tracing point is moving at any point is along the tangent line at that point.

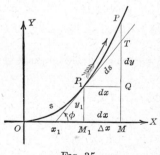

Fig. 35.

Let (x, y) be the coördinates of the moving point.

Evidently, y is changing non-uniformly with respect to x. Suppose the moving point has reached P_1. Here y is evidently changing at the same rate it would if the point were moving along the tangent line at P_1. If then the change in y is to *become* and *remain* uniform with respect to x, the point *must move along the tangent*.

It follows that at the point P_1, if the increment of x is $\Delta x = M_1 M$, $dx = \Delta x$, and $dy = QT$.

It is to be noted that the corresponding increment of y is $\Delta y = QP$.

In the right triangle QP_1T, $\tan QP_1T = \tan \varphi$, the slope of the tangent line. Hence $dy = dx \tan \varphi$.

Again, if s is the length of the curve traced, then corresponding to dx and dy the change in s if this change becomes and remains uniform, is $ds = P_1T$; and since P_1QT is a right triangle,

[11] $$ds^2 = dx^2 + dy^2.$$

The triangle P_1QT is called the **differential triangle**.

51. Relation between differentials and derivatives. Since the slope of the tangent line at any point is equal to the value of the derivative, $\dfrac{dy}{dx}$, for that point, then, if $f'(x)$ is used instead of $\dfrac{dy}{dx}$ to avoid confusion, the equation $dy = dx \tan \varphi$ becomes

[12] $$dy = f'(x)dx.$$

Since dy and dx are finite quantities, dividing by dx,

$$\frac{dy}{dx} = f'(x).$$

This is an extremely important and useful relation, which stated in words is: *the first derivative and the ratio of the differentials can be used interchangeably.*

It is to be noted that [12] gives a general method for finding the differential of a function. It is stated in the following:

RULE. *If y is a function of x, then dy corresponding to dx equals the derivative of y with respect to x times dx.*

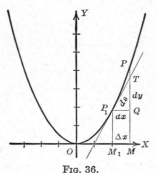

FIG. 36.

Example. A point is moving along the parabola $y = \frac{1}{2}x^2$. When it has reached the point whose abscissa is 2, find dy and ds corresponding to $dx = 1$. Plot the curve and show dx, dy, and ds.

Solution. First find the derivative of y with respect to x.

$$y = \frac{1}{2}x^2.$$
$$\frac{dy}{dx} = x.$$
$$dy = x\,dx \text{ for any value of } x.$$

When $x = 2$, and $dx = 1$, $dy = 2 \cdot 1 = 2$.

And $ds = \sqrt{dx^2 + dy^2} = \sqrt{1^2 + 2^2} = 2.236+$.

The values are represented graphically in Fig. 36.

EXERCISES

1. When a train is passing a certain mile post it is moving at a rate of 60 mi. an hour. Using t for time and s for distance, find ds when dt has each of the values 1 hr., 1 min., and 1 sec.

2. A stream of water 3 in. in diameter is flowing from a reservoir at a uniform rate of 5 ft. a second. Using V for volume in cu. ft., and t for time, find dV corresponding to $dt = 1$ sec.; for $dt = 1$ min.

3. The right triangle, Fig. 37, is being generated by the altitude moving uniformly to the right. If the variable base is x and the area A, show that dA corresponding to dx is the rectangle M_1MQP_1.

4. The area of the upper half of the area of the parabola $y^2 = 4x$ is being generated by the ordinate moving toward the right. If A

is the variable area, show that $dA = 2\sqrt{x}\, dx$ for any value of x. Draw the figure.

5. If the upper half of the area of the circle $x^2 + y^2 = r^2$ is being generated by the ordinate moving uniformly toward the right, show that $dA = \sqrt{r^2 - x^2}\, dx$.

6. The area above the x-axis between $y = \sin x$ and the x-axis is being generated by its ordinate. Show that $dA = \sin x\, dx$. For the part below the x-axis show that $dA = -\sin x\, dx$.

7. A point is moving on the circle $x^2 + y^2 = 25$. Find dy and ds corresponding to a change in x of $dx = 0.2$ at the point in the first quadrant where $x = 3$.

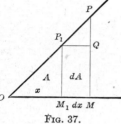

FIG. 37.

8. A point is moving on the ellipse $\dfrac{x^2}{36} + \dfrac{y^2}{16} = 1$. Find dy corresponding to $dx = 0.4$ at the point in the first quadrant where $x = 2$. In the second quadrant where $x = -2$.

In the following find dy for any x.

9. $y = 3x^2 + 2x - 1$.

10. $y = x^3 + 4x + 2$.

11. $y = x^4 - 3x^3 + 2x^2$.

12. $\dfrac{x^2}{16} - \dfrac{y^2}{9} = 1$.

13. $y = \sqrt{x^2 + 4}$.

14. $x^{\frac{2}{3}} + y^{\frac{2}{3}} = 4$.

15. $x^{\frac{1}{2}} + y^{\frac{1}{2}} = 2$.

16. $y = \dfrac{1}{\sqrt{x^2 + 5}}$.

17. The distance s that a body will fall in t seconds is given by the formula $s = \frac{1}{2}gt^2$. Find ds for any value of t. Find ds when $t = 2$ and corresponding to $dt = 1$. (Use $g = 32$.)

CHAPTER VIII

RATE OF CHANGE. SPEED, VELOCITY, ACCELERATION

52. Rate of change.—It is customary to think of the rate of change of any quantity as the change that takes place in a unit of time. If then the measure of the magnitude of a change is divided by the number of units of time during which it occurs, the quotient is the measure of the rate of change.

If the change is uniform, this quotient represents the rate of change at any instant during the time in which the change is taking place. If the change is not uniform, the quotient represents the *average* rate of change.

Thus, if a train runs 400 mi. in 10 hr., the rate is 40 mi. an hour and is an average rate.

In the above there are an independent and a dependent variable, time being the independent variable.

Rate of change without reference to time is frequently considered. For instance, the change which occurs in the length of a bar of steel when the temperature is changed. Here the rate of change of the length per unit change in temperature is found by dividing the change in length by the corresponding change in temperature. In this illustration temperature is the independent variable.

If a point is moving along a straight line plotted in rectangular coördinates, then the rate of change of y with reference to x is the change in y divided by the corresponding change in x, and may be represented by $\frac{\Delta y}{\Delta x}$.

Further, since the changes are uniform with respect to each other, the rate of change is represented by $\frac{dy}{dx}$ for any point on the line. (See **Art. 50.**)

53. Rate of change when not uniform.—The **rate of change at any instant** during the change of a variable is the differential of the variable, divided by the corresponding differential of the time.

This is taken as the definition of the **instantaneous rate,** and can readily be worded to apply when the independent variable is not time. It is chosen as a definition because it is in close agreement with the common idea regarding rate at a given instant. For instance, if one should say that an automobile is going at such a rate that it would go 60 mi. in 3 hr., it is generally understood that the rate at the instant considered is 20 mi. an hour, and is found by dividing the distance by the time. Recalling the meaning of a differential, it is seen that the instantaneous rate is the differential of the distance divided by the corresponding differential of the time. In general, if V is the variable that is changing in time,

$$\textbf{instantaneous rate of change} = \frac{dV}{dt}.$$

If the rate of change is uniform, $\frac{dV}{dt}$ is constant; and if not uniform, $\frac{dV}{dt}$ is a variable.

Since the quotient of the differentials is always equal to the derivative, the instantaneous rate of change is equal to the derivative for that particular value of the independent variable.

54. Speed and velocity.—It is not usual in common talk to make any distinction between the ideas of speed and velocity. Here, however, a distinction will be made. A point is in **motion** with reference to another point when its position is changing with reference to the other point. Change of position is due to (1) change of direction or (2) change of distance or (3) change of both direction and distance.

As illustrations: (1) A point moving along the circumference of a circle remains at the same distance from the center of the circle but the direction changes. (2) A point moving along a straight line changes its distance from the starting point but not its direction. (3) A point moving along a curve in general changes both its distance and direction from its starting point.

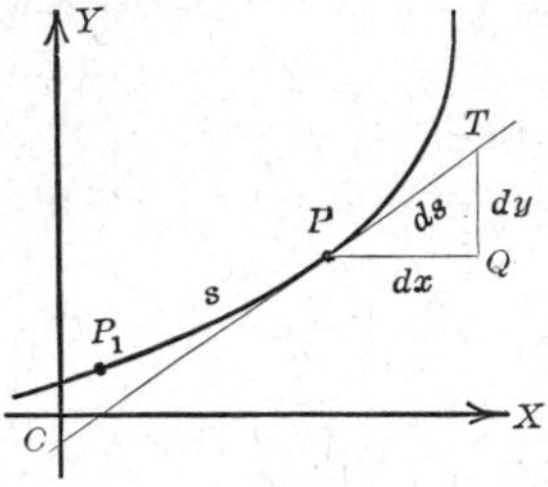

Fig. 38.

The **speed of a body** is the distance passed over in a unit of time.

The **velocity of a body** is its change in position in a unit of time, and involves both distance and direction, of which either may be constant. The rate of change of the distance is called the **magnitude of the velocity.**

When a point changes its position it moves along a straight or curved path. If the point starts at P_1, Fig. 38, its velocity at any point P has the direction of the tangent line PT, and a magnitude equal to $\dfrac{ds}{dt}$, where dt is the differential of the time corresponding to dx, dy, and ds.

From the differential triangle PQT, $ds^2 = dx^2 + dy^2$.

Dividing by dt^2, $\left(\dfrac{ds}{dt}\right)^2 = \left(\dfrac{dx}{dt}\right)^2 + \left(\dfrac{dy}{dt}\right)^2$.

Hence
$$\mathbf{\frac{ds}{dt} = \sqrt{\left(\frac{dx}{dt}\right)^2 + \left(\frac{dy}{dt}\right)^2}.}$$

But $\dfrac{dx}{dt}$ and $\dfrac{dy}{dt}$ are the components of the velocity along the x-axis and the y-axis respectively. (**P. M. IV, Art. 60; H. S., Art. 397.**)

Hence the magnitude of the instantaneous velocity of a point along a curve is equal to the square root of the sum of the squares of the components along the x-axis and the y-axis; and the direction of the velocity is along the line of slope $\tan \varphi = \dfrac{dy}{dx}$.

The instantaneous speed is the same as the magnitude of the velocity at that instant.

If a point moves in a straight line with uniform speed, it has uniform, or constant velocity.

In many questions where it is not necessary to distinguish between speed and velocity, it is customary to use velocity in the sense of speed.

55. Acceleration.—The rate of change of a velocity or speed is an **acceleration.**

If v is the speed or the magnitude of a velocity, and α the acceleration,

then $v = \dfrac{ds}{dt}$ is the time rate of change of s with respect to t,

and $\alpha = \dfrac{dv}{dt} = \dfrac{d^2s}{dt^2}$, the time rate of change of the speed, is the acceleration along the path of motion.

Example. The distance s that a body will fall from rest in a vacuum in time t seconds is given by the formula $s = \frac{1}{2}gt^2$. Find its velocity after t_1 seconds and its acceleration.

Solution. $\qquad s = \frac{1}{2}gt^2.$

Differentiating, $v = \dfrac{ds}{dt} = gt.$

Differentiating, $\alpha = \dfrac{dv}{dt} = \dfrac{d^2s}{dt^2} = g.$

Hence the velocity when $t = t_1$ is gt_1, and the acceleration is a constant g.

56. Solving rate problems.—Since a problem involving rates is apt to cause trouble unless care is taken in the arrangement of the work, we will formulate with some care the steps in a solution. If an equation is given connecting the variables involved in the problem, only steps (5) and (6) are required, and, in any case, it will not always be necessary to follow the order rigidly.

(1) Read the problem to understand exactly what is being considered.

(2) Select all the variables involved and represent them by suitable letters.

(3) State carefully what is given and what is to be found.

(4) Write an equation or equations connecting the variables.

(5) Differentiate with respect to the independent variable.

(6) Substitute values given and solve for that which is to be found.

In order to write the equation one must have exact knowledge of the subject that is involved. This may be geometry, physics, chemistry, electricity, etc.

Example 1.   A point is moving along the parabola $x^2 = 4y$ at such a rate that x is increasing uniformly at the rate of 4 in. a second. How rapidly is y increasing when $x = 3$?

Solution.   Here the equation connecting the variables x and y is given. The independent variable is time t, for both x and y are functions of t.

Given $\qquad\qquad y = \tfrac{1}{4}x^2$.

Differentiating, $\qquad \dfrac{dy}{dt} = \tfrac{1}{2}x\dfrac{dx}{dt}.$

But $\qquad\qquad \dfrac{dx}{dt} = 4$ for any value of t.

Hence when $x = 3$, $\dfrac{dy}{dt} = \tfrac{1}{2} \times 3 \times 4 = 6.$

∴ y is increasing at the rate of 6 in. a second when $x = 3$.

Example 2. A square sheet of metal 10 in. on a siae is expanded by increasing its temperature so that each side of the square increases 0.005 in. a second. At what rate is the area of the square increasing at the end of 20 sec.?

Solution. Let x = a side of the square, and A = its area at any time. Also let t = the time in seconds.

Given $\dfrac{dx}{dt} = 0.005$ for any value of t.

To find $\dfrac{dA}{dt}$ when $t = 20$.

The equation connecting the variables is
$$A = x^2.$$
Differentiating, $\dfrac{dA}{dt} = 2x\dfrac{dx}{dt}.$

At any time t, $x = 10 + 0.005t.$

When $t = 20$, $\dfrac{dA}{dt} = 2(10 + 0.005 \times 20)0.005 = 0.101.$

∴ the area is increasing at the rate of 0.101 sq. in. a second at the end of 20 sec.

Example 3. A ship A sails due north at the rate of 8 mi. an hour. A ship B, 10 mi. south and 32 mi. west of A, sails due east at the rate of 16 mi. an hour. At what rate is the distance between them decreasing? How far does the ship B go before the distance between A and B begins to increase?

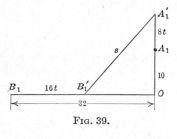

Fig. 39.

Solution. Let t = number of hours measured from the instant that the ships are in the positions A_1 and B_1, Fig. 39.

Let s = the distance between the ships when in any positions A_1' and B_1' after t hours.

Then $s = \sqrt{B_1'O^2 + OA_1'^2}$.

But $B_1'O = 32 - 16t$, and $OA_1' = 10 + 8t$.

Hence $s = \sqrt{(32 - 16t)^2 + (10 + 8t)^2}$

$\qquad = \sqrt{1124 - 864t + 320t^2}$.

Differentiating, $\dfrac{ds}{dt} = \dfrac{-432 + 320t}{\sqrt{1124 - 864t + 320t^2}}$.

When the ships are in the position A_1 and B_1 respectively, $t = 0$, and

$$\frac{ds}{dt} = -\frac{432}{\sqrt{1124}} = -12.9-.$$

The negative sign means that s is decreasing. Hence the ships are approaching each other at a rate of 12.9 mi. an hour at the instant that they are in the positions A_1 and B_1.

The distance between the ships will begin to increase when $\dfrac{ds}{dt} = 0$, or when $-432 + 320t = 0$.

Solving this for t, $t = 1\frac{7}{20}$ = the number of hours before the distance begins to increase.

Hence the ship B goes 16 mi. $\times 1\frac{7}{20} = 21.6$ mi. before the distance begins to increase.

EXERCISES

1. A ball rolling down an incline gains speed as the time increases. If the distance it has rolled in t seconds is s feet where $s = 6t^2$, find its speed for any instant. Find its speed when $t = 1$, when $t = 5$, when $t = 10$.

2. The space x in feet described in the time t in seconds by a point moving in a straight line is given by the formula

$$x = 40t + 16t^2.$$

Find the velocity and the acceleration at the end of 2 sec.

3. As in the preceding, if the formula is $x = 100t - 16t^2$, find t when the velocity is zero.

4. A bullet was fired straight upward at such a velocity that its height after t seconds was $y = 2000t - 16t^2$. What was its velocity at the start? What was its greatest height? What was its velocity at the end of 10 sec.?

5. If x is increasing uniformly, find the ratio between the rates of increase of $(2x)^{\frac{3}{2}}$ and $4x\sqrt[3]{3x}$ when $x = 8$.

6. If the height h miles which a balloon will rise in t minutes is given by the formula

$$h = \frac{10t}{\sqrt{4000 + t^2}},$$

at what rate is the balloon rising at the end of 10 min.? At the end of 30 min.? Give the answers in miles per hour.

7. From Regnault's experiments it is found that the number of heat units, Q, necessary to raise the temperature of b grams of water from $0°$ to $T°$ centigrade, is given by the formula

$$Q = (T + 2T^2 10^{-5} + 3T^3 10^{-7})b.$$

If heat is being supplied to 40 g. of water at the rate of 20 heat units per second, find the rate at which the temperature is rising when $T° = 30°$. When $T° = 50°$.

Suggestion. Find the derivative with respect to t and substitute the values.

8. If $y = \dfrac{3x}{1 - \sqrt{1 - x^2}}$, find the rate at which y is increasing when $x = \frac{1}{3}$ and is increasing at the rate of $\frac{1}{2}$ in. a second.

9. As a man walks out along a springboard OE, Fig. 40, he sinks to a distance $y = \frac{1}{15}x^2(x + 2)$ inches when he is x feet from the fixed end. If he moves so that x increases at the rate of 2 ft. a second, how fast is he sinking when he starts at O? When $x = 8$ ft.? When $x = 12$ ft.?

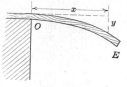

Fig. 40.

10. A point moves in the curve whose equation is $x^{\frac{2}{3}} + y^{\frac{2}{3}} = a^{\frac{2}{3}}$ so that the velocity component along the x-axis is a constant k. Find the acceleration in the direction of the y-axis.

11. Air expands according to the adiabatic law $pv^{1.41} = C$. When the pressure is 40 lb. per square inch, the volume is 5 cu. ft., and is increasing at the rate of 0.2 cu. ft. per second. Find the rate at which the pressure is changing.

12. A point moves along the arc of the parabola $y^2 = 2px$ with a velocity v. Find its velocity parallel to each coördinate axis.

Solution. Since v is velocity along arc, $v = \dfrac{ds}{dt}$, where s is the length of the path measured from any point.

We are to find $\dfrac{dx}{dt}$ and $\dfrac{dy}{dt}$.

The given equation is $y^2 = 2px$.

Differentiating, $\dfrac{dy}{dt} = \dfrac{p}{y}\dfrac{dx}{dt}$.

But $\left(\dfrac{ds}{dt}\right)^2 = \left(\dfrac{dx}{dt}\right)^2 + \left(\dfrac{dy}{dt}\right)^2$.   By **Art. 54.**

Then $v^2 = \left(\dfrac{dx}{dt}\right)^2 + \dfrac{p^2}{y^2}\left(\dfrac{dx}{dt}\right)^2$.

$\therefore \dfrac{dx}{dt} = \dfrac{vy}{\sqrt{y^2 + p^2}}$, and $\dfrac{dy}{dt} = \dfrac{pv}{\sqrt{y^2 + p^2}}$.

13. Heat is being applied to a circular metal plate so that its radius increases at the rate of $\frac{1}{8}$ in. a minute. At what rate does its area increase when its diameter is 4 in.?

Suggestion. Let r = radius and A = area.

Given $\dfrac{dr}{dt} = \frac{1}{8}$ in. a minute.

Find $\dfrac{dA}{dt}$ when $r = 2$.

Use the relation $A = \pi r^2$, differentiate, and find the value of $\dfrac{dA}{dt}\Big|_{r\,=\,2}$.

14. A stone dropped into still water produces a series of waves in continually enlarging concentric circles. If the radius of one of these circles is increasing at the rate of 5 ft. a second, find the rate its area is increasing when its diameter is 20 ft.

15. A rectangular parallelepiped of cast iron expands 0.0000062 part of each of its linear dimensions for each degree of increase in temperature. At what rate per degree of temperature change is its volume increasing when its linear dimensions are respectively 3, 4, and 6 in.?

16. The point P, Fig. 41, moves along the line $y = 10$ at the uniform rate of 8 ft. a minute   How fast is the middle point of OP receding from $Q(0, 10)$ when $OP = 20$ ft.?

17. A ball is dropped from a height of 100 ft. above level ground. The sun is at an altitude of 40°. Find the rate at which the shadow of the ball is travelling along the ground when it has fallen 50 ft. When it reaches the ground.

Suggestion. The distance that the ball is above the ground at any time t seconds after it is dropped is $s = 100 - \frac{1}{2}gt^2$.

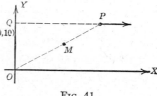

Fig. 41.

18. Two locomotives are moving along two straight lines of railway which intersect at an angle of 60°. One is approaching the intersection at the rate of 30 mi. an hour, and the other is receding from it at the rate of 40 mi. an hour. Find the rate per hour at which they are separating from each other when each is 10 mi. from the intersection if they are each 10 mi. from the intersection at the same instant.

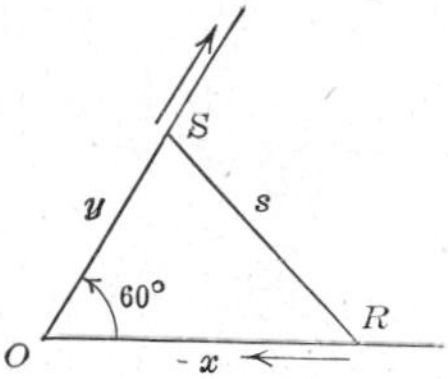

Solution. Let the trains at some instant be in the positions R and S respectively, Fig. 42.

Also let $x = OR$ be the distance the first train is from the station O at any instant, $y = OS$ be the distance the second train is from the station, and let $s = RS$ be the distance the trains are apart at that instant.

Fig. 42.

Given $\dfrac{dx}{dt} = -30$, and $\dfrac{dy}{dt} = 40$.

To find $\dfrac{ds}{dt}$ when $x = y = 10$.

By the cosine law of trigonometry
$$s = \sqrt{x^2 + y^2 - 2xy \cos 60°} = \sqrt{x^2 + y^2 - xy}.$$

Differentiating, $\dfrac{ds}{dt} = \dfrac{2x\dfrac{dx}{dt} + 2y\dfrac{dy}{dt} - x\dfrac{dy}{dt} - y\dfrac{dx}{dt}}{2\sqrt{x^2 + y^2 - xy}}.$

Then $\dfrac{ds}{dt}\Big|_{x=y=10} = \dfrac{-600 + 800 - 400 + 300}{2\sqrt{100 + 100 - 100}} = 5.$

Hence they are separating from each other at 5 mi. per hour at the instant when each is 10 mi. from the station.

19. A boy is running on a horizontal plane directly towards the foot of a tower that is 60 ft. high, at the rate of 5 mi. an hour. At what rate is he approaching the top when he is 80 ft. from the base?

20. A boy is running at the rate of 8 mi. an hour on a horizontal plane directly towards the foot of a tower 100 ft. high. How much faster is he approaching the foot than the top of the tower when he is 50 ft. from the foot? How far from the foot of the tower is he when he is approaching the top $\frac{1}{2}$ as fast as he is approaching the foot?

21. One end of a string wound in a ball is fastened to the top of a pole 50 ft. high, and a man holding the ball 5 ft. above the ground walks away from the base of the pole at the rate of 4 mi. an hour. What is the man's distance from the pole when the string is unwinding at the rate of 2 mi. an hour?

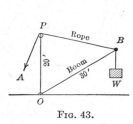

Fig. 43.

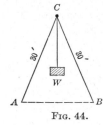

Fig. 44.

22. An aeroplane flying horizontally at a rate of 100 ft. a second passes directly over a fort at a height of 8000 ft. How fast is its distance from the fort increasing 1 min. later?

23. The rope *APB*, Fig. 43, runs over a fixed pulley at *P* 20 ft. above *O*, and is fastened at *B* to the end of the boom *OB*, 30 ft. in length. A weight *W* hangs from *B*. The rope is being wound in at the rate of 4 ft. per second. How rapidly is *W* rising when *PB* is horizontal?

24. A weight *W* is being lifted by a pair of shears having legs *AC* = *BC* = 30 ft., Fig. 44. How fast is *W* being raised when *A* and *B* are 20 ft. apart if they are being drawn together at the rate of 9 in. per second?

CHAPTER IX

INTEGRATION

57. The inverse of differentiation.—Just as division is the operation that is the inverse of multiplication, and the extraction of a root is the inverse of raising to a power, so differentiation has its inverse operation. Here, as usual, the inverse operation is the more difficult. In fact, it is frequently impossible to do the inverse of a differentiation except approximately.

The process of doing the inverse of a differentiation is called **integration.** The result obtained is called an **integral.**

Before proceeding with the methods of integrating, it will be well to consider with some care just what is meant by the inverse of differentiation. The student should now read again **Arts. 14, 15,** and **49–51,** and think through once more the ideas involved in the derivative and the differential. He should consider carefully the meaning of related changes in variables and rate of change of variables, and how they are expressed. He should keep in mind always that the ideas involved are of *first* importance.

Heretofore the questions have dealt with the rates of change in variables when the relations of the variables were known, or with corresponding changes in the related variables. Now the starting point will be with the rates of change or with the related changes in the variables. That is, the rate of change of a function is given and it is required to find the value of the function.

If the rate of change of a function is constant, the finding of the value of the function is merely a question of arithmetic. For instance, it is required to find the distance s that a train will run in 3 hr. at a constant rate of 40 mi. an hour.

As a second illustration, let it be required to find the quantity Q, in cubic feet, of water in a tank if it has been running in at a constant rate of r, in cubic feet a minute, for t minutes, provided there were C cubic feet of water in the tank at the beginning. Here it is evident that, by simple arithmetic

$$Q = rt + C.$$

If, however, in either of these illustrations the rate is not constant, then the question cannot be answered so readily; but such questions arise frequently, and one must have a way to answer them.

58. Inverse processes.—Any process in mathematics has its inverse, that is, for any given process there is always a second process that neutralizes the first. Division neutralizes multiplication, extraction of a root neutralizes raising to a power, finding the number corresponding to a logarithm neutralizes finding the logarithm of a number.

In teaching mathematics it is a good policy to present first the easier of two processes that are the inverse of each other. For this reason, the process that we usually call the inverse is the more difficult process. Thus, the process of extracting the root of a number is more difficult than raising a number to a power, and it is taught second.

It is well to notice also that often the inverse process does not give a definite result as does the first process. For instance, the square of 3 is 9 and nothing else, while the square root of 9 is either $+3$ or -3. Another illustration is, given an angle to find its sine; and its converse, given the sine of the angle to find the angle. Thus, $\sin 30° = \frac{1}{2}$ and nothing else, while $\sin^{-1} \frac{1}{2} = 30°$, $150°$, $390°$, $510°$, etc. Here we should have to know something else than the sine of the angle in order to determine one definite angle. For instance, if it were also known that the angle was an acute angle of a triangle, then $\sin^{-1} \frac{1}{2} = 30°$, and no other value would be permissible.

This will be found to be the case in integration, that is, *some other information besides the rate of change of a function will be necessary in order to find a definite value of the function.*

59. Fundamental question in integral calculus.—Integral calculus deals with questions that are the inverse of those considered in differential calculus. That is, the fundamental question in integral calculus is: Given the rate of change of a quantity and the value of the quantity at some certain instant to find the value of the quantity at any instant This statement is made with the understanding that the independent variable is time. A more general statement is as follows: Given the rate of change of the dependent variable, or function, with respect to the independent variable together with the value of the dependent variable for a certain value of the independent variable, to find the value of the dependent variable corresponding to any value of the independent variable. In symbols this is: Given $\dfrac{dy}{dx} = f(x)$, or $dy = f(x)dx$, and the value of y corresponding to a particular value of x, to find the relation $y = F(x)$.

60. Notation.—In trigonometry the inverse of $\sin \theta = a$ is $\sin^{-1} a = \theta$. The same symbols for the inverse might be used in calculus, but it is not customary to use this form. The symbol for the inverse of differentiation is $\int$, an elongated S. This symbol indicates that the differential before which it is placed is to be integrated.

Thus, $\int dy$ indicates that a function is to be found of which dy is the differential. The form $\int x^2 dx$ indicates that a function is to be found of which $x^2 dx$ is the differential.

The form $\int f(x)dx$ is read "the integral of $f(x)dx$."

The word *integral* implies the *total amount*. The expression "integral of the rate" means precisely "the total made from the rate."

61. Indefinite integral.—If one is to find $\int 2x\, dx$ it is only necessary to know a function of x such that its differential is $2x\, dx$. Such a function is evidently x^2; but x^2 is not the only function of which the differential is $2x\, dx$, for the differential of $x^2 + C$, where C is any constant, is $2x\, dx$. Thus $2x\, dx$ is the differential of $x^2 + 3, x^2 + 7, x^2 + \sin 30°$, etc.

$$\therefore \int 2x\, dx = x^2 + C.$$

In general, $\qquad \int f'(x)dx = f(x) + C.$

Since in such an integral there is no indication of what the constant may be, the integral is called an **indefinite integral.**

The constant C that is supplied when integrating is called the **constant of integration.**

62. Methods of integrating.—To determine the integrals of various differentials that may arise requires very definite knowledge of differentiation, facility in manipulating algebraic and trigonometric expressions, and much ingenuity. In general, an indefinite integral is found by one of the following:

(1) *By recognizing at once a function whose differential is the given differential.*

(2) *By reversing the rules of differentiation.*

(3) *By reference to a table of integrals.*

In the following exercises occur integrals that should be recognized at once.

EXERCISES

To test ability to write the indefinite integrals in simple cases, cover the results given in exercises 1–24 by a piece of paper and write the results, then compare with the text.

1. $\int dx = x + C$

2. $\int dy = y + C.$

3. $\int x\,dx = \frac{1}{2}x^2 + C.$

4. $\int 3x\,dx = \frac{3}{2}x^2 + C.$

5. $\int 6x\,dx = 3x^2 + C.$

6. $\int 3x^2dx = x^3 + C.$

7. $\int 4x^3dx = x^4 + C.$

8. $\int 5x^4dx = x^5 + C.$

9. $\int 3x^3dx = \frac{3}{4}x^4 + C.$

10. $\int x^5dx = \frac{1}{6}x^6 + C.$

11. $\int x^ndx = \dfrac{1}{n+1}\,x^{n+1} + C$

12. $\int x^{\frac{1}{2}}dx = \frac{2}{3}x^{\frac{3}{2}} + C.$

13. $\int \frac{4}{3}x^{\frac{1}{3}}dx = x^{\frac{4}{3}} + C.$

14. $\int \frac{7}{2}x^{\frac{5}{2}}dx = x^{\frac{7}{2}} + C.$

15. $\int x^{\frac{2}{3}}dx = \frac{3}{5}x^{\frac{5}{3}} + C.$

16. $\int 2u\,du = u^2 + C.$

17. $\int 2(x + 1)dx = (x + 1)^2 + C.$

18. $\int (x + 1)^2dx = \frac{1}{3}(x + 1)^3 + C.$

19. $\int 2(x^2 + 1)2x\,dx = (x^2 + 1)^2 + C.$

20. $\int 3(x^2 - 1)^22x\,dx = (x^2 - 1)^3 + C.$

21. $\int 3(x^3 + 1)^23x^2dx = (x^3 + 1)^3 + C.$

22. $\int (x^4 + 1)^34x^3dx = \frac{1}{4}(x^4 + 1)^4 + C.$

23. $\int (2x^2 - 6)^34x\,dx = \frac{1}{4}(2x^2 - 6)^4 + C.$

24. $\int 2(x^2 + 2x)(2x + 2)dx = (x^2 + 2x)^2 + C.$

In exercises 25–36 integrate to find the value of the dependent variable, that is, the function, and test the result by differentiation.

25. $dy = 4x\,dx.$

26. $dy = -3x^2dx.$

27. $dy = -10x\,dx.$

28. $dy = 0.02x^2dx.$

29. $dy = (x^2 - 3)^22x\,dx.$

30. $dy = 0.01x^8dx.$

31. $ds = -32t\,dt.$

32. $ds = at\,dt.$

33. $ds = 0.006t^2dt.$

34. $dv = 3t^{-2}dt.$

35. $dv = 4t^{-\frac{1}{2}}dt.$

36. $dp = kv^{-2.41}dv.$

Determine the functions whose derivatives are given in exercises 37–48 and test by finding the derivatives of the results. These may be put in the form of the preceding by multiplying by the differential of the independent variable.

37. $\dfrac{dy}{dx} = 4x^2$.

43. $\dfrac{dv}{dt} = -4t^{-3}$.

38 $\dfrac{dy}{dx} = 2x(x^2 + 6)$.

44. $\dfrac{dv}{dt} = -0.01t^{-0.4}$.

39. $\dfrac{dy}{dx} = x^{-3}$.

45. $\dfrac{dp}{dv} = 2v^{-2.41}$.

40. $\dfrac{dy}{dx} = 0.015x^4$.

46. $\dfrac{dy}{dx} = 4.5x^{-7}$.

41. $\dfrac{ds}{dt} = 10t^{-6}$.

47. $\dfrac{dy}{dx} = 3x^2(x^3 + 5)^2$.

42. $\dfrac{ds}{dt} = \frac{1}{2}t^{-\frac{2}{3}}$.

48. $\dfrac{dy}{dx} = 4(x^3 + 2x^2)^3(3x^2 + 4x)$.

63. Determination of the constant of integration.—As was stated in **Art. 58,** some other information besides the rate of change or the differential of the function is necessary in order that the constant of integration may be found. When such other facts are given, a definite value of the function can be found. This can be best illustrated by examples.

Example 1.   Find the equation of a straight line which has a slope of 2, and passes through the point (2, 7).

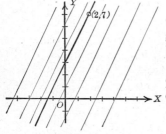

FIG. 45.

Solution. The equation could, of course, be written by analytic geometry, but here it is solved by calculus.

Since the slope of any line is $\dfrac{dy}{dx}$, we have, $\dfrac{dy}{dx} = 2$.

Multiplying by dx, $dy = 2dx$.

Integrating, $\qquad y = 2x + C$.

This equation is not the equation of a definite line, but is the general equation of all lines having a slope of 2. Some of these lines are shown in Fig. 45. Evidently one, and only one, of these lines can pass through the point (2, 7), and for this particular line the constant C of the equation will have a definite value. To find this value of C we make the line pass through (2, 7), that is, we substitute the coördinates of this point for x and y in the equation and solve for C.

Substituting $x = 2$ and $y = 7$, $7 = 2 \cdot 2 + C$. $\therefore C = 3$.

Putting this value of C in the equation, $y = 2x + 3$.

Therefore this is the equation of the particular line sought.

Example 2. Find the equation of a curve such that the slope of its tangent line at any point shall be equal to the abscissa of the point if, further, it is given that the curve passes through the point (2, 4).

Solution. Since $\dfrac{dy}{dx}$ = slope of tangent, and x = abscissa of point of tangency,

$$\frac{dy}{dx} = x.$$

Considering $\dfrac{dy}{dx}$ as the ratio of dy to dx, and multiplying by dx

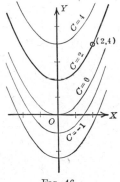

Fig. 46.

$$dy = x \, dx.$$

Then $\int dy = \int x \, dx$, and

$$y = \tfrac{1}{2}x^2 + C.$$

Here C is any constant, and the equation represents all parabolas having their axes on the y-axis and opening upward. Some of these are represented in Fig. 46.

It is evident that one such parabola can pass through any particular point of the plane. The one sought passes through (2, 4), and therefore these values must satisfy the equation $y = \tfrac{1}{2}x^2 + C$.

Substituting (2, 4) in this equation,

$$4 = \tfrac{1}{2} \cdot 2^2 + C. \therefore C = 2.$$

The equation of the curve satisfying both conditions is then

$$y = \tfrac{1}{2}x^2 + 2.$$

Example 3. Find the area bounded by the parabola $y^2 = 4x$ and the double ordinate corresponding to $x = 8$.

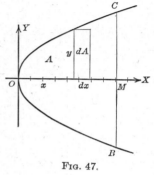

Fig. 47.

Solution. The parabola $y^2 = 4x$ is shown in Fig. 47, and is symmetrical with respect to the x-axis. Then one-half of the area is above the x-axis and is the area *OMC*.

Consider the area A as generated by an ordinate moving from the origin toward the right. When it has advanced any distance x

$$dA = y\,dx.$$

But $y = +2\sqrt{x}$ since y is positive.
Then $dA = 2\sqrt{x}\,dx.$
Integrating, $A = \tfrac{4}{3}x^{\frac{3}{2}} + C.$ (1)

A further fact about the area A is that $A = 0$ when $x = 0$.
Substituting these values in (1) gives

$$0 = 0 + C. \therefore C = 0.$$

Hence for any value of x, $A = \tfrac{4}{3}x^{\frac{3}{2}} + 0$.
And for $x = 8$, $A = \tfrac{4}{3}\cdot 8^{\frac{3}{2}} = \tfrac{64}{3}\sqrt{2} = 30.17-$.
$\therefore$ the total area $= 2A = 60.34 -$ square units.

Example 4. A body falls from a height of 200 ft. above the earth's surface. It is given that the velocity of a falling body is $32t$ ft. a second for any time t seconds after it starts to fall. Find its distance from the surface of the earth 3 sec. after it starts to fall.

Solution. Let s = the number of feet the body is above the earth's surface at any time.

Then since s is decreasing as t is increasing,

$$\frac{ds}{dt} = -32t.$$

Multiplying by dt, $ds = -32t\ dt$.
Integrating, $s = -16t^2 + C$.
To determine C we know that $s = 200$ when $t = 0$. Substituting these values,

$$200 = -16 \cdot 0 + C. \quad \therefore\ C = 200.$$

Then at any time t seconds after the body starts,

$$s = -16t^2 + 200.$$

When $t = 3$, $s = -16 \cdot 3^2 + 200 = 56$.

Hence at the end of 3 sec. the body is 56 ft. above the earth's surface.

EXERCISES

1. Find the equation of the straight line which has a slope of $\frac{1}{2}$ and passes through the point $(-4, -2)$.

2. A body is moving at the rate $\dfrac{dx}{dt} = \frac{3}{2}t^2$, where x is distance in feet and t is time in seconds. Find the distance it will move in t seconds if $x = 0$ when $t = 0$.

3. Find the equation of the curve whose slope at any point is equal to three times the abscissa of that point, and which passes through the point $(2, 6)$.

4. Find the equation of the curve whose slope at any point is equal to the square of its abscissa at that point, and which passes through the point $(1, 1)$.

5. Find the equation of the curve whose slope at any point is equal to the square root of its abscissa at that point, and which passes through the point $(2, 4)$.

6. Find the area enclosed by the parabola $y^2 = 2x$ and the double ordinate corresponding to $x = 4$.

7. Find the area enclosed by the parabola $y^2 = 3x$, the x-axis, and the ordinates corresponding to $x = 2$ and $x = 8$.

8. Find the area between the curve $y = 2x$ and the x-axis from the origin to the ordinate corresponding to $x = 10$.   Check by finding the area considered as a triangle.

9. Find the area between the curve $y = x^3$ and the x-axis from the origin to the ordinate corresponding to $x = 4$.

10. Find the area between the curve $y = x^3$ and the x-axis from the ordinate corresponding to $x = -3$ to the origin.

Suggestion.   Here, since the area lies below the x-axis, the value of y is negative.   Then in order that the area may be positive

$$dA = -ydx.$$

11. Find the area enclosed by the semi-cubical parabola $y = x^{\frac{3}{2}}$ and the double ordinate corresponding to $x = 4$.

12. Find the area enclosed by the curve $y = x^{-\frac{1}{2}}$, the x-axis, and the ordinates corresponding to $x = \frac{1}{2}$ and $x = 8$.

64. The $u^n du$ formula.—While a knowledge of differentiation enables one to write at once the integrals of many differentials, there are formulas that help in integrating forms that occur frequently. The following formula enables one to write at once the integral of $u^n du$ where u is any function of the independent variable and n is any constant except -1.

$$[13] \qquad \int u^n du = \frac{u^{n+1}}{n+1} + C.$$

The formula can be proved by finding the differential of the result, and noting that it is the differential of which the integral is to be found.

$$\text{Thus, } d\left(\frac{u^{n+1}}{n+1} + C\right) = d\left(\frac{u^{n+1}}{n+1}\right) + dC$$
$$= \frac{1}{n+1}(n+1)u^n du + 0 = u^n du.$$

Before applying the formula one must be *certain* that the differential which is to be integrated is *exactly* of the form $u^n du$.   The following are examples of such forms:

Example 1.   Find $\int x^4 dx$.
Here $u = x$, $du = dx$, and $n = 4$.
∴ $\int x^4 dx = \frac{1}{5}x^5 + C$.

Example 2.   Find $\int x^{-\frac{1}{2}} dx$.
Here $u = x$, $du = dx$, and $n = -\frac{1}{2}$.
∴ $\int x^{-\frac{1}{2}} dx = 2x^{\frac{1}{2}} + C$.

Example 3.   Find $\int (x^3 + x^2)^2(3x^2 + 2x)dx$.
Here $u = x^3 + x^2$, $du = (3x^2 + 2x)dx$, and $n = 2$.
∴ $\int (x^3 + x^2)^2(3x^2 + 2x)dx = \frac{1}{3}(x^3 + x^2)^3 + C$.

Example 4.   Find $\int \sqrt{x^2 + 1}\ 2x\ dx$.
Here $u = x^2 + 1$, $du = 2x\ dx$, and $n = \frac{1}{2}$.
∴ $\int \sqrt{x^2 + 1}\ 2x\ dx = \frac{2}{3}(x^2 + 1)^{\frac{3}{2}} + C$.

Example 5.   Find y if $\dfrac{dy}{dx} = \dfrac{1}{\sqrt{x^3}}$.

Multiplying by dx, $dy = \dfrac{dx}{\sqrt{x^3}} = x^{-\frac{3}{2}}dx$

Then $u = x$, $du = dx$, and $n = -\frac{3}{2}$.

∴ $y = \int x^{-\frac{3}{2}}dx = -2x^{-\frac{1}{2}} + C = -\dfrac{2}{\sqrt{x}} + C$.

Example 6.   Find s if $\dfrac{ds}{dt} = \dfrac{2t + 3}{\sqrt{(t^2 + 3t)^5}}$.

Multiplying by dt, $ds = (t^2 + 3t)^{-\frac{5}{2}}(2t + 3)dt$.
Then $u = t^2 + 3t$, $du = (2t + 3)dt$, and $n = -\frac{5}{2}$.
∴ $s = \int (t^2 + 3t)^{-\frac{5}{2}}(2t + 3)dt = -\frac{2}{3}(t^2 + 3t)^{-\frac{3}{2}} + C$,

$= \dfrac{2}{3\sqrt{(t^2 + 3t)^3}} + C$.

65. The formula $\int c\ du = c\int du$.—Another very useful fact is given in the following formula, which states that *any constant factor of a differential can be written before or after the integral sign at pleasure.*

[14] $\int c\ du = c\int du$.

Proof. Since $d(cu) = c \, du$, by differentiation,

then $\qquad cu = \int c \, du$. $\qquad$ By definition of integral.

But $\quad \int du = u$. $\qquad\qquad$ By [13] where $n = 0$.

And $\quad c \int du = cu$. $\qquad\qquad$ By an axiom.

$\therefore \int c \, du = c \int du$. $\qquad$ Equating values of cu.

Formula [14] enables one to put many integrals in the form of [13] whenever the change can be made by multiplying by a constant.

Example 1. Find $\int 6x^2 dx$.

By [14], $\qquad\qquad\qquad \int 6x^2 dx = 6 \int x^2 dx$.

By [13], $6 \int x^2 dx = 6(\frac{1}{3}x^3 + C') = 2x^3 + 6C' = 2x^3 + C$.

Example 2. Find $\int (x^3 + 3)^3 x^2 dx$.

Since multiplying and dividing by the same number does not change the value,

$$\int (x^3 + 3)^3 x^2 dx = \int \tfrac{1}{3}(x^3 + 3)^3 \, 3x^2 dx.$$

By [14], $\int \frac{1}{3}(x^3 + 3)^3 3x^2 dx = \frac{1}{3} \int (x^3 + 3)^3 3x^2 dx$.

By [13], $\frac{1}{3} \int (x^3 + 3)^3 3x^2 dx = \frac{1}{12}(x^3 + 3)^4 + C$.

$\therefore \int (x^3 + 3)^3 x^2 dx = \frac{1}{12}(x^3 + 3)^4 + C$.

66. Formula $\int (du + dv + \cdots) = \int du + \int dv + \cdots$

It frequently happens that a differential that is to be integrated can be put into forms like [13] by applying the formula

[15] $\quad \int (du + dv + \cdots) = \int du + \int dv + \cdots,$

where u and v may be any functions of the independent variable.

The formula may be stated in words as follows: *The integral of the sum of two or more differentials is equal to the sum of the integrals of these differentials.*

Proof for two differentials.

$\qquad\qquad d(u + v) = du + dv$. $\qquad$ By differentiation.

Then $\int (du + dv) = u + v$. $\quad$ By definition of integral.

But $u = \int du$ and $v = \int dv$. $\qquad\qquad$ By [13].

$\therefore \int (du + dv) = \int du + \int dv$.

This can readily be extended to the integral of the sum of any number of differentials.

Example 1.   Find $\int(x^3 + 3x^2 - x + 1)dx$.
By [15] $\int(x^3 + 3x^2 - x + 1)dx$
$$= \int x^3dx + \int 3x^2dx - \int xdx + \int dx$$
$$= \tfrac{1}{4}x^4 + x^3 - \tfrac{1}{2}x^2 + x + C.   \text{By [13] and [14]}.$$

Here C is the sum of the several constants of integration.

Example 2.   Find $\int \dfrac{x^4 - 3x^3 - 5x^2 + 7}{x^2}dx$.
By dividing,
$$\int \frac{x^4 - 3x^3 - 5x^2 + 7}{x^2}dx = \int(x^2 - 3x - 5 + 7x^{-2})dx.$$
By [15], $\int(x^2 - 3x - 5 + 7x^{-2})dx$
$$= \int x^2dx - \int 3xdx - \int 5dx + \int 7x^{-2}dx$$
$$= \tfrac{1}{3}x^3 - \tfrac{3}{2}x^2 - 5x - \frac{7}{x} + C.   \text{By [13] and [14]}.$$

EXERCISES

Integrate the following and test the results by differentiation:

1. $\int(4 + 5x^2)x \, dx$.

2. $\int(3x^5 - 8x^4)dx$.

3. $\int(6t^4 - 5t^3 + 3t^2)dt$.

4. $\int(x - 1)(x + 1)dx$.

5. $\int(x^3 + 1)^{\frac{3}{2}}x^2 \, dx$.

6. $\int(2x^{\frac{1}{2}} - 3x^{-\frac{1}{2}})dx$.

7. $\int(x^2 + 1)^2dx$.

8. $\int(x^2 + 1)^2x \, dx$.

9. $\int(\sqrt{x} + 2\sqrt[3]{x^2})dx$.

10. $\int(\sqrt{x} + 2\sqrt[3]{x^2})^2dx$.

11. $\int(x^2 + a^2)\sqrt{x} \, dx$.

12. $\int(a^2 - x^2)\sqrt[3]{x} \, dx$.

13. $\int(x^2 + 3x)^3(2x + 3)dx$.

14. $\int(x^4 + 4x)^7(x^3 + 1)dx$.

15. $\int 4\sqrt{x^2 + 3x + 2}(2x + 3)dx$.

16. $\int\sqrt{ax^2 + bx + c} \, (2ax + b)dx$.

17. $\int(x^{\frac{2}{3}} - \dfrac{a}{x^5})dx$.

18. $\int\dfrac{dx}{\sqrt{x + 1}}$.

19. $\int\dfrac{dt}{\sqrt{1 - 2t}}$.

20. $\int\dfrac{(1 - x)dx}{(2x - x^2)^2}$.

Find the function from each of the following derivatives.

21. $\dfrac{dy}{dx} = x(1 - x^2)^3$.

25. $\dfrac{dy}{dx} = 0.06x^2 - 0.04x^3$

22. $\dfrac{dy}{dx} = x^2(x^3 - 2)^{\frac{1}{2}}$.

26. $\dfrac{dy}{dx} = \dfrac{x}{(9 - 4x^2)^2}$.

23. $\dfrac{dy}{dx} = (3x^2 + x)(2x^3 + x^2)^3$.

27. $\dfrac{dy}{dx} = (\sqrt{c} - \sqrt{x})^3$.

24. $\dfrac{dv}{dt} = 6t^3 - 3t^{-2}$.

28. $\dfrac{ds}{dt} = \dfrac{t^2}{\sqrt{5t^3 + 7}}$.

29. Find the area that is below the x-axis and is enclosed by the parabola $y = x^2 - 4x + 3$ and the x-axis.

30. Find the area that is below the x-axis and is enclosed by the curve $y = x^3 - 4x^2 + 3x$ and the x-axis.

31. Find the area bounded by the semi-cubical parabola $4y^2 = x^3$ and the double ordinate corresponding to $x = 8$.

Suggestion. The curve is symmetrical with respect to the x-axis. The area can then be found by finding the area above the x-axis and multiplying by 2. The differential of the area is $dA = \frac{1}{2}x^{\frac{3}{2}}dx$. When $x = 0$, $A = 0$.

32. In dealing with a falling body, $\dfrac{dv}{dt} = g$, where v is the velocity and $g = 32$. Find the value of v when $t = 4$ if $v = 0$ when $t = 0$.

33. In dealing with a falling body, the velocity v feet a second at any time t seconds after it starts is given by the formula $v = gt + v_0$, where v_0 is the initial velocity. Find the distance s a body will fall in 4 sec. if it is started downward with a velocity $v_0 = 20$.

Suggestion. Since $v = \dfrac{ds}{dt}$, $\dfrac{ds}{dt} = gt + v_0$.

Multiplying by dt, $ds = (gt + v_0)dt$.

Integrate and note that $s = 0$, when $t = 0$.

34. As in the preceding exercise, if a body is thrown vertically downward with a velocity of 10 ft. a second, how far will it have moved at the end of 8 sec.?

35. If the acceleration of a body is proportional to the time and if $v = v_0$ and $s = s_0$, when $t = 0$, show that the total distance s a body will have moved at the end of t seconds is

$$s = \frac{kt^3}{6} + v_0 t + s_0.$$

Solution. Since the acceleration is proportional to the time, and $\frac{dv}{dt} = \frac{d^2s}{dt^2}$ = acceleration,

$$\frac{dv}{dt} = kt.$$

Multiplying by dt, $dv = ktdt$.
Integrating, $v = \frac{1}{2}kt^2 + C_1$.
But $v = v_0$ when $t = 0$. Substituting these values,
$$v_0 = \frac{1}{2}k \cdot 0 + C_1. \qquad\qquad \therefore C_1 = v_0.$$
Then $\qquad\qquad\qquad\qquad v = \frac{1}{2}kt^2 + v_0$.
Since $v = \frac{ds}{dt}$, $\qquad\qquad \frac{ds}{dt} = \frac{1}{2}kt^2 + v_0$.
Multiplying by dt, $\qquad ds = \frac{1}{2}kt^2dt + v_0dt$.
Integrating, $\qquad\qquad s = \frac{1}{6}kt^3 + v_0t + C_2$.
But $s = s_0$ when $t = 0$. Substituting these values,
$$s_0 = \frac{1}{6}k \cdot 0 + v_0 \cdot 0 + C_2. \quad \therefore C_2 = s_0$$
Then $\qquad\qquad s = \frac{1}{6}kt^3 + v_0t + s_0$.

36. A car starts and continues at a rate per second of $v = \frac{1}{8}t^2$. Knowing that $\frac{ds}{dt} = v$, find the formula for the distance s when it has moved t seconds. How far will it go in 4 sec.?

37. A flywheel starts and continues at an angular speed in radians per second of $\omega = 0.001t^3$. What is the time of the first revolution? Of the second? Of the eighth?

Suggestion. Let θ = the number of radians it turns through.

Then $\qquad\qquad\qquad \frac{d\theta}{dt} = \omega = 0.001t^3$.

Multiplying by dt, $\qquad d\theta = 0.001t^3dt$.
Integrating, $\qquad\qquad \theta = 0.00025t^4 + C$.
Substituting $\theta = 0$ when $t = 0$, $0 = 0 + C$. $\therefore C = 0$.
Then $\qquad\qquad\qquad \theta = 0.00025t^4$.

To find the time of the first revolution, it is necessary to find the time that has elapsed while θ has changed from 0 to 2π.

When $\theta = 0$, $t = 0$.

When $\theta = 2\pi$, $t = \sqrt[4]{\dfrac{2\pi}{0.00025}} = 12.59$.

$\therefore$ the first revolution is made in 12.59 sec.

38. The angular speed in radians per second of a flywheel while stopping is $\omega = 80 - 10t$. How many revolutions will it make before it stops?

39. Determine the equation of a curve passing through the point (1, 4), which has a slope at any point (x, y) proportional to $1 + x$.

40. A bullet is fired directly upward with a muzzle velocity of 2000 ft. per second. Find its velocity after it has risen 10,000 ft. (Neglect the action of the air.)

Suggestion. The acceleration is $g = 32$ ft. per second per second. Then $\frac{dv}{dt} = -32$.

Find $v = -32t + C$, and determine C from $v = 2000$ when $t = 0$.

Next put $\frac{ds}{dt} = v$, integrate, and substitute $s = 0$ when $t = 0$ to find the constant.

41. A wheel revolves so that its angular speed is $0.001t^2$ radians per second. If it starts from rest, how many revolutions will it make in 3 min.? How long will it take to make the first 100 revolutions?

42. Water is flowing from an opening in the side of a cylindrical tank having a cross section of 80 sq. ft. The speed of the water in the jet is equal to $\sqrt{2gh}$, where g is the the acceleration of gravity and h is the height of the surface of the water above the opening. If the cross section of the jet has an area of 0.05 sq. ft., how long will it take the surface of the water in the tank to lower from 80 ft. above the opening to 60 ft. above the opening?

Suggestion. As the water is lowering in the tank the differential of the volume at any instant in time dt is

$$dV = -80dh,$$

where $-dh$ corresponds to dt, since h is decreasing as t increases.

This same volume of water runs out through the opening in time dt, and is given by

$$dV = 0.05\sqrt{2gh}\, dt.$$
$$\therefore\ -80dh = 0.05\sqrt{2gh}\, dt.$$

Solving for dt, $dt = -\dfrac{1600}{\sqrt{2g}}\, h^{-\frac{1}{2}}dh.$

Integrate and note that $h = 80$ when $t = 0$.

CHAPTER X

TRIGONOMETRIC FUNCTIONS

67. In the previous chapters only algebraic functions have been used in finding derivatives and integrals. In the present chapter the derivatives and differentials of the trigonometric functions will be found, and some of the simple integrals considered.

Since the formulas for the differentiation of trigonometric functions are simpler when the angles are expressed in radians, the circular, or radian measure, for the angles will be used instead of degrees. However, when computations are to be made and numerical values found in problems, it will be frequently necessary to change radians to degrees, minutes, and seconds so that reference can be made to tables of trigonometric functions. The student should then review these subjects before proceeding with the work, of this chapter. **P. M. III, Art. 52; IV, Arts. 25, 26; H. S., Arts. 361, 362.**

The following relations are given for reference:

2π radians $= 360°$.

$$1 \text{ radian} = 360° \div 2\pi = 57.2957795° +.$$
$$= 57° \ 17' \ 44.8''.$$
$$1° = 2\pi \text{ radians} \div 360 = 0.0174533 + \text{ radians.}$$

68. Derivative of sin u and cos u.—Let O be a unit circle generated by the point $P(x, y)$ moving in the positive direction, Fig. 48.

117

Let u be the measure of the angle XOP in radians, and let s be the measure of the arc XP in linear units.

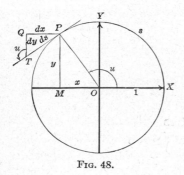

FIG. 48.

Then $u = s$, $x = \cos u$, and $y = \sin u$.

Differentiating, $du = ds$, $dx = d(\cos u)$, and
$$dy = d(\sin u).$$

In the differential triangle PQT,
$dx = PQ$, $dy = QT$, and $ds = PT$.

Also the angle at T through which the tangent has turned is equal to u.

Now $dy = ds \cos u$, $\cos u$ and dy having the same sign. But $dy = d(\sin u)$ and $ds = du$.

$\therefore d(\sin u) = \cos u \, du$.

Dividing by dx gives the derivative formula:

[16]
$$\frac{d(\sin u)}{dx} = \cos u \frac{du}{dx}.$$

Also $dx = -ds \sin u$, $\sin u$ and dx having opposite signs. But $dx = d(\cos u)$ and $ds = du$.

$\therefore d(\cos u) = -\sin u \, du$.

Dividing by dx gives the derivative formula:

[17]
$$\frac{d(\cos u)}{dx} = -\sin u \frac{du}{dx}.$$

Formulas [16] and [17] may be stated respectively in the following rules:

The derivative of the sine of an angle is equal to the cosine of the angle times the derivative of the angle.

The derivative of the cosine of an angle is equal to the negative of the sine of the angle times the derivative of the angle.

It should be noted that in handling trigonometric functions where algebraic operations on these functions are indicated, the rules for finding the derivatives of algebraic functions are to be used.

Thus, $\dfrac{d}{dx}(\sin u + \cos u) = \dfrac{d(\sin u)}{dx} + \dfrac{d(\cos u)}{dx}\cdot$ By [**15**].

$$\dfrac{d(\sin^4 u)}{dx} = 4 \sin^3 u \ \dfrac{d(\sin u)}{dx}\cdot \qquad \text{By [10].}$$

69. Derivation of formula for derivative of sin u by method of limits.—This derivation of the formula for the derivative of sin u may be found easier to follow than the method of the preceding article. Here the fundamental method (**Art. 15**) is used.

Given $y = \sin u$, where u is a function of x.

Let $x = x_1$, $\qquad\qquad y_1 = \sin u$.

Let $x = x_1 + \Delta x$, $y_1 + \Delta y = \sin (u_1 + \Delta u)$.

Subtracting, $\qquad \Delta y = \sin(u_1 + \Delta u) - \sin u_1$

$\qquad = 2 \cos (u_1 + \tfrac{1}{2}\Delta u) \sin \tfrac{1}{2}\Delta u$. By trigonometry.

(P. M. IV. Art. 88, [30]; H. S. Art. 427, [87].)

Dividing by Δx, $\dfrac{\Delta y}{\Delta x} = 2 \cos (u_1 + \tfrac{1}{2}\Delta u)\dfrac{\sin \tfrac{1}{2}\Delta u}{\Delta x}$

$$= \cos (u_1 + \tfrac{1}{2}\Delta u) \ \dfrac{\sin \tfrac{1}{2}\Delta u}{\tfrac{1}{2}\Delta u}\cdot\dfrac{\Delta u}{\Delta x}\cdot$$

Let $\Delta x \to 0$, then by **Art. 12** (5),

$\lim\limits_{\Delta x \to 0}\left[\dfrac{\Delta y}{\Delta x}\right]$

$\qquad = \lim\limits_{\Delta x \to 0}\left[\cos (u_1 + \tfrac{1}{2}\Delta u)\right]\lim\limits_{\Delta x \to 0}\left[\dfrac{\sin\tfrac{1}{2}\Delta u}{\tfrac{1}{2}\Delta u}\right]\lim\limits_{\Delta x \to 0}\left[\dfrac{\Delta u}{\Delta x}\right].$

Now $\lim\limits_{\Delta x \to 0}\left[\dfrac{\Delta y}{\Delta x}\right] = \dfrac{dy}{dx}$ by definition;

$\qquad \lim\limits_{\Delta x \to 0}[\cos(u_1 + \tfrac{1}{2}\Delta u)] = \cos u_1$, for $\Delta u \to 0$ as $\Delta x \to 0$;

$\qquad \lim\limits_{\Delta x \to 0}\left[\dfrac{\sin \tfrac{1}{2}\Delta u}{\tfrac{1}{2}\Delta u}\right] = 1$ by **Art. 70**;

and $\lim\limits_{\Delta x \to 0} \left[\dfrac{\Delta u}{\Delta x}\right] = \dfrac{du}{dx}$ by definition.

Hence $\dfrac{dy}{dx} = \cos u \, \dfrac{du}{dx}.$

70. Relation between sin θ, θ, and tan θ, for small angles.

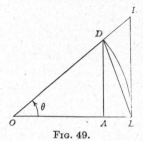

FIG. 49.

Draw angle $BOE = \theta$, in radians, Fig. 49. With O as center and $OB = 1$ as radius, describe the arc BD. Draw DA perpendicular to OB and BE tangent to the arc at B.

Then $\sin \theta = AD$, $\theta = $ arc BD, having the same measure, and $\tan \theta = BE$. Also

area of triangle $OBD <$ sector $OBD <$ area of triangle OBE.

But area of triangle $OBD = \frac{1}{2}OB \times AD$,

area of sector $OBD = \frac{1}{2}\overline{OB}^2 \times \theta$,

and   area of triangle $OBE = \frac{1}{2}OB \times BE$.

Hence $\frac{1}{2}OB \times AD < \frac{1}{2}\overline{OB}^2 \times \theta < \frac{1}{2}OB \times BE$.

Dividing by $\frac{1}{2}$ and substituting $OB = 1$, $AD = \sin \theta$, and $BE = \tan \theta$,

(1) $\sin \theta < \theta < \tan \theta.$

Dividing by $\sin \theta$ and remembering that $\tan \theta = \dfrac{\sin \theta}{\cos \theta}$,

$$1 < \frac{\theta}{\sin \theta} < \sec \theta.$$

But as $\theta \to 0$, $\sec \theta \to 1$, then since $\dfrac{\theta}{\sin \theta}$ is always between 1 and a quantity which approaches 1 as a limit, we have

[18] $\lim\limits_{\theta \to 0}\left[\dfrac{\theta}{\sin \theta}\right] = 1.$

Again dividing (1), by $\tan \theta$ and simplifying,

$$\cos \theta < \frac{\theta}{\tan \theta} < 1.$$

But as $\theta \to 0$, cos $\theta \to 1$, then

[19] $$\lim_{\theta \to 0}\left[\frac{\theta}{\tan \theta}\right] = 1.$$

By computing the following table the student will verify the formulas [18] and [19] as the angles become small.

Angle θ in degrees	Angle θ in radians	sin θ	tan θ	$\dfrac{\theta}{\sin \theta}$	$\dfrac{\theta}{\tan \theta}$
20°	0.3491				
10°	0.1745				
5°	0.0873				
4°	0.0698				
3°	0.0524				
2°	0.0349				
1°	0.0175				
$\frac{1}{2}$°	0.0087				

These results show that for small angles sin θ and tan θ may be replaced by θ in radians in any computation and the results will be approximately correct. It should be carefully noted that this statement does not mean that the limits are not exactly 1.

71. Illustrative examples.—In using the calculus, the trigonometric functions that occur most frequently are the sine and cosine. In differentiating or integrating these functions it is evident that only sines and cosines are obtained.

The formulas for integrating sine or cosine can be obtained by taking the inverse of formulas [17] and [16]. They are as follows:

[20] $\int \text{sin u du} = -\cos u + C.$

[21] $\int \cos u \, du = \sin u + C.$

In all computations the angles of the formulas are measured in radians.

Example 1.   Given $y = \sin^3 x$, find $\dfrac{dy}{dx}$.

Solution. $\dfrac{dy}{dx} = 3 \sin^2 x \dfrac{d(\sin x)}{dx}$.   By [**10**].

$\dfrac{dy}{dx} = 3 \sin^2 x \cos x$.   By [**16**].

Example 2.   Given $y = \sin (3x^2 + 4x - 1)$, find $\dfrac{dy}{dx}$.

Solution. $\dfrac{dy}{dx} = \dfrac{d \sin (3x^2 + 4x - 1)}{dx}$

$= \cos (3x^2 + 4x - 1) \dfrac{d(3x^2 + 4x - 1)}{dx}$.   By [**16**].

But $\dfrac{d(3x^2 + 4x - 1)}{dx} = \dfrac{d(3x^2)}{dx} + \dfrac{d(4x)}{dx} - \dfrac{d1}{dx} = 6x + 4.$

$\therefore \dfrac{dy}{dx} = (6x + 4) \cos (3x^2 + 4x - 1).$

Example 3.   Find the maximum and minimum points of the curve $y = \cos x$.

Solution. $\dfrac{dy}{dx} = -\sin x.$

Putting $\dfrac{dy}{dx} = 0$ gives $-\sin x = 0.$

$\therefore x = n\pi$, where $n = 0, \pm 1, \pm 2, \cdot \cdot \cdot \cdot$.

For values of x near an even number of times π, but less, $-\sin x$ is positive; and for values of x near an even number of times π, but greater, $-\sin x$ is negative.   Hence the curve is rising before and falling after $x = 2n\pi$.

$\therefore$ maximum points are the points for which $x = 2n\pi$.

Likewise minimum points are the points for which

$$x = (2n + 1)\pi.$$

Note that $2n$ is an even number and $2n + 1$ is an odd number.

A portion of the curve is shown in Fig. 50. Maximum points are at A, B, and C. Minimum points arc at E, F, G, and H.

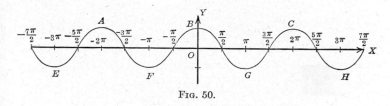

FIG. 50.

Example 4. Find the area enclosed by an arch of the curve $y = \sin x$ and the x-axis.

Solution. The curve $y = \sin x$ is shown in Fig. 51. The area sought extends from $x = 0$ to $x = \pi$.

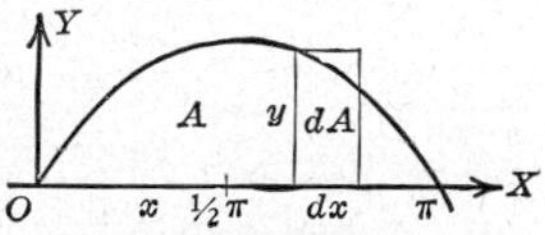

Consider this area A as being generated by an ordinate moving toward the right.

FIG. 51.

Then $dA = y\,dx = \sin x\,dx$.

Integrating, $A = -\cos x + C$.   By [**20**].

To find the value of C we know that $A = 0$ when $x = 0$. Substituting these values, $0 = -\cos 0 + C$, or $C = 1$.

When $x = \pi$, $A = -\cos \pi + 1 = 2 =$ number of square units in area.

Example 5. Find $\int \sin^3 x \cos x\,dx$.

Solution. Since $\cos x\,dx$ is the differential of $\sin x$, $\int \sin^3 x \cos x\,dx$ is of the form $\int u^n du$, where $\sin x = u$ and $\cos x\,dx = du$.

$\therefore \int \sin^3 x \cos x\,dx = \frac{1}{4}\sin^4 x + C.$ By [**13**].

EXERCISES

In exercises 1–32 find the derivatives.

1. $y = \sin 3x$.

2. $y = \cos 6x$.

3. $y = \sin x \cos x$.

4. $y = \cos^5 x$.

5. $y = \sin^n x$.

6. $y = \sin^2 x \cos x$.

7. $y = \sin 2x \cos 3x$.

8. $y = \sin^2 x \cos 3x$.

9. $y = \sin \frac{1}{2}x \cos 5x$.

10. $y = \sqrt{\sin 3x}$.

11. $\rho = a \cos^2 \theta$.

12. $\rho = \sqrt{1 - \cos \theta}$.

13. $y = \dfrac{\sin x}{\cos x}$.

14. $y = \dfrac{1}{\cos^2 x}$.

15. $y = \dfrac{\cos x}{\sin x}$.

16. $y = \dfrac{1 - \cos x}{1 + \cos x}$.

17. $x = a(\theta - \sin \theta)$.

18. $y = x \sin x$.

19. $y = x^2 \sin x$.

20. $y = x^3 \cos x$.

21. $y = \sin (x^2 + 2x - 3)$.

22. $y = \cos (2x^2 - 3x)$.

23. $y = \sin^2 (x^2 - 3)$.

24. $y = \frac{1}{3} \sin^4 x + 3x^2 + 2$.

25. $y = \sin^3 x \cos^2 x$.

26. $y = \cos^2 x \sqrt{\cos 2x}$.

27. $\rho = a(\sin 2\theta + \cos 2\theta)$.

28. $y = \sin 3x - 4 \sin^3 x$.

29. $y = \dfrac{1 - \sin^3 \theta}{\cos \theta}$.

30. $y = \dfrac{\sin^2 \theta}{\sqrt{\cos \theta}}$.

31. $y = \sqrt{\dfrac{1 - \cos x}{1 + \cos x}}$.

32. $y = a \sin \theta + a\theta \cos \theta$.

In exercises 33–46 find the indefinite integrals.

33. $\int \sin 3x \cdot 3dx$.

34. $\int \cos 2x \cdot 2dx$.

35. $\int \sin 2x \, dx$.

36. $\int \cos 4x \, dx$.

37. $\int \cos (2x + 1)2 \, dx$.

38. $\int \sin (3x + 2)dx$.

39. $\int \sin (5x - 16)dx$.

40. $\int \sin x \cos x \, dx$.

41. $\int \cos^2 x \sin x \, dx$.

42. $\int \sin^n x \cos x \, dx$.

43. $\int \cos^n x \sin x \, dx$.

44. $\int \sin^3 (x + 2) \cos (x + 2) \, dx$.

45. $\int \cos^2 (2x - 1) \sin (2x - 1) \, dx$.

46. $\int (\sin^3 x - \sin^2 x) \cos x \, dx$.

47. Given $x = a(\theta - \sin \theta)$ and $y = a(1 - \cos \theta)$, find dx and dy, then by division find $\dfrac{dy}{dx}$.

48. Find the area enclosed by one arch of the curve $y = \cos x$ and the x-axis.

49. Find the slope of the tangent to the curve $y = \sin x$ at the point where $x = \frac{1}{4}\pi$.   Where $x = 2$.

50. Find the slope of the tangent to the cycloid $x = a(\theta - \sin \theta)$, $y = a(1 - \cos \theta)$ at the point where $\theta = \frac{1}{2}\pi$.   Where $\theta = \pi$.   Where $\theta = 0$.   (See Art. 204.)

Suggestion.   To find $\dfrac{dy}{dx}$, first find dy and dx and then divide dy by dx.

51. Find the maximum and minimum points, and the points of inflection of the curve $y = \sin x$.

52. Find the equation of the curve passing through the point $(\pi, 0)$, if the slope of the tangent at any point is equal to the cosine of the abscissa of that point.

53. The range m in miles of a projectile is given by the formula

$$m = 165v^2 \sin 2\alpha,$$

where α is the angle of elevation of the gun and can be varied, and v is the muzzle velocity in miles per second.   Find the value of α for the maximum range, and find the maximum range for a muzzle velocity of 3000 ft. per second.

54. An ice cream cone holds $\frac{1}{8}$ pint. If it is a right circular cone with the vertex angle 2θ, find the value of θ that will make the amount of material in the cone a minimum.

F_IG._ 52.

Solution.   Let r = radius of base, h = altitude, s = slant height, S = lateral area of cone, and V = volume.

It is required to find θ when S is a minimum.

(1) $S = \pi rs$.   By geometry.

(2) $V = \frac{1}{3}\pi r^2 h$.   By geometry.

But $V = \frac{1}{8}$ pint $= \frac{2\,3\,1}{6\,4}$ cu. in., $r = s \sin \theta$, $h = s \cos \theta$.

Substituting in (2), $\frac{2\,3\,1}{6\,4} = \frac{1}{3}\pi s^2 \sin^2 \theta\, s \cos \theta = \frac{1}{3}\pi s^3 \sin^2 \theta \cos \theta$.

Solving for s^3, $s^3 = \dfrac{693}{64\pi \sin^2 \theta \cos \theta}$.

Substituting in (1), $S = \pi \sin \theta \left(\dfrac{693}{64\pi \sin^2 \theta \cos \theta} \right)^{\frac{2}{3}}$.

Or $\qquad S = \dfrac{693^{\frac{2}{3}}\pi^{\frac{1}{3}}}{16} \dfrac{1}{(\sin \theta)^{\frac{1}{3}}(\cos \theta)^{\frac{2}{3}}}$.

By Art. **43** (2) and (6) S will be a minimum when $(\sin \theta)^{\frac{1}{3}} (\cos \theta)^{\frac{2}{3}}$ is a maximum.   Put it equal to M.

Then $\qquad M = (\sin \theta)^{\frac{1}{3}}(\cos \theta)^{\frac{2}{3}}$.

Differentiating, $\dfrac{dM}{d\theta} = -\tfrac{2}{3}(\sin\,\theta)^{\frac{4}{3}}(\cos\,\theta)^{-\frac{4}{3}} + \tfrac{1}{3}(\cos\,\theta)^{\frac{5}{3}}(\sin\,\theta)^{-\frac{2}{3}}.$

Putting $\dfrac{dM}{d\theta} = 0,$ $-\dfrac{2(\sin\,\theta)^{\frac{4}{3}}}{3(\cos\,\theta)^{\frac{4}{3}}} + \dfrac{(\cos\,\theta)^{\frac{5}{3}}}{3(\sin\,\theta)^{\frac{2}{3}}} = 0,$

or $\dfrac{-2\sin^2\theta + \cos^2\theta}{3(\cos\,\theta)^{\frac{4}{3}}(\sin\,\theta)^{\frac{2}{3}}} = 0.$

Then $-2\sin^2\theta + \cos^2\theta = 0.$

Dividing by $\cos^2\theta,$ $\tan^2\theta = \tfrac{1}{2}.$

$$\tan\theta = \tfrac{1}{2}\sqrt{2} = 0.7071.$$

$\therefore$ $\theta = 35°\ 15.8'.$

Since this is the only acute value of θ, and since there must be a minimum for S, we decide that it is the proper value.

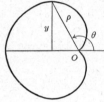

55. Find the value of ρ and θ for the highest point of the cardioid $\rho = 2a(1 - \cos\,\theta).$

Suggestion. The curve is as shown in Fig. 53. $y = \rho \sin\,\theta$ is to be a maximum. The equation is in polar coördinates.

Fig. 53.

56. A circle of radius 1 is being generated by a point moving with uniform velocity in the counter-clockwise direction, Fig. 54. At what part of the first quadrant of the arc is the arc being generated twice as rapidly as the sine of the angle is changing?

Solution. The rate that the sine of the angle is changing is

$$\frac{d(\sin\,\theta)}{dt} = \cos\,\theta\frac{d\theta}{dt}.$$

The rate that the arc is changing is represented by $\dfrac{ds}{dt}.$

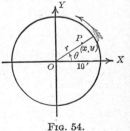

But $s = \theta.$

Then $\dfrac{ds}{dt} = \dfrac{d\theta}{dt}.$

$$\therefore \frac{d\theta}{dt} = 2\cos\,\theta\frac{d\theta}{dt}.$$

Fig. 54.

Solving for θ, $\theta = \cos^{-1}\tfrac{1}{2} = 60°.$

57. A wheel of radius 10 ft. is revolving uniformly about a fixed axis at 4 revolutions a minute, and a point P is moving outward along a radius at the rate of 6 ft. a minute. When the point P is 8 ft. from the center O, the angle the radius that the point is on makes with the horizontal is 60°. For this position find the horizontal and vertical velocities of P.

Solution. In Fig. 55, let P be the point that is revolving and at the same time is moving outward along the radius.

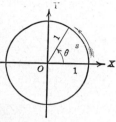

Let x and y be the coördinates of the point P, let r be its distance from the center, and let θ be the angle that OP makes with OX.

Since r is increasing at 6 ft. a minute, $\dfrac{dr}{dt} = 6$.

Since the point is revolving at the rate of 4 revolutions a minute, $\dfrac{d\theta}{dt} = 8\pi$.

Fig. 55.

The rates to be found are $\dfrac{dx}{dt}$ and $\dfrac{dy}{dt}$ when $\theta = 60°$ and $r = 8$.

The relations between the variables are $x = r \cos \theta$ and $y = r \sin \theta$.

Differentiating, $\quad \dfrac{dx}{dt} = -r \sin \theta \cdot \dfrac{d\theta}{dt} + \cos \theta \cdot \dfrac{dr}{dt}$,

$$\dfrac{dy}{dt} = r \cos \theta \cdot \dfrac{d\theta}{dt} + \sin \theta \cdot \dfrac{dr}{dt}.$$

When $\theta = 60°$ and $r = 8$, $\dfrac{dx}{dt} = -8 \sin 60° \cdot 8\pi + \cos 60° \cdot 6$

$$= -171.12 = \text{number of feet a minute.}$$

and $\qquad\qquad \dfrac{dx}{dt} = 8 \cos 60° \cdot 8\pi + \sin 60° \cdot 6$

$$= 105.73 = \text{number of feet a minute.}$$

58. In measuring an electric current with a tangent galvanometer, the percentage of error due to an error in the reading x, is proportional to $(\tan x + \cot x)$. Show that the percentage of error is least when $x = 45°$.

72. Derivatives of other trigonometric functions.— The following formulas complete the list of formulas for differentiating trigonometric functions, both the ordinary and the inverse. Their derivation can easily be carried out as exercises. They are not stated in words but the student can do so if he wishes. These formulas should be carefully memorized in order to deal readily with such functions.

[22] $$\frac{d(\tan u)}{dx} = \sec^2 u \frac{du}{dx}.$$

[23] $$\frac{d(\cot u)}{dx} = -\csc^2 u \frac{du}{dx}.$$

[24] $$\frac{d(\sec u)}{dx} = \sec u \tan u \frac{du}{dx}.$$

[25] $$\frac{d(\csc u)}{dx} = -\csc u \cot u \frac{du}{dx}.$$

[26] $$\frac{d(\text{vers } u)}{dx} = \sin u \frac{du}{dx}.$$

[27] $$\frac{d(\sin^{-1} u)}{dx} = \frac{\frac{du}{dx}}{\sqrt{1 - u^2}}.$$

[28] $$\frac{d(\cos^{-1} u)}{dx} = -\frac{\frac{du}{dx}}{\sqrt{1 - u^2}}.$$

[29] $$\frac{d(\tan^{-1} u)}{dx} = \frac{\frac{du}{dx}}{1 + u^2}.$$

[30] $$\frac{d(\cot^{-1} u)}{dx} = -\frac{\frac{du}{dx}}{1 + u^2}.$$

[31] $$\frac{d(\sec^{-1} u)}{dx} = \frac{\frac{du}{dx}}{u\sqrt{u^2 - 1}}.$$

[32] $$\frac{d(\csc^{-1} u)}{dx} = -\frac{\frac{du}{dx}}{u\sqrt{u^2 - 1}}.$$

[33] $$\frac{d(\text{vers}^{-1} u)}{dx} = \frac{\frac{du}{dx}}{\sqrt{2u - u^2}}.$$

73. Derivations and suggestions.—In deriving the formulas of the preceding article, the general plan of procedure is to express the function, of which the derivative is to be found, in terms of some function or functions of which the derivative has already been found.

Formula [**22**]. Let $y = \tan u$.

Since $\tan u = \dfrac{\sin u}{\cos u}$, $y = \dfrac{\sin u}{\cos u}$.

Then by [**9**], $\dfrac{dy}{dx} = \dfrac{\cos^2 u \dfrac{du}{dx} + \sin^2 u \dfrac{du}{dx}}{\cos^2 u}$

$$= \frac{1}{\cos^2 u}\frac{du}{dx} = \sec^2 u \frac{du}{dx}.$$

$$\therefore \frac{d(\tan u)}{dx} = \sec^2 u \frac{du}{dx}.$$

Formula [**23**]. Let $y = \cot u$, put $\cot u = \dfrac{\cos u}{\sin u}$, and use [**9**].

Formula [**24**]. Let $y = \sec u$, put $\sec u = \dfrac{1}{\cos u}$, and use [**9**]

Formula [**27**]. Let $y = \sin^{-1} u$.

Then $\sin y = u$.

Differentiating, $\cos y \dfrac{dy}{dx} = \dfrac{du}{dx}$.

Dividing by $\cos y$, $\dfrac{dy}{dx} = \dfrac{\dfrac{du}{dx}}{\cos y}$.

But $\cos y = \sqrt{1 - \sin^2 y} = \sqrt{1 - u^2}$.

$$\therefore \frac{d(\sin^{-1} u)}{dx} = \frac{\dfrac{du}{dx}}{\sqrt{1 - u^2}}.$$

Example 1. Given $y = \sec^3 2x$, find $\dfrac{dy}{dx}$.

Solution. $\dfrac{dy}{dx} = 3 \sec^2 2x \dfrac{d(\sec 2x)}{dx}$, By [**10**].

$\qquad = 3 \sec^2 2x \sec 2x \tan 2x \dfrac{d(2x)}{dx}$, By [**24**].

$\qquad = 6 \sec^3 2x \tan 2x.$ By [**8**].

Example 2.   Given $y = \tan^{-1}\dfrac{x + a}{1 - ax}$, find $\dfrac{dy}{dx}$.

Solution. $\dfrac{dy}{dx} = \dfrac{\dfrac{d}{dx}\left(\dfrac{x + a}{1 - ax}\right)}{1 + \left(\dfrac{x + a}{1 - ax}\right)^2}$,   By [29].

$$= \dfrac{\dfrac{(1 - ax) + a(x + a)}{(1 - ax)^2}}{\dfrac{1 + a^2x^2 + a^2 + x^2}{(1 - ax)^2}} = \dfrac{1}{1 + x^2}.$$

EXERCISES

Find the derivatives in exercises 1–24.

1. $y = \tan 2x$.

2. $y = \sec^2 x$.

3. $y = \csc 3x$.

4. $y = \tan^3 5x$.

5. $y = m \cot^n qx$.

11. $y = \dfrac{3 \tan x + 1}{\tan x + 3}$.

12. $y = \dfrac{\sec 3x}{\tan 3x + 1}$.

13. $y = \sin^{-1}\dfrac{x}{a}$.

14. $y = \cos^{-1}\dfrac{x}{a}$.

15. $y = \sin x \sin^{-1} x$.

21 $y = \tan^{-1}(\sec x + \tan x)$.

22. $y = \sin^{-1}\left(\dfrac{\sin x - \cos x}{\sqrt{2}}\right)$.

23. $y = \text{vers}^{-1}\dfrac{2x^2}{1 + x^2}$.

24. $y = \sqrt{2ax - x^2} + a \cos^{-1}\dfrac{\sqrt{2ax - x^2}}{a}$.

6. $\rho = \tan 3\theta + \sec 3\theta$.

7. $\rho = \frac{1}{3} \tan^3 \theta - \tan \theta + \theta$.

8. $y = \sin^2 x\sqrt{\sec x}$.

9. $y = \tan x \sec 2x$.

10. $y = (2 \sec^4 x + 3 \sec^2 x) \sin x$

16. $y = \sin^{-1}\dfrac{x}{\sqrt{1 + x^2}}$.

17. $y = \sec^{-1}\dfrac{a}{\sqrt{a^2 - x^2}}$.

18. $y = \csc^{-1}(x^2 + 2x)$.

19. $y = \tan^{-1}\dfrac{3a^2x - x^3}{a^3 - 3ax^2}$.

20. $y = \frac{1}{2}x\sqrt{a^2 - x^2} + \dfrac{a^2}{2} \sin^{-1}\dfrac{x}{a}$.

25. Derive the formula for the derivative of $\cos u$ by taking $\cos u = \sin\left(\frac{1}{2}\pi - u\right)$.

26. Derive the formula for the derivative of cot u by taking cot $u = \tan\left(\frac{1}{2}\pi - u\right)$.

27. Given $\sin 2\theta = 2 \sin \theta \cos \theta$, by differentiating derive the formula $\cos 2\theta = \cos^2 \theta - \sin^2 \theta$.

28. Given $\sin 3\theta = 3 \sin \theta - 4 \sin^3 \theta$, by differentiating derive the formula $\cos 3\theta = 4 \cos^3 \theta - 3 \cos \theta$.

Find $\dfrac{dy}{dx}$ in the implicit functions in exercises 29–34.

29. $y \sin x = 1.$ **32.** $xy = \tan^{-1} \dfrac{x}{y}.$

30. $y \tan^{-1} x - y^2 + x^2 = 0.$ **33.** $\cos (x - y) = 2x.$

31. $xy - y \sin x - x \cos y = 0.$ **34.** $y \sin x - \cos(x - y) = 0.$

35. Find $\dfrac{dy}{dx}$ and $\dfrac{d^2y}{dx^2}$ when $y = \cos^2 x - \sin^2 x$.

CHAPTER XI

LOGARITHMIC AND EXPONENTIAL FUNCTIONS

74. Formulas for differentiation.—A logarithmic function is one that involves a logarithm of a variable.

Thus, $\log x$, $\log (x^2 + 3x)$, and $\log \sin x$ are logarithmic functions; but $\log 25$ and $\log \sin 30°$ are not logarithmic functions, they are constants.

An **exponential function** is one in which a variable appears in an exponent.

Thus, 5^x, e^{x^2}, x^x, and $a^{\log x}$ are exponential functions; but x^5 and $(x^2 + 3x)^3$ are not exponential functions, they are algebraic functions.

The following five formulas are those usually given for differentiating logarithmic and exponential functions.

[34]
$$\frac{d(\log_e u)}{dx} = \frac{1}{u}\frac{du}{dx}.$$

[35]
$$\frac{d(\log_a u)}{dx} = \frac{1}{u}\frac{du}{dx}\log_a e.$$

[36]
$$\frac{d(a^u)}{dx} = a^u\frac{du}{dx}\log_e a.$$

[37]
$$\frac{d(e^u)}{dx} = e^u\frac{du}{dx}.$$

[38]
$$\frac{d(u^v)}{dx} = vu^{v-1}\frac{du}{dx} + u^v\frac{dv}{dx}\log_e u.$$

75. Exponents and logarithms.—Before proceeding to the proof of these formulas, the student who is not perfectly familiar with the principles used in dealing with logarithms and exponents should review them carefully.

P. M. II, Chapt. XIII; IV, Chapt. I; H. S., Chapts. XXIX and XXXIII.

In calculus logarithms to the base e are used for the sake of simplicity, where $e = 2.71828 \cdots$. In calculus, then, when no base is expressed, the base e is understood; while in trigonometry, when no base is expressed, the base 10 is understood.

The following relations are given for reference:

[39] $$\log_{10} e = 0.434294 = M.$$

The number $M = 0.434294$ is *the modulus of the common system of logarithms with reference to the natural system.*

[40] $$\log_e 10 = 2.302585 = \frac{1}{M}.$$

The number $\frac{1}{M} = 2.302585$ is *the modulus of the natural system of logarithms with reference to the common system.*

In changing logarithms from base 10 to base e or from base e to base 10, the following formulas are used, where N is any number of which a logarithm can be found.

[41] $$\log_e N = 2.302585 \log_{10} N.$$
[42] $$\log_{10} N = 0.434294 \log_e N.$$

All the decimal places given for the value of M and $\frac{1}{M}$ need not be used unless the desired accuracy makes it necessary. For most work it is sufficient to use the values $M = 0.4343$ and $\frac{1}{M} = 2.3026$.

Formulas [41] and [42] depend upon the following theorem the proof of which may be omitted by the student if he so wishes.

THEOREM. *Given the logarithm of a number N to the base a then the logarithm of N to the base b is given by the relation:*

[43] $$\log_b N = \frac{1}{\log_a b} \log_a N.$$

Proof.   Let $x = \log_b N$; then $b^x = N$.

Taking logarithm to base a, $\log_a b^x = \log_a N$,

or $\qquad\qquad x \log_a b = \log_a N.$

$$\therefore\quad x = \frac{1}{\log_a b} \log_a N.$$

But $\qquad\qquad x = \log_b N.$

(1) $\qquad\qquad \therefore\ \log_b N = \frac{1}{\log_a b} \log_a N.$

The constant multiplier, $\dfrac{1}{\log_a b}$, is called the **modulus** of the system of which the base is b with reference to the system of which the base is a.

If a is put for N in (1),

$$\log_b a = \frac{1}{\log_a b} \log_a a.$$

Then, since $\log_a a = 1$, $\log_b a = \dfrac{1}{\log_a b}.$

(2) $\qquad\qquad \therefore\ \log_b a \log_a b = 1.$

It follows from (1) that the modulus of the natural system with reference to the common system is $\dfrac{1}{\log_{10} e}$, and the modulus of the common system with reference to the natural system is $\dfrac{1}{\log_e 10}.$ That is,

(3) $\qquad\qquad \log_e N = \frac{1}{\log_{10} e} \log_{10} N,$

(4) and $\qquad \log_{10} N = \frac{1}{\log_e 10} \log_e N.$

The modulus $\dfrac{1}{\log_e 10} = \log_{10} e = 0.43429448\ \cdots$, is usually represented by M.

The modulus $\dfrac{1}{\log_{10} e} = \log_e 10 = 2.302585\ \cdots$, is represented by $\dfrac{1}{M}.$

76. Derivative of $\log_e$ u.—Making the start in deriving the formulas [34]–[38] is the difficult task. The following derivation is perhaps as simple as any that can be given. If, however, the reader finds it too difficult to follow, he should remember that he can use the formula even though he cannot derive it.

We will first find $\dfrac{dy}{dx}$ when $y = \log_e x$.

Let $x = x_1$, then $y_1 = \log_e x_1$, or $x_1 = e^{y_1}$.

Let $x = x_1 + \Delta x$, and $x_1 + \Delta x = e^{y_1 + \Delta y}$.

Subtracting, $\Delta x = e^{y_1 + \Delta y} - e^{y_1} = e^{y_1}(e^{\Delta y} - 1)$.

Dividing by Δy, $\dfrac{\Delta x}{\Delta y} = e^{y_1} \cdot \dfrac{e^{\Delta y} - 1}{\Delta y} = x_1 \cdot \dfrac{e^{\Delta y} - 1}{\Delta y}$.

Or $$\frac{\Delta y}{\Delta x} = \frac{1}{x_1} \frac{\Delta y}{e^{\Delta y} - 1}.$$

Then since $\Delta y = 0$, when $\Delta x = 0$,

$$\lim_{\Delta x \to 0} \left[\frac{\Delta y}{\Delta x} \right] = \frac{1}{x_1} \lim_{\Delta y \to 0} \left[\frac{\Delta y}{e^{\Delta y} - 1} \right].$$

Or $$\frac{dy}{dx} = \frac{1}{x_1} \lim_{\Delta y \to 0} \left[\frac{\Delta y}{e^{\Delta y} - 1} \right].$$

But it can be shown that $\lim\limits_{\Delta y \to 0} \left[\dfrac{\Delta y}{e^{\Delta y} - 1} \right] = 1$.

Then, dropping the subscripts, $\dfrac{dy}{dx} = \dfrac{1}{x}$, or $dy = \dfrac{1}{x} dx$.

Evidently, if $y = \log_e u$, then $dy = \dfrac{1}{u} du$.

Dividing by dx, $\dfrac{dy}{dx} = \dfrac{1}{u} \dfrac{du}{dx}$.

[34] $$\therefore \quad \frac{d(\log_e u)}{dx} = \frac{1}{u} \frac{du}{dx}.$$

This formula may be stated in words as follows: *The derivative of the logarithm of a function to the base e equals unity divided by the function, times the derivative of the function.*

77. Derivative of $\log_a$ u.—Let a be any base.

Since by [43], $\log_a u = \log_e u \log_a e$,

then $\dfrac{d(\log_a u)}{dx} = \dfrac{d(\log_e u)}{dx} \log_a e$.   By [8].

[35] $\therefore \dfrac{d(\log_a u)}{dx} = \dfrac{1}{u} \dfrac{du}{dx} \log_a e$.   By [34].

If in [35], $a = 10$, $\log_{10} u$ expresses the common logarithm of u, and

$$\frac{d(\log_{10} u)}{dx} = \frac{1}{u} \frac{du}{dx} M,$$

where $M = 0.4343 -$.

78. Derivative of a^u and e^u.—Let $y = a^u$.

Then $\log_e y = u \log_e a$.

Taking the derivative of each side of this equation by [34] and [8],

$$\frac{1}{y} \frac{dy}{dx} = \frac{du}{dx} \log_e a.$$

Or $$\frac{dy}{dx} = y \frac{du}{dx} \log_e a.$$

[36] $\therefore \dfrac{d(a^u)}{dx} = a^u \dfrac{du}{dx} \log_e a$.

If a is put equal to e, and noting that $\log_e e = 1$, we have

[37] $$\frac{d(e^u)}{dx} = e^u \frac{du}{dx}.$$

79. Derivative of u^v.—Let $y = u^v$, where u and v are functions of x.

Then $\log_e y = v \log_e u$.

Taking the derivative of each side of this equation by [34] and [7],

$$\frac{1}{y}\frac{dy}{dx} = \frac{v}{u}\frac{du}{dx} + \frac{dv}{dx}\log_e u.$$

$$\frac{dy}{dx} = y \cdot \frac{v}{u}\frac{du}{dx} + y \cdot \frac{dv}{dx}\log_e u$$

$$= u^v\frac{v}{u}\frac{du}{dx} + u^v\frac{dv}{dx}\log_e u.$$

[38] $$\therefore \frac{d(u^v)}{dx} = vu^{v-1}\frac{du}{dx} + u^v\frac{dv}{dx}\log_e u.$$

The application of formulas [10], [36] and [38] should be carefully distinguished. Formula [10] is used when a variable is affected by a constant exponent; [36] is used when a constant is affected by a variable exponent; and [38] is used when a variable is affected by a variable exponent.

It is customary in calculus to omit the base when writing logarithms to the base e, and to express the base when it is not e. Thus, log 5 means $\log_e 5$.

80. Illustrative examples.

Example 1. Given $y = \log(x^2 + 3x)$, find $\frac{dy}{dx}$.

$$\frac{dy}{dx} = \frac{1}{x^2 + 3x}\frac{d(x^2 + 3x)}{dx}, \qquad \text{By [34].}$$

$$= \frac{1}{x^2 + 3x}(2x + 3). \qquad \text{By [6], [10], [4], [5].}$$

$$\therefore \frac{dy}{dx} = \frac{2x + 3}{x^2 + 3x}.$$

Example 2. Given $y = \log_{10}(1 + 3x)$, find $\frac{dy}{dx}$ and the slope of the tangent at the point on the curve where $x = 0$.

$$\frac{dy}{dx} = \frac{1}{1 + 3x}\frac{d(1 + 3x)}{dx}\log_{10} e, \qquad \text{By [35].}$$

$$= \frac{1}{1 + 3x} \cdot 3\log_{10} e. \qquad \text{By [6], [5], [8], [4].}$$

$$\therefore \frac{dy}{dx} = \frac{3}{1 + 3x} \log_{10} e.$$

$$\frac{dy}{dx}\bigg|_{x=0} = \frac{3}{1 + 3 \cdot 0} \log_{10} e = 1.3029-, \text{ the slope.}$$

Example 3.   Given $y = e^{x^2+x}$, find $\frac{dy}{dx}$.

$$\frac{dy}{dx} = e^{x^2+x} \frac{d(x^2 + x)}{dx}, \qquad \text{By [37].}$$

$$= e^{x^2+x}(2x + 1). \quad \text{By [6], [10], [4].}$$

$$\therefore \frac{dy}{dx} = (2x + 1)e^{x^2+x}.$$

Example 4.   Given $y = \log \sin^2 x$, find $\frac{dy}{dx}$.

$$\frac{dy}{dx} = \frac{1}{\sin^2 x} \frac{d(\sin^2 x)}{dx}, \qquad \text{By [34].}$$

$$= \frac{1}{\sin^2 x} \cdot 2 \sin x \cos x. \quad \text{By [10], [16], [4].}$$

$$\therefore \frac{dy}{dx} = 2 \cot x.$$

Example 5.   Given the catenary $y = \frac{1}{2}a(e^{\frac{x}{a}} + e^{-\frac{x}{a}})$, find the slope of the curve at the point whose abscissa is 0.

Solution.   Given $y = \frac{1}{2}a(e^{\frac{x}{a}} + e^{-\frac{x}{a}})$.

$$\frac{dy}{dx} = \frac{1}{2}a\left[e^{\frac{x}{a}} \frac{d\left(\frac{x}{a}\right)}{dx} + e^{-\frac{x}{a}} \frac{d\left(-\frac{x}{a}\right)}{dx} \right], \text{By [8], [37].}$$

$$= \frac{1}{2}a\left(e^{\frac{x}{a}} \cdot \frac{1}{a} - e^{-\frac{x}{a}} \cdot \frac{1}{a} \right). \qquad \text{By [8], [4].}$$

$$\therefore \frac{dy}{dx} = \frac{1}{2}(e^{\frac{x}{a}} - e^{-\frac{x}{a}}).$$

And $\dfrac{dy}{dx}\bigg|_{x=0} = \frac{1}{2}(e^0 - e^0) = 0.$

$\therefore$ the slope of the catenary at the point where $x = 0$ is 0.

EXERCISES

In each of the exercises 1 to 60 find the derivative of the dependent variable with respect to the independent variable.

1. $y = \log x^2$.

2. $y = \log x^3$.

3. $y = \log x^n$.

4. $y = \log (x^2 + 3x)$.

5. $y = \log (2x^3 + x)$.

6. $y = \log (x^3 + 7x)$.

7. $y = \log \dfrac{1}{x}$.

8. $y = \log \dfrac{3x + 1}{x^2}$.

9. $y = \frac{1}{2} \log \dfrac{1 - x}{1 + x}$.

10. $y = \log(x + \sqrt{x^2 - a^2})$.

11. $y = \log \sin x$.

12. $y = \log \sec x$.

13. $y = \log (\sec x + \tan x)$.

14. $y = \log \tan (x^2 + a^2)$.

15. $y = \log \sin (x^2 + 3x)$.

16. $y = \log (\log x)$.

17. $s = \log \sqrt{\dfrac{t}{1 - t}}$.

18. $y = \log \dfrac{(1 + x^2)^3}{(1 - x^2)^4}$.

19. $y = \log \dfrac{3 \tan x + 1}{\tan x + 3}$.

20. $y = \dfrac{1}{a} \log (\sec ax + \tan ax)$.

21. $y = \log_{10} x^2$.

22. $y = \log_{10} x^{-2}$.

23. $y = \log_{10} (1 + 3x)$.

24. $s = \log_{10} \dfrac{t}{1 + t^2}$.

25. $y = (\log_{10} x)^2$.

26. $y = \log_b x^3$.

27. $y = \log_{10} \sin x$.

28. $y = \log_{10} \dfrac{2x + 5}{x^2 + 5x}$.

29. $y = e^{2x}$.

30. $y = e^{3x^2 + 4}$.

31. $y = a^{2x}$.

32. $y = 10^{2x + 3}$.

33. $y = e^{\sqrt{1 - x^2}}$.

34. $y = a^{\tan x}$.

35. $i = be^{-\alpha t}$.

36. $i = Ie^{-\frac{Rt}{L}}$.

37. $y = e^{e^x}$.

38. $y = \frac{1}{2}(e^x + e^{-x})$.

39. $y = e^x \log x$.

40. $y = x^2 e^{3x}$.

41. $y = x^x$.

42. $y = \sqrt[x]{\sin x}$.

43. $y = e^x \sin x$.

44. $y = e^{-x} \sin x$.

45. $y = x \cdot 10^{2x + 3}$.

46. $y = x + \log (1 - x^2)$.

47. $i = e^{-\frac{1}{3}t} \sin (2t + \frac{1}{2}\pi)$.

48. $y = (3x + 2)e^{-x^2}$.

49. $y = (x^2 + 1)^{2x + 3}$.

50. $y = x^2 \log x^2$.

51. $y = x^{\sin x}$.

52. $y = \log \sqrt{\dfrac{1 - \cos x}{1 + \cos x}}$.

53. $y = \dfrac{\sin x + \cos x}{e^x}$.

54. $y = (x^2 + bx + c)e^x$.

55. $y = \dfrac{e^{-x^2}}{1 + x^2}$.

56. $y = e^x \sin^{-1} x$.

57. $y = \cos^{-1} \dfrac{e^x - e^{-x}}{e^x + e^{-x}}$.

58. $y = \tan^{-1} \dfrac{e^x - e^{-x}}{2}$.

59. $y = x^5 \cdot 5^x$.

60. $y = a^{\tan x \sec^2 x}$.

Find $\dfrac{dy}{dx}$ of the following implicit functions:

61. $e^x \sin y = 0$.

62. $x - y = \log(x + y)$.

63. $e^{x-y} = x + y$.

64. $e^x + e^y = 1$.

65. $ye^{ny} = ax^m$.

66. $xy = a^2 \log \dfrac{x}{a}$.

67. Find the slope of the tangent to the curve $y = e^x$ at the point where $x = 0$. Where $x = 2$.

68. Find the slope of the tangent to the curve $y = \log_{10} x$ at the point where $x = 1$. Where $x = 10$.

69. Find the minimum point of the curve $y = \log(x^2 - 2x + 3)$.

70. Find the maximum and minimum points of the curve whose equation is $y = 2x^2 - \log x$.

71. Show that the rate of change of y with respect to x for any point on the curve $y = ae^{kx}$ is proportional to y.

72. Find the points of inflection of the curve $y = e^{-x^2}$.

Suggestion. Given $y = e^{-x^2}$.

$$\frac{dy}{dx} = -2e^{-x^2}x.$$

$$\frac{d^2y}{dx^2} = 4e^{-x^2}x^2 - 2e^{-x^2}.$$

Putting $\dfrac{d^2y}{dx^2} = 0$, $4e^{-x^2}x^2 - 2e^{-x^2} = 0$.

Factoring, $2e^{-x^2}(2x^2 - 1) = 0$.

The only finite value of x is found from the factor $2x^2 - 1$ put equal to zero. $\therefore x = \pm\frac{1}{2}\sqrt{2}$.

73. Find the points of inflection of the curve $xy = 4 \log \dfrac{x}{2}$.

74. Find the values of x for which the curve $y = x^2e^{-x}$ has maximum points; for which it has minimum points.

75. The rate in kilometers per second that a signal can be transmitted by a submarine cable 1 cm. in diameter and insulated with a covering of guttapercha t cm. thick is given by the formula

$$r = \frac{10^7 \log_e t}{15t^2}.$$

What is the maximum rate and for what thickness of insulation?

Suggestion. Given $r = \dfrac{10^7 \log t}{15t^2}$.

Differentiating, $\dfrac{dr}{dt} = \dfrac{10^7}{15} \cdot \dfrac{t - 2t \log t}{t^4} = \dfrac{10^7}{15} \cdot \dfrac{1 - 2 \log t}{t^3}$.

For a maximum rate $\dfrac{dr}{dt} = 0$, and this is so when the numerator of the fraction equals zero.

Then $\qquad\qquad 1 - 2 \log t = 0.$

Whence $\qquad \log t = \tfrac{1}{2}$ and $t = e^{\frac{1}{2}} = 1.649.$

Substituting this in the formula for r gives

$$r = 122,600.$$

Hence the rate is 122,600 Km. when the thickness of the insulation is 1.649 cm.

81. Logarithmic differentiation.—Sometimes the work of differentiating a function is shortened by first taking the logarithm of the function, and then applying the rules of differentiation. The advantages of this method are most marked for exponential functions, especially those of the form u^v. The following examples illustrate the method. It will be noted that by this method the derivative is expressed as an implicit function of the variables, but can readily be expressed as an explicit function of the independent variable if desired.

Example 1. Given $y = \dfrac{\sqrt{x - 1}}{\sqrt[3]{x + 3}}$, find $\dfrac{dy}{dx}$.

Taking the logarithm of each side,

$$\log y = \tfrac{1}{2} \log (x - 1) - \tfrac{1}{3} \log (x + 3).$$

Differentiating, $\dfrac{1}{y} \dfrac{dy}{dx} = \dfrac{1}{2(x - 1)} - \dfrac{1}{3(x + 3)}.$

$$\therefore \dfrac{dy}{dx} = \dfrac{y(x + 11)}{6(x^2 + 2x - 3)}.$$

Example 2.   Given $y = x^{2x+3}$, find $\dfrac{dy}{dx}$.

Taking the logarithm of each side,

$$\log y = (2x + 3) \log x.$$

Differentiating, $\dfrac{1}{y}\dfrac{dy}{dx} = (2x + 3)\dfrac{1}{x} + 2 \log x.$ By [7].

$$\therefore \frac{dy}{dx} = \left(\frac{2x + 3}{x} + \log x^2\right)y = \left(\frac{2x + 3}{x} + \log x^2\right)x^{2x+3}.$$

Example 3.   Given $y = x^{\frac{1}{\log x}}$, find $\dfrac{dy}{dx}$.

Taking the logarithm of each side,

$$\log y = \frac{1}{\log x}\log x = 1.$$

Differentiating, $\dfrac{1}{y}\dfrac{dy}{dx} = 0.$ $\therefore \dfrac{dy}{dx} = 0.$

82. Logarithmic derivative.   Relative rate of increase.—
The form $\dfrac{1}{y}\dfrac{dy}{dx}$ is called the **logarithmic derivative** of y with
respect to x.   This is the mathematical expression for an
idea that is of considerable use, and will be illustrated
more fully later (**Art. 92**).   This idea is known as the
relative rate of increase, and is defined to be the rate of
increase of the function per unit value of the function.
This, of course, can be expressed by dividing the rate of
increase by the value of the function.

Thus, if $y = f(x)$, then the total rate of increase of y with
respect to x is expressed by $\dfrac{dy}{dx}$ and the

$$\textbf{relative rate of increase} = \frac{1}{y}\frac{dy}{dx},$$

which is exactly the logarithmic derivative.

The **rate per cent of increase** is the rate of increase per
100 units of the function, and therefore is represented

by 100 times the relative rate of increase; that is, if $y = f(x)$, the

rate per cent of increase $= 100 \dfrac{1}{y} \dfrac{dy}{dx}.$

The expression $\dfrac{1}{y} \dfrac{dy}{dx}$ can be found by taking the logarithm of both sides of $y = f(x)$ and then finding the derivative, or it can be found by finding the ordinary derivative, $\dfrac{dy}{dx}$, and then dividing by the value of the function.

Example 1.   Given $y = 3e^{\frac{1}{2}x}$, find the relative rate of increase of y and the rate per cent of increase.

Solution.   Given $y = 3e^{\frac{1}{2}x}$.

Taking logarithms, $\log y = \log 3 + \frac{1}{2}x$.

Differentiating, $\dfrac{1}{y} \dfrac{dy}{dx} = \frac{1}{2} =$ the relative rate of increase.

And $\qquad 100 \dfrac{1}{y} \dfrac{dy}{dx} = 50 =$ per cent rate of increase.

Example 2.   If a square sheet of metal is heated, show that the relative rate of increase in its area is twice the coefficient of expansion of the material.   The **coefficient of expansion** is the increase in length per unit length for one degree increase in temperature, and is therefore the relative rate of increase.

Solution.   Let $x =$ the length of a side of the square and y the area.

Then $\qquad\qquad\qquad y = x^2.$

Coefficient of expansion is $\dfrac{1}{x} \dfrac{dx}{dt}$, by definition, where t is temperature.

Relative rate of increase of area is found by taking the logarithm of each side of $y = x^2$ and finding the derivative.

Taking logarithms, $\log y = 2 \log x.$

Differentiating, $\dfrac{1}{y}\dfrac{dy}{dt} = 2\dfrac{1}{x}\dfrac{dx}{dt}$.

Hence the relative rate of increase of the area equals twice the coefficient of expansion of the material.

EXERCISES

Find the logarithmic derivative and the ordinary derivative in exercises 1 to 12.

1. $y = 3e^{2x}$.

2. $y = 10^{3x+2}$.

3. $y = e^{-x^2+3x^3}$.

4. $y = x^{\sin x}$.

5. $y = x^n n^x$.

6. $y = (x + 1)^{\frac{2}{3}}(2x + 5)^{\frac{3}{4}}$.

7. $y = \dfrac{\sqrt{1 + x^2}}{\sqrt{1 - x^2}}$.

8. $y = (2 - 3x^2)e^{2x^2-1}$.

9. $y = x^{\sqrt{x}}$.

10. $s = (t^2 + 1)^{2t+3}$.

11. $y = uv$, where u and v are functions of x.

12. $y = uvw$, where u, v, and w are functions of x.

13. Find $\dfrac{dy}{dx}$ in the implicit function $e^{x+y} = xy$.

14. Find $\dfrac{dy}{dx}$ in the implicit function $x^y = y^x$.

15. If a circular sheet of metal is heated, show that the relative rate of increase in its area is 2 times the coefficient of expansion of the material.   (See example 2, Art. 82.)

16. Find the relative rates of each of the following pairs of functions and compare their values:

(1) e^{ax} and e^{ax+c}.

(2) e^{ax} and e^{-ax}.

(3) e^{ax} and 10^{ax}

(4) $\sin x$ and $\cos x$.

17. The number of bacteria in a certain culture is given by the formula

$$N = 1000\, e^{0.4t},$$

where N is the number and t is time in hours.   Find the relative rate of increase and the per cent rate of increase.

83. Simple integrals involving logarithmic and exponential functions.—The integrals $\int \dfrac{du}{u}$, $\int e^u du$, and $\int a^u du$

are readily evaluated and occur frequently in applications of calculus.

[44] $$\int \frac{du}{u} = \log u + C.$$

This can be readily proved by finding the differential of the right-hand member.

For $\qquad d(\log\ u + C) = \dfrac{du}{u}.$ By [34].

[45] $$\int e^u du = e^u + C.$$

For $\qquad d(e^u + C) = e^u du.$ By [37].

[46] $$\int a^u du = \frac{a^u}{\log a} + C.$$

For $\qquad d\!\left(\dfrac{a^u}{\log a} + C\right) = a^u du.$ By [36].

84. Illustrative examples.—*Example* 1. Find $\displaystyle\int \frac{2x\,dx}{x^2 + 4}.$

Here $u = x^2 + 4$, and $du = 2x\ dx$.

$$\therefore \int \frac{2x\,dx}{x^2 + 4} = \log(x^2 + 4) + C. \qquad \text{By [44]}$$

Example 2. Find $\displaystyle\int a^{2x+3} dx.$

Here if $u = 2x + 3$, $du = 2dx$.

Then the integral is put in the form $\displaystyle\int a^u du$ by multiplying and dividing by 2

$$\therefore \int a^{2x+3} dx = \tfrac{1}{2} \int a^{2x+3} 2dx = \frac{a^{2x+3}}{2\log a} + C. \qquad \text{By [46].}$$

Example 3. Find $\displaystyle\int e^{\sin x} \cos x\ dx.$

Here $u = \sin x$, and $du = \cos x\ dx$.

$$\therefore \int e^{\sin x} \cos x\ dx = e^{\sin x} + C. \qquad \text{By [45]}.$$

Example 4.   Find the equation of a curve such that the slope of its tangent line at any point is proportional to the ordinate of that point, if it is further known that the curve passes through the point (0, 1).

Solution.   Since $\dfrac{dy}{dx}$ represents the slope of the tangent,

$$\frac{dy}{dx} = ky.$$

Dividing by y and multiplying by dx, to put it in a form that can be integrated.

$$\frac{dy}{y} = k\, dx.$$

Then $\displaystyle\int \frac{dy}{y} = \int k\, dx.$

Hence $\log y = kx + C$.

$$\therefore y = e^{kx+c} = e^{kx}e^{c} = C_1 e^{kx}.$$

Since the curve is to pass through the point (0, 1), substituting these values gives

$$1 = C_1 e^{k\cdot 0}.   \therefore C_1 = 1.$$

Hence the curve passing through the point (0, 1) is

$$y = e^{kx}.$$

Giving k different values will give different curves; but they will all pass through the point (0, 1), and will have a slope at any point equal to k times the ordinate of that point.

Example 5.   Find the area bounded by the equilateral hyperbola $xy = 4$, the x-axis, and the ordinates corresponding to $x = 1$ and $x = 8$.

Solution.   The hyperbola is shown in Fig. 56 and the area sought is $MNQR$.

Consider the area A as generated by the ordinate moving **toward** the right.

Then $\qquad dA = ydx.$

And $\qquad \int dA = \int y\,dx = \int \dfrac{4}{x}dx = 4\int \dfrac{dx}{x}.$

$$\therefore\ A = 4\log x + C.$$

When $x = 1$, $A = 0$.

$$\therefore\ 0 = 4\log 1 + C,\ \text{or}\ C = -4\log 1.$$

When $x = 8$, $A = 4\log 8 - 4\log 1$.

$$\therefore\ A = 4 \times 2.079 - 4 \times 0 = 8.316.$$

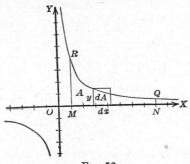

Fig. 56.

Therefore the area sought is 8.316 square units.

Example 6. The dying away of an electric current, i, on the sudden removal of the e.m.f. from a certain circuit is given by the equation

$$\frac{di}{dt} = -60i,$$

where t is the time in seconds. Derive the formula for i at any time after the e.m.f. is removed if $i = 30$ when $t = 0$.

Solution. Here we have given the rate of change of the current with respect to the time, and hence the problem is the inverse of differentiation.

Given $\qquad \dfrac{di}{dt} = -60i.$

Multiplying by dt and dividing by i,
$$\frac{di}{i} = -60dt.$$

Then $\int \frac{di}{i} = -60\int dt.$

Integrating, $\log i = -60t + C.$

$\therefore\ i = e^{-60t+c} = e^{-60t}e^{C} = C_1 e^{-60t}.$

It is also given that $i = 30$ when $t = 0$. Substituting these values,

$$30 = C_1 e^0, \text{ and therefore } C_1 = 30.$$
$$\therefore\ i = 30e^{-60t}.$$

This formula expresses the value of i at any time t seconds after the electro-motive force is cut off.

Thus, after $\frac{1}{60}$ second the current is

$$i = 30e^{-1} = \frac{30}{2.718} = 11.04-.$$

Example 7. The law for the rate of many chemical reactions states that the rate of the chemical reaction with respect to the time is proportional to the quantity of changing substance present in the mixture, that is, to the quantity still unchanged. This is the same as stating that the relative rate is constant, or the logarithmic derivative equals a constant. Let q be the quantity still unchanged at any time t seconds after the reaction starts, and q_0 the original quantity, and find an expression for q at any time t after the reaction starts.

Solution. By the law stated in the example,

$$\frac{dq}{dt} = kq.$$

Multiplying by dt and dividing by q,

$$\frac{dq}{q} = k\,dt.$$

Integrating, $\quad \log q = kt + C.$

$$\therefore q = e^{kt+C} = e^{kt}e^C = C_1 e^{kt}.$$

But $\qquad\qquad q = q_0$ when $t = 0.$

Then $\qquad\qquad q_0 = C_1 e^0,$ and therefore $C_1 = q_0.$

$$\therefore q = q_0 e^{kt}.$$

Since q is a decreasing function the constant k is negative. In **Art. 94** this is assumed at first.

EXERCISES

Find the indefinite integrals in exercises 1–10.

1. $\int e^{2x}dx.$

2. $\int a^{3x}dx.$

3. $\int e^{x^2}x\, dx.$

4. $\int \dfrac{dx}{x-1}.$

5. $\int \dfrac{3}{x}\, dx$

6. $\int \dfrac{x+1}{x}\, dx.$

7. $\int \dfrac{\cos x\, dx}{\sin x}.$

8. $\int \dfrac{x^3 - 2x^2 + x}{x^2}\, dx$

9. $\int (e^x + 4)e^{-x}dx.$

10. $\int (e^{2x+1} + x)dx.$

11. Find the area bounded by the equilateral hyperbola $xy = 1$, the x-axis, and the ordinates corresponding to $x = 1$ and $x = 10$.

12. Find the area bounded by the curve $y = x + \dfrac{1}{x}$, the x-axis, and the ordinates corresponding to $x = 2$ and $x = 4$.

13. Find the equation of the curve passing through the point $(0, 1)$ if the slope of any point of the curve is equal to xy.

Suggestion $\quad \dfrac{dy}{dx} = xy. \qquad\qquad \therefore \dfrac{dy}{y} = x\, dx.$

14. When capacity C is involved in an electric circuit, $i = -C\dfrac{dE}{dt}$, where i is the current, E the e.m.f., and t the time in seconds. But $i = \dfrac{E}{r}$, where r is resistance, and therefore

$$\frac{E}{r} = -C\frac{dE}{dt}.$$

Here C and r are constants and E and t are variables.   By integrating solve and find

$$E = E_0 e^{-\frac{t}{Cr}},$$

where e is the base of the natural system of logarithms, and E_0 is the e.m.f. when $t = 0$.

Suggestion.   Put $\dfrac{E}{r} = -C\dfrac{dE}{dt}$ in the form $\dfrac{dE}{E} = -\dfrac{1}{Cr}\,dt$ and integrate.

15. The decomposition of radium takes place automatically so that the relative rate is constant.   Consider an original quantity q_0, then if q is the quantity remaining after any time t,

$$\frac{1}{q}\frac{dq}{dt} = k.$$

Solve this as in example **7** and find

$$q = q_0 e^{kt}.$$

Now it has been determined that $q = \frac{1}{2}q_0$ when $t = 1800$ years. Using these values, find k and find the value of q in 500 years.   In 1 year.

16. The number of bacteria in a culture increased according to the law

$$\frac{1}{N}\frac{dN}{dt} = 0.3,$$

where N is the number at any time and t is in hours.   If at the start $N = 100$, derive the formula giving the value of N at any time.

17. When an iron rod is heated its length L increases according to the law

$$\frac{1}{L}\frac{dL}{dT} = 0.00001,$$

where T is temperature.   Derive the formula giving the length at any temperature if $L = 10$ when $T = 0$.   At what temperature will L have increased 1 per cent?

18. A body that is hotter than the surrounding medium cools according to Newton's law of cooling which is

$$\frac{d\theta}{dt} = -k\theta,$$

where θ is the difference in temperature between the body and the surrounding medium, and t is the time in seconds. If $\theta = \theta_0$ when $t = 0$, derive the formula

$$\theta = \theta_0 e^{-kt.}$$

Find k if θ falls from $100°$ to $90°$ in 40 sec.

19. Assuming that the retardation (negative acceleration) of a boat moving in still water is proportional to its velocity, derive a formula for the distance s passed over in time t after the engine was shut off if the boat was moving at the rate of m miles an hour when the engine was shut off.

20. When light passes through glass the intensity of the light at any point varies with the distance it has penetrated the glass. For a certain specimen of glass the variation is expressed by the relation

$$\frac{di}{dx} = -0.02i,$$

where i is the intensity and x the distance penetrated. If i was originally 100, find a formula for i at any distance.

21. In rising above sea level the pressure of the atmosphere varies according to the relation

$$\frac{dp}{dh} = -0.00004p,$$

where p is the height of the barometric column in inches and h is the height in feet above the sea level. If $p = 30$ when $h = 0$, derive a formula giving p for any h. Compute p when $h = 10,000$.

CHAPTER XII

THREE IMPORTANT TYPES OF FUNCTIONS

85. The subjects that a practical man studies are selected, in most cases, because of their apparent uses and applications. The methods that he uses are those that seem best suited to his needs. It is unnecessary to state that, among the many methods and schemes listed in mathematics, some are more important and useful than others, and that one gives the most attention to the most useful methods.

In mathematics functions are used to express relations between quantities. It follows, then, that the functions which are of most use, and hence of greatest interest to the practical man, are those most frequently employed in expressing phenomena in nature.

86. The types of functions to be especially considered.— A survey of the problems so far considered in his study of mathematics would lead the student to select a certain few types of functions as those most frequently used. The most useful functions in studying phenomena of nature fall under three main types.

(1) The **power function** expressed by the form ax^n, where a and n are constants.

(2) The **exponential function** expressed by the form ab^x, where a and b are constants; or by the form ae^{kx}, where a, e, and k are constants, e being the base of the natural system of logarithms.

(3) The **periodic function** expressed usually by $\sin x$ or $\cos x$.

In this chapter the equations, and the curves of the equations, making use of these types, will be studied, and some suggestions given as to the reasons why they are of major importance.

THE POWER FUNCTION

87. Occurrence of power functions.—In nature it is very common for one quantity to vary directly or inversely as some constant power of another quantity. All such quantities are said to vary according to the **power law,** and when such a law of relation is expressed as an equation a power function is used. The power law may be stated as follows:

In any power function, if one quantity changes by a fixed multiple, the other also changes by a fixed multiple.

Whenever two variable quantities are found by experiment or otherwise to obey this law, the relation between them can be expressed by a power function. One can easily satisfy himself that the power law holds. For instance, suppose the relation is given by the equation

$$y = x^3,$$

then the following are pairs of values of x and y:

$$x = 1, 2, 4, 8, 16, \cdot \ \cdot \ \cdot \ ,$$
$$y = 1, 8, 64, 512, 4096, \ \cdot \ \cdot \ \cdot \ .$$

Here x changes by the constant multiple 2 and y changes by the constant multiple 8. Any other multiple could be chosen for x and a corresponding multiple could be found for y.

Numerous examples of this law can be found in geometry, physics, chemistry, electricity, mechanics, and engineering practice. **P. M. II, Chapt. XV; IV, pp. 29–37; H. S., Chapt. XXXI, and pp. 456–463.**

(1) The area of a circle is given by the formula, $A = \pi r^2$, where π is the constant and r varies for different circles. The formula states that the area of a circle varies directly as the square of the radius.

(2) The volume of a sphere is given by the formula, $V = \frac{4}{3}\pi r^3$, where $\frac{4}{3}\pi$ is the constant. The formula states that the volume of a sphere varies directly as the cube of the radius.

(3) The distance s, that a body falls is given by the formula, $s = \frac{1}{2}gt^2$, where $\frac{1}{2}gt^2$ is of the form ax^n.

(4) The heat generated by an electric current in a given time varies as the square of the number of amperes of current.

(5) The strength of a beam supported at each end varies as the square of the depth.

(6) The size of a stone that will be carried by a swiftly flowing stream varies as the sixth power of the velocity.

(7) The intensity of light from a lamp varies inversely as the square of the distance from the source of light. That is, if I is the illumination and d the distance, $I = \dfrac{k}{d^2}$ or $I = kd^{-2}$. Here kd^{-2} is of the form ax^n where n is a negative number.

(8) The quantity, Q, of water that will flow through a V-shaped notch is given by the formula $Q = kh^{\frac{5}{2}}$, where h is the height of the surface of the water above the bottom of the notch.

(9) In long water pipes, when the discharge and length are constant, the head varies inversely as the fifth power of the diameter, that is, $H = kd^{-5}$, where H is the head and d the diameter.

(10) In gas pressure the formula $pv^n = C$ is frequently used. Such a form is $pv^{1.37} = C$, which can be written $p = Cv^{-1.37}$.

From these examples it is evident that for direct variation the exponent is positive, while for inverse variation the exponent is negative.

Equations of the form $y = ax^n$, where n is positive, are said to be of the **parabolic type.**

Equations of the form $y = ax^n$, where n is negative, are said to be of the **hyperbolic type.**

88. Parabolic type. y = ax^n, n > 0. For the curves shown in this article the constant a is taken equal to 1. If a is different from 1, the general form of the curve is not changed, the ordinates being multiplied by a.

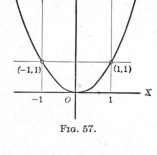

Fig. 57.

(1) When $n = 2$, $y = x^2$. The curve is the ordinary **parabola** with its axis on the y-axis, and is shown in Fig. 57. The slope of any point can be found from the derivative,

$$\frac{dy}{dx} = 2x.$$

It is then evident from the derivative that the curve is falling when $x < 0$, rising when $x > 0$, and has a minimum point when $x = 0$.

(2) When $n = 3$, $y = x^3$. The curve is called the **cubical parabola,** and has the form shown in Fig. 58.

Discussion. When $x = 0$, $y = 0$, and the curve passes through the origin. When $x = 1$, $y = 1$; when $x = -1$, $y = -1$; and the curve passes through the points $(1, 1)$ and $(-1, -1)$. The curve is symmetrical with respect to the origin, but not with respect to either coördinate axis. Why?

For any positive value of x, y is positive; and for any negative value of x, y is negative. Hence the curve lies

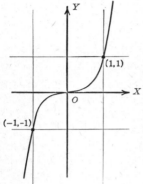

wholly in the first and third quadrants.

Since $\dfrac{dy}{dx} = 3x^2$, the derivative is never negative, and the curve is rising for all values of x that are positive or negative. When $x = 0$, $\dfrac{dy}{dx} = 0$, and the tangent at the origin is along the x-axis.

Since $\dfrac{d^2y}{dx^2} = 6x$, it is evident that the second derivative is positive for all positive values of x, and the curve is concave upward; while for negative values *of* x the second derivative is negative, and the curve is concave downward.

FIG. 58.

This information together with a few points makes it possible to sketch the curve with considerable accuracy.

(3) When $n = \frac{3}{2}$, $y = x^{\frac{3}{2}}$. The curve is called the **semi-cubical parabola**, and has the form shown in Fig. 59.

Discussion. When $x = 0$, $y = 0$, and the curve passes through the origin. Writing $y = x^{\frac{3}{2}}$ in the form $y^2 = x^3$, it is seen that the curve is symmetrical with respect to the x-axis.

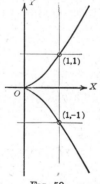

FIG. 59.

For any positive value of x, y has two values numerically equal but opposite in sign. For any negative value of x, y is imaginary. Hence the curve lies wholly in the first and fourth quadrants.

Finding the first and second derivatives,

$$\frac{dy}{dx} = \frac{3x^2}{2y}, \text{ and } \frac{d^2y}{dx^2} = \frac{3x}{4y}.$$

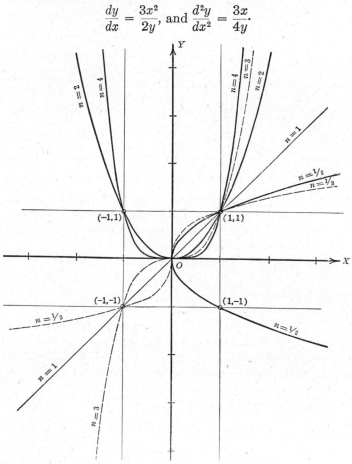

Fig. 60. $y = x^n$, $n = \frac{1}{3}, \frac{1}{2}, 1, 2, 3, 4$.

From the first derivative it is seen that the curve is rising in the first quadrant and falling in the fourth quadrant.

From the second derivative it is seen that the curve is concave upward in the first quadrant and concave downward in the fourth quadrant.

This information together with a few points makes it possible to sketch the curve with considerable accuracy.

Finally, in Fig. 60, are represented several curves of the parabolic type, including those already given. Those not already dealt with should be plotted and discussed.

89. Hyperbolic type. $y = ax^n$, $n < 0$. —As with the parabolic type, the curves in this article are plotted for $a = 1$.

(1) When $n = -1$, $y = x^{-1}$ or $xy = 1$. The curve is the ordinary **equilateral hyperbola,** and lies in the first and third quadrants as shown in Fig. 61.

Discussion. No finite value of x will make $y = 0$, and no finite value of y will make $x = 0$. Hence the curve does not meet either of the coördinate axes.

The curve is not symmetrical with respect to either coördinate axis, but is symmetrical with respect to the origin. Why?

When x is near 0 and positive, y becomes large and positive. When x is near 0 and negative, y becomes large and negative. When y is near 0 and positive, x becomes large and positive. When y is near 0 and negative, x becomes large and negative. In such a case, the curve is said to be **asymptotic** to the coördinate axes, and the lines $x = 0$ and $y = 0$ are the **asymptotes** to the curve.

Since it is necessary that both x and y are positive or both negative, the curve lies only in the first and third quadrants. Since the coördinates of the points $(1, 1)$ and $(-1, -1)$ satisfy the equation, the curve passes through these points.

Finding the first and second derivatives,

$$\frac{dy}{dx} = -\frac{1}{x^2}, \text{ and } \frac{d^2y}{dx^2} = \frac{2}{x^3}.$$

From the first derivative it is seen that the curve is always falling since $-\dfrac{1}{x^2}$ is negative for both positive and negative values of x.

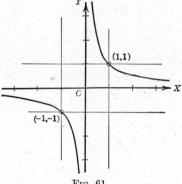

Since the second derivative is positive when $x > 0$ and negative when $x < 0$, the curve is concave upward in the first quadrant and concave downward in the third quadrant.

This information together with a few points enables one to sketch the curve with considerable accuracy.

FIG. 61.

(2) When $n = -2$, $y = x^{-2}$ or $x^2 y = 1$. The curve has the form shown in Fig. 62.

The discussion is similar to that in (1). It is to be noted that the curve lies wholly in the first and second quadrants,

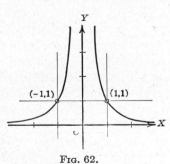

FIG. 62.

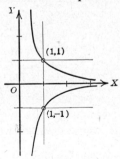

FIG. 63.

passes through the points $(1, 1)$ and $(-1, 1)$, and is asymptotic to the coördinate axes.

(3) When $n = -\frac{3}{2}$, $y = x^{-\frac{3}{2}}$ or $x^{\frac{3}{2}} y = 1$. The curve has the form shown in Fig. 63. The discussion and plotting

is left as an exercise. It is to be noted that the curve lies wholly in the first and fourth quadrants, passes through the points (1, 1) and (1, −1), and is asymptotic to both coördinate axes.

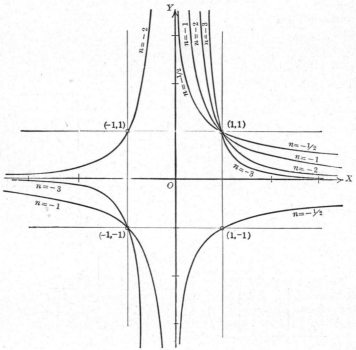

Fig. 64. $y = x^n, n = -\frac{1}{2}, -1, -2, -3.$

Finally, in Fig. 64 are represented several curves of the hyperbolic type, including those already given. Those not already dealt with should be plotted and discussed.

90. Regions in which curves of power functions lie.—In summary of curves of the parabolic and hyperbolic types whose equations are of the form $y = x^n$, it is to be noted that they are confined to certain regions of the plane; and that each passes through two of the points $(1, 1)$, $(-1, 1)$, $(-1, -1)$, and $(1, -1)$. In particular, the curves of the parabolic type are confined to the shaded portions of Fig. 65, and the hyperbolic types are confined to the unshaded portions.

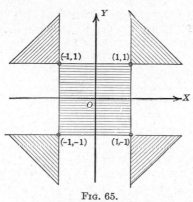

FIG. 65.

EXERCISES

Plot each group of the following equations upon the same set of coördinate axes, by first discussing the equation and then finding a few points.

1. (1) $y = x^2$,　(2) $y = x^4$,　(3) $y = x^6$.

2. (1) $y = x$,　(2) $y = x^3$,　(3) $y = x^5$.

3. (1) $y = x^{\frac{1}{2}}$　(2) $y = x^{\frac{3}{2}}$,　(3) $y = x^{\frac{5}{2}}$.

4. (1) $y = x^{\frac{1}{3}}$　(2) $y = x^{\frac{2}{3}}$.

5. (1) $y = x^{-1}$,　(2) $y = x^{-3}$.

6. (1) $y = x^{-2}$,　(2) $y = x^{-4}$.

7. (1) $y = x^{-\frac{1}{2}}$,　(2) $y = x^{-\frac{3}{2}}$.

8. (1) $y = x^{-\frac{1}{3}}$,　(2) $y = x^{-\frac{2}{3}}$.

9. In what quadrants does a parabolic curve always lie if n is an even integer? If an odd integer?

10. In what quadrants does a parabolic curve always lie if n is a fraction and both numerator and denominator odd integers? If the numerator is even and the denominator odd? If the numerator is odd and the denominator even?

11. Answer the same questions as in exercise 9 for hyperbolic curves.

12. Answer the same questions as in exercise 10 for hyperbolic curves.

13. What is the effect upon the regions in which the curves of the parabolic and hyperbolic types lie if $a = -1$ instead of $a = 1$?

14. Plot the curves of $y = x^2$, $y = 3x^2$, and $y = \frac{1}{3}x^2$ on the same set of axes.

15. Plot the curves of $y = x^{-2}$, $y = 3x^{-2}$, and $y = \frac{1}{3}x^{-2}$ on the same set of axes.

16. What effect does a change in the value of the constant a in the equation $y = ax^n$ have on the regions shown in Fig. 65?

17. If p is the pressure and t the absolute temperature of a gas in adiabatic expansion, $p = kt^{\frac{\gamma}{\gamma-1}}$, where k is a constant and $\gamma = 1.41$ for air. If $p = 2700$ when $t = 300$, find k, and plot the equation for values of t from 200 to 400.

18. In a mixture in a gas engine expanding without gain or loss of heat, it is found that the law of expansion is given by the equation $pv^{1.37} = c$. Given that $p = 188.2$ when $v = 11$, find the value of the constant c, and plot the curve of the equation using this value of the constant. Consider values of v from 10 to 25.

THE EXPONENTIAL FUNCTION

91. Occurrence of exponential functions.—While in nature it is frequently the case that two quantities so depend upon each other that the relation may be expressed by an exponential function, such relations are not so easily discerned as are those that may be expressed by the power law. Often such a relation is apparent only after some mathematical consideration, while again it will be seen after some carefully performed experiment.

The exponential law is the law that holds when two variables are so related that when one changes in arithmetical progression the other changes in geometrical progression, that is, by a constant factor. As an illustration, suppose x and y are two variables so related that their corresponding values are as follows:

$x = 0, 1, 2, 3, 4, 5, 6, \cdots$
$y = 1, 2, 4, 8, 16, 32, 64, \cdots$

The equation expressing this relation is evidently

$$y = 2^x.$$

To make this illustration clearer let us see if we can find a particular example to make it concrete. For instance, bacteria increase by each individual dividing into two bacteria, then each of these dividing in a similar manner, and so continuing. Now under ideal conditions this process will continue indefinitely. Suppose the conditions are such that each individual divides every 30 min. Then, if the unit of time be taken as 30 min. and we start with one individual, the relation between the time t and the number of bacteria y is as follows:

$t = 0, 1, 2, 3, 4, 5, 6, 7, 8, \cdots$
$y = 1, 2, 4, 8, 16, 32, 64, 128, 256, \cdots$
$$\therefore y = 2^t.$$

Then the number of bacteria at any time can be found by this formula. For instance, after 10 hr., $t = 20$, and

$$y = 2^{20} = 1,048,576.$$

The above example is an illustration of *organic growth*. It will be found that the exponential function expresses the relation in all organic growth. For this reason it is often called the **law of organic growth.** It can be applied to the growth of timber in a forest as well as to the healing of a wound. This law is usually expressed in the form

$$y = ae^{kx},$$

where $e = 2.71828 \cdots$, the base of the natural system of logarithms, and a and k are constants to be determined in each particular case. Because of its frequent occurrence in problems involving conditions in nature, the base e is sometimes called "a constant of nature."

Many applications of the exponential function will be found as we proceed, but the following uses are suggestive:

(1) To express the pressure of the atmosphere at any height.

(2) In physics and electricity, it is used in considering damped vibrations.

(3) In medicine and surgery, to express the progress of the healing of a wound.

(4) In biology, to determine the growth of bacteria.

(5) In chemistry, to express the progress of a chemical action.

(6) In mechanics, in connection with the slipping of a belt on a pulley.

92. Rate of change proportional to the function.—If one considers the *rate of increase* in the number of bacteria in the example of the previous article, he will see that the rate of increase at any instant is directly proportional to the number of bacteria at that instant. That is, when there are ten bacteria the rate of increase is just twice as fast as when there are five. This relation can be stated in the following:

THEOREM. *If the rate of change of a function y with respect to the independent variable t is proportional to the function itself, the relation between the function and its variable is expressed by the exponential equation*

$$y = ae^{kt};$$

and, conversely, if the relation between a function y and its variable t is expressed by the exponential equation $y = ae^{kt}$, *the rate of change of the function is proportional to the function itself.*

Proof. Since the rate of change of y with respect to t is expressed by the derivative,

$$\frac{dy}{dt} = ky.$$

Dividing by y and multiplying by dt,

$$\frac{dy}{y} = k\,dt.$$

Integrating, $\qquad \log y = kt + C.$

Then $\qquad\qquad y = e^{kt+C} = e^C e^{kt}.$

But e^C is a constant. Putting it equal to a,

$$y = ae^{kt}$$

Proof of converse. Given $y = ae^{kt}$.

Differentiating, $\dfrac{dy}{dt} = ake^{kt} = ky.$

But k is a constant and therefore the rate of change of the function is proportional to the function.

93. The compound interest law.—If A stands for amount, P for principal, r for rate per cent, and t for time in years, for compound interest we have, when the interest is compounded annually,

$$A = P(1 + r)^t.$$

When the interest is compounded semi-annually,

$$A = P\left(1 + \frac{r}{2}\right)^{2t}$$

When the interest is compounded at n equal intervals each year,

$$A = P\left(1 + \frac{r}{n}\right)^{nt}.$$

It is also seen from the meaning of interest that the rate of increase of A during any interval is proportional to the value of A at the beginning of that period.   It follows then that if the interest is compounded *continually*, that is, if the number of intervals in a year becomes infinite, the rate of increase of A at any instant is proportional to the value of A at that instant, the proportionality factor being r.

$$\therefore \frac{dA}{dt} = rA.$$

Dividing by A and multiplying by dt,

$$\frac{dA}{A} = rdt.$$

Integrating, $\log A = rt + C.$

Then $A = e^{rt+C} = e^{C}e^{rt}.$

But e^{C} is a constant.   Putting it equal to a,

$$A = ae^{rt}.$$

To determine the constant a, we have $A = P$ when $t = 0$. Substituting these values,

$$P = ae^{0} = a.$$

Substituting P for a, the formula for finding the amount of any principal P at a rate per cent r for a time t years when compounded continually is

$$A = Pe^{rt}.$$

It is because of this relation that Lord Kelvin called the exponential law "the compound interest law," a name that is still often used.

Example.   Find the amount of \$500 at compound interest at 6 per cent per annum for 10 yr., (*a*) if compounded continually, (*b*) if compounded annually.

Solution.   (*a*) Substituting in the formula $A = Pe^{rt}$,

$$A = 500 \times 2.71828^{0.6} = 911.20.$$

(*b*) Substituting in the formula $A = P(1 + r)^{t}$,

$$A = 500(1 + 0.06)^{10} = 895.50.$$

The difference between the amounts when compounded continually and when compounded annually is

$$\$911.20 - \$895.50 = \$15.70.$$

Here a four place table of logarithms was used. A five place table makes, the result $0.16 less.

94. The law of organic decay.—In many cases in nature the exponential law occurs as a decreasing function. This is so in organic decay, and in many cases of retarded motion, as in the slowing up of the speed of a flywheel after the power has been shut off. The exponential law then occurs in the form

$$y = ae^{-kx}.$$

Example. A circular disk is rotating in a horizontal plane and in a liquid. If the retardation of its velocity due to friction of the liquid is proportional to its angular velocity ω, find its angular velocity after t seconds, the initial angular velocity being ω_0.

Solution. Since the angular velocity is decreasing,

$$\frac{d\omega}{dt} = -k\omega.$$

Dividing by ω and multiplying by dt,

$$\frac{d\omega}{\omega} = -k \, dt.$$

Integrating, $\qquad \log \omega = -kt + C.$

Then $\qquad \omega = e^{-kt+C} = e^C e^{-kt}.$

But e^C is a constant. Putting it equal to a,

$$\omega = ae^{-kt}.$$

To find a we know that $\omega = \omega_0$ when $t = 0$. Substituting these values,

$$\omega_0 = ae^0. \quad \therefore \ a = \omega_0.$$

The formula giving the angular velocity at any instant is then

$$\omega = \omega_0 e^{-kt},$$

where the constant k depends upon the viscosity of the liquid, and could be determined by experiment.

Further examples of this type are given in exercises 15 and 18 to 21, page 150.

95. Graphs of exponential functions.—An equation of the form $y = b^x$, where b is any positive constant, is called an **exponential equation.** If the exponent is fractional and involves even roots of b, only the positive values of these roots are used.

Example 1. Discuss the equation $y = b^x$ when $b > 1$. Plot the curve when $b = 1.5$.

Intercepts. When $x = 0$, $y = b^0 = 1$. This shows that the curve passes through the point $(0, 1)$ for *any* value of b.

If $y = 0$, $b^x = 0$, which is impossible for any finite value of x. This shows that the curve neither meets nor crosses the x-axis. However, for sufficiently large negative values of x, the value of b^x can be made to become as near zero as desired. The curve is then asymptotic to the x-axis in the negative direction.

Symmetry. Since changing x to $-x$ or y to $-y$ changes the equation, the curve is not symmetrical with respect to either coördinate axis.

Extent. Since no integral value of x can make y negative, and since only positive values of b^x are to be taken when x is a fraction, the curve is wholly above the x-axis.

Further, since y is not imaginary for any value of x, and increases as x increases, the curve lies in the first and second quadrants, exists for all values of x, and continually rises from left to right.

Plotting. The curve of $y = 1.5^x$ can be plotted as accurately as desired by finding points. Taking logarithms of both sides of the equation,

$$\log_{10} y = x \log_{10} 1.5 = 0.1761x.$$

The following points are readily found, and the curve is as shown in (1) of Fig. 66.

x	-3	-2	-1	0	1	2	3	4	5
$\log_{10} y$	$\bar{1}.4717$	$\bar{1}.6478$	$\bar{1}.8239$	0	0.1761	0.3522	0.5283	0.7044	0.8805
y	0.296	0.444	0.667	1	1.5	2.25	3.375	5.063	7.595

Example 2. Discuss the equation $y = b^x$ when $b < 1$. Plot the curve when $b = \frac{1}{2}$.

The discussion is similar to that of example 1. It is to be noted that y decreases as x increases, and the curve is asymptotic to the x-axis in the positive direction.

Plotting. Points for plotting $y = (\frac{1}{2})^x$ are found and the curve is as shown in (2) of Fig. 66.

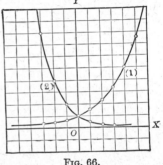

Fig. 66.

x	-5	-4	-3	-2	-1	0	1	2	3	4
y	32	16	8	4	2	1	0.5	0.25	0.125	0.0625

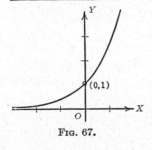

Fig. 67.

It should be noted that these curves always pass through the point $(0, 1)$, and are asymptotic to the x-axis in the positive or negative direction.

The most interesting of these curves is for the equation $y = e^x$. This curve is shown in Fig. 67.

Since when $y = e^x$, $\dfrac{dy}{dx} = e^x$, and since $\dfrac{dy}{dx}$ gives the slope of the curve at any point, it follows that the slope of the curve at any point is equal to the ordinate of that point.

It is well worth while to fix in mind the general shape of the curve of an exponential equation.

EXERCISES

Plot the curves of the following exponential equations:

1. $y = 2^x$.

2. $y = 3^x$.

3. $y = (0.75)^x$.

4. $y = (0.4)^x$.

5 $y = 1^{-x}$.

6. $y = 2^{-x}$.

7. $y = e^{-x}$.

8. $y = x^x$, $x > 0$.

9. Discuss the effect upon the curve of $y = b^x$ when $b < 1$ and increases to 1.

10. Discuss the effect upon the curve of $y = b^x$ when $b > 1$ and increases from 1.

11. Plot the curve of $i = be^{-at}$, where i and t are the variables. Choose $b = 1.5$ and $a = 0.4$.

12. If a body is heated to a temperature T_1 above the surrounding bodies, and suspended in air, its excess of temperature T above the surrounding bodies at any time, t seconds thereafter, is given by Newton's law of cooling expressed by the equation $T = T_1 e^{-at}$, where a is a constant that can be determined by experiment. Given $T_1 = 20$ and $a = 0.014$, plot a curve showing the temperature at any time t up to 100 seconds.

13. The dying away of the current on the sudden removal of the e.m.f. from a circuit containing resistance and self-induction, is expressed by the equation, $i = Ie^{-\frac{Rt}{L}}$, where i is the current at any time, t seconds, after the e.m.f. is removed, R is the resistance, and L the coefficient of self-induction. Plot a curve to show the current at any time from $t = 0$ to $t = 0.2$, if $I = 10$ amperes, $R = 0.1$ ohm, and $L = 0.01$ henry.

96. Hyperbolic functions.—In books and magazine articles where mathematics is applied, the reader frequently

meets functions known as hyperbolic functions. These functions are somewhat analogous to trigonometric functions and are related to the equilateral hyperbola somewhat as the trigonometric functions are connected with the circle. They can then be visualized, but the establishing of these relations will not be attempted here. For our purpose what are known as the exponential definitions of the hyperbolic functions will be sufficient. Whenever one finds these functions in his reading, he can express them in exponential functions by these definitions, and then he can manipulate them at pleasure.

The names of the hyperbolic functions, their abbreviations, and their definitions are as follows where the value of e is 2.71828 $\cdots$.

Hyperbolic sine u or sinh $u = \dfrac{e^u - e^{-u}}{2}$.

Hyperbolic cosine u or cosh $u = \dfrac{e^u + e^{-u}}{2}$.

Hyperbolic tangent u or tanh $u = \dfrac{\sinh u}{\cosh u} = \dfrac{e^u - e^{-u}}{e^u + e^{-u}}$.

Hyperbolic cotangent u or coth $u = \dfrac{\cosh u}{\sinh u} = \dfrac{e^u + e^{-u}}{e^u - e^{-u}}$.

Hyperbolic secant u or sech $u = \dfrac{1}{\cosh u} = \dfrac{2}{e^u + e^{-u}}$.

Hyperbolic cosecant u or csch $u = \dfrac{1}{\sinh u} = \dfrac{2}{e^u - e^{-u}}$.

Relations analogous to those connecting trigonometric functions exist between hyperbolic functions, and formulas for differentiating them can readily be established. Some of these are given in the following exercises. In doing these exercises the student will acquire some familiarity with the hyperbolic functions.

EXERCISES

By making use of the definitions show that the following identities are true relations between the hyperbolic functions.

1. $\cosh^2 u - \sinh^2 u = 1$.

Proof. $\cosh u = \dfrac{e^u + e^{-u}}{2}$ and $\sinh u = \dfrac{e^u - e^{-u}}{2}$.   By Def.

Squaring and subtracting,

$$\cosh^2 u - \sinh^2 u = \frac{e^{2u} + 2 + e^{-2u}}{4} - \frac{e^{2u} - 2 + e^{-2u}}{4} = \frac{4}{4} = 1.$$

2. $\tanh^2 u + \operatorname{sech}^2 u = 1$.

3. $\coth^2 u - \operatorname{csch}^2 u = 1$.

4. $\sinh (x \pm y) = \sinh x \cosh y \pm \cosh x \sinh y$.

5. $\cosh (x \pm y) = \cosh x \cosh y \pm \sinh x \sinh y$.

6. $\tanh (x \pm y) = \dfrac{\tanh x \pm \tanh y}{1 \pm \tanh x \tanh y}$.

7. $\sinh 2u = 2 \sinh u \cosh u$.

By making use of the definitions show that the following derivative formulas are true, where u is a function of x.

8. $\dfrac{d \sinh u}{dx} = \cosh u \dfrac{du}{dx}$.

Put $\sinh u = \dfrac{e^u - e^{-u}}{2}$

Then $\dfrac{d \sinh u}{dx} = \dfrac{d}{dx}\left(\dfrac{e^u - e^{-u}}{2}\right) = \dfrac{e^u \dfrac{du}{dx} + e^{-u}\dfrac{du}{dx}}{2} = \cosh u \dfrac{du}{dx}$.

9. $\dfrac{d \cosh u}{dx} = \sinh u \dfrac{du}{dx}$.

10. $\dfrac{d \tanh u}{dx} = \operatorname{sech}^2 u \dfrac{du}{dx}$.

11. $\dfrac{d \coth u}{dx} = -\operatorname{csch}^2 u \dfrac{du}{dx}$.

12. $\dfrac{d \operatorname{sech} u}{dx} = -\operatorname{sech} u \tanh u \dfrac{du}{dx}$.

13. $\dfrac{d \operatorname{csch} u}{dx} = -\operatorname{csch} u \coth u \dfrac{du}{dx}$.

97. The catenary.—When a cord that is perfectly flexible and inextensible and of uniform cross section and density is suspended from two points A and B in Fig. 68, it assumes a position as shown. The curve along which the cord hangs is called a **catenary,** and has the equation

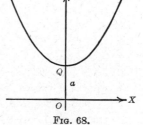

$$y = \frac{a}{2}(e^{\frac{x}{a}} + e^{-\frac{x}{a}}).$$

If $x = 0, y = \frac{a}{2}(e^{\frac{0}{a}} + e^{-\frac{0}{a}}) = a.$

Hence the curve intersects the y-axis at the point $(0, a)$.

Fig. 68.

If x is replaced by $-x$, $y = \frac{a}{2}(e^{-\frac{x}{a}} + e^{\frac{x}{a}})$, which is the same as the original equation. Hence the curve is symmetrical with respect to the y-axis.

It may be noted that if a in the equation of the catenary is 1, the equation becomes

$$y = \frac{e^x + e^{-x}}{2} = \cosh x.$$

It follows then that the curve of the hyperbolic cosine is a catenary.

EXERCISES

1. Discuss and plot the catenary $y = \dfrac{e^x + e^{-x}}{2}$, which is also $y = \cosh x$.

First plot $y_1 = \frac{1}{2}e^x$ and $y_2 = \frac{1}{2}e^{-x}$. Then plot $y = \dfrac{e^x + e^{-x}}{2}$ by adding the ordinates y_1 and y_2 to find y for the different values of x. Use values of e^x and e^{-x} given in tables on page 409.

2. A wire, weighing 0.2 lb. per foot, is suspended from two points in a horizontal line 50 ft. apart. The horizontal tension at each end is 10 lb. Plot the catenary formed by the wire. The constant a in the formula, $y = \frac{1}{2}a(e^{\frac{x}{a}} + e^{-\frac{x}{a}})$, is found by dividing the horizontal. tension by the weight per unit length of the wire.

THE PERIODIC FUNCTION

98. Occurrence of periodic functions.—In nature there are many motions that are recurrent. Sound waves, light waves, and water waves are familiar examples. Motions in machines are repeated in a periodic manner. The vibration of a pendulum is a simple case, as is also the piston-rod motion in an engine. Other familiar illustrations are the vibration of a piano string, breathing movements, heart beats, and motion of tides. An alternating electric current has periodic changes. It increases to a maximum value in one direction, decreases to zero and on down to a minimum, that is, to a maximum value in the opposite direction, rises again, and repeats these changes. It is thus an *alternating* current passing from a maximum in one direction to a maximum in the other direction, say, 60 times a second.

Before physical quantities that change in a periodic fashion can be dealt with mathematically, it is necessary to find a mathematical statement for a periodic function. For this reason we will now make a study of some simple periodic functions expressed in mathematical symbols, and then endeavor to see how certain periodic physical phenomena can be represented by these functions. This will require very attentive study for there are new ideas and many definitions.

99. The sine curve.—While the student may be quite familiar with the sine function, the discussion and plotting of $y = \sin x$ will smooth the way for the treatment of the topics considered in the following articles.

Discussion. When $x = 0$, $y = 0$. Hence the curve passes through the origin. When $y = 0$, $\sin x = 0$, and $x = n\pi$ radians, where n is any integer either positive or negative. Hence the curve crosses the x-axis at an indefinite number of points both to the right and to the left of the origin. To the right these are $x = \pi, 2\pi, 3\pi, \cdots n\pi$; and to the left they are $x = -\pi, -2\pi, -3\pi, \cdots -n\pi$.

Putting $-y$ for y or $-x$ for x, changes the equation. Hence the curve is not symmetrical with respect to either axis; but, putting $-y$ for y and $-x$ for x, does not change the equation. Hence the curve is symmetrical with respect to the origin.

Since there is a sine for any angle, the curve extends indefinitely in both positive and negative directions along the x-axis. Since the sine of an angle is not greater than 1 nor less than -1, the curve does not extend above the line $y = 1$ nor below the line $y = -1$.

Taking the first and second derivatives,

$$\frac{dy}{dx} = \cos x,$$

$$\frac{d^2y}{dx^2} = -\sin x.$$

Putting $\frac{dy}{dx} = 0$, $\cos x = 0$.

$$\therefore x = \pm\tfrac{1}{2}\pi, \pm \tfrac{3}{2}\pi, \pm \tfrac{5}{2}\pi, \pm\tfrac{7}{2}\pi, \cdots.$$

Substituting these values in $\frac{d^2y}{dx^2} = -\sin x$, it is found that the curve has maximum points when

$$x = \tfrac{1}{2}\pi, \tfrac{5}{2}\pi, \tfrac{9}{2}\pi, \cdots, \text{ and } -\tfrac{3}{2}\pi, -\tfrac{7}{2}\pi, -\tfrac{11}{2}\pi \cdots,$$

and minimum points when

$$x = \tfrac{3}{2}\pi, \tfrac{7}{2}\pi, \tfrac{11}{2}\pi, \cdots, \text{ and } -\tfrac{1}{2}\pi, -\tfrac{5}{2}\pi, -\tfrac{9}{2}\pi, \cdots.$$

In passing from left to right the curve is rising between a minimum point and the following maximum point, and falling between a maximum point and the following minimum point.

Putting $\frac{d^2y}{dx^2} = 0$, $-\sin x = 0$.

$$\therefore x = \pm\pi, \pm 2\pi, \pm 3\pi, \cdots.$$

It follows that there are points of inflection for these values of x, which are the points where the curve crosses the x-axis.

Plotting. Any length can be chosen as a unit on the coördinate axes. What may be called the **proper sine curve** is plotted by choosing as a unit on the y-axis the same length that is chosen to represent one radian on the x-axis. The curve is shown in Fig. 69.

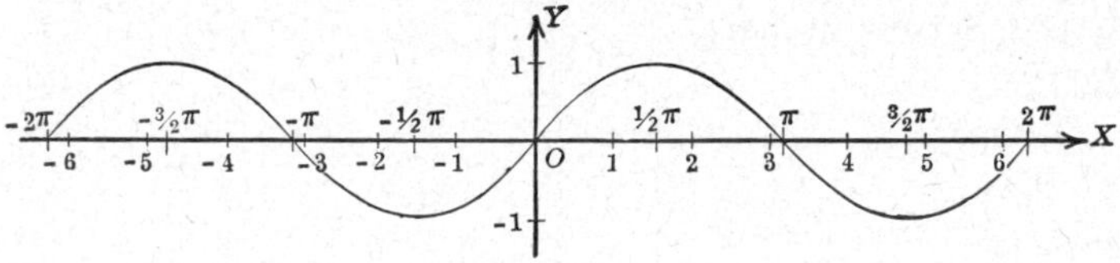

Fig. 69.

x	0	$\frac{1}{6}\pi$	$\frac{1}{4}\pi$	$\frac{1}{3}\pi$	$\frac{1}{2}\pi$	$\frac{2}{3}\pi$	$\frac{3}{4}\pi$	$\frac{5}{6}\pi$	π	$\frac{7}{6}\pi$	$\frac{5}{4}\pi$	$\frac{4}{3}\pi$	$\frac{3}{2}\pi$	$\frac{5}{3}\pi$	$\frac{7}{4}\pi$	$\frac{11}{6}\pi$	2π
y	0	.5	.707	.866	1	.866	.707	.5	0	−.5	−.707	−.866	−1	−.866	−.707	−.5	0

From 2π radians to 4π radians or from -2π radians to 0, these values repeat. They also repeat for each interval of 2π radians in both directions.

Definitions. A curve that repeats in form as illustrated by the sine curve is called a **periodic curve.** The function that gives rise to a periodic curve is called a **periodic function.** The least repeating part of a periodic curve is called a **cycle** of the curve. The change in the value of the variable necessary for a cycle is called the **period** of the function. The greatest absolute value of the ordinates of a periodic function is called the **amplitude** of the function.

Example 1. Find the period of $\sin nx$, and plot $y = \sin 2x$.

Since, in finding the value of sin nx, the angle x is multiplied by n before finding the sine, the period is $\dfrac{2\pi}{n}$.

The curve for $y = \sin 2x$ is shown in Fig. 70. The period of the function is π radians, and there are two cycles of the curve in 2π radians.

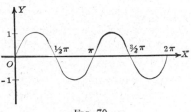

The number n in sin nx is called the **periodicity factor.**

Example 2. Find the amplitude of b sin x, and plot $y = 2 \sin x$.

Fɪɢ. 70.

Since, in finding the value of b sin x, sin x is found and then multiplied by b, the amplitude of the function is b, for the greatest value of sin x is 1.

The curve for $y = 2 \sin x$ is shown in Fig. 71. The amplitude is 2.

The number b in b sin x is sometimes called the **amplitude factor.**

By a proper choice of a periodicity factor and an amplitude factor a function of any amplitude and any period desired can be found.

Fɪɢ. 71.

While the sine function is perhaps the most frequently used of the periodic functions, the cosine function can be used quite as readily. By a proper choice and combination of sines and cosines a function can be built up that will represent exactly or approximately any periodic phenomenon. Just how this can be done can hardly be explained here.

EXERCISES

1. Plot $y = \sin x$ using several different lengths on the x-axis as units.

2. Discuss and plot $y = \cos x$. Give its period. By means of the derivative find where the curve is rising and where falling.

3. Discuss and plot $y = \tan x$ and $y = \cot x$ on the same set of axes. Give the period of each.

4. Plot $y = \sin x + \cos x$.

Suggestion. Plot $y_1 = \sin x$ and $y_2 = \cos x$ on the same set of axes. Then find the points on the curve $y = \sin x + \cos x$ from the relation $y = y_1 + y_2$, by adding the ordinates for various values of x.

5. Plot $y = \sin^2 x$ and $y = \cos^2 x$ on the same set of axes. Note that the curves never extend below the x-axis.

6. Plot $y = \frac{1}{2} \sin x$, $y = \sin x$, $y = 2 \sin x$, and $y = \frac{3}{2} \sin x$ on the same set of axes. Give the period and the amplitude of each.

7. Plot $y = \sin \frac{1}{2}x$, $y = \sin x$, $y = \sin 2x$, and $y = \sin \frac{3}{2}x$ on the same set of axes. Give the period and the amplitude of each.

8. Plot $y = \sin 2x + 2 \cos x$, and give the period.

9. Plot $y = \sin x + x$. Is this periodic?

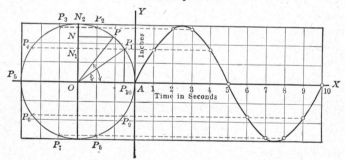

Fig. 72.

100. Projection of a point having uniform circular motion.

—*Example* 1. A point P, Fig. 72, moves around a vertical circle of radius 3 in. in a counter-clockwise direction. It starts with the point at A and moves with an angular velocity of 1 revolution in 10 sec. Plot a curve showing the distance the projection of P on the vertical diameter is from O at any time t, and find its equation.

Plotting. Let OP be any position of the radius drawn to the moving point. OP starts from position OA and at the end of 1 sec. is in position OP_1, having turned through an angle of $36° = 0.6283$ radians. At the end of 2 sec. it has turned to OP_2, through an angle of $72° = 1.2566$ radians, and so on to positions $OP_3, OP_4, \cdots, OP_{10}$.

The points $N_1, N_2 \cdots$ are the projections of $P_1, P_2 \cdots$, respectively, on the vertical diameter.

Produce the horizontal diameter OA through A, and lay off the seconds on this to some scale, taking the origin at A.

For each second plot a point whose ordinate is the corresponding distance of N from O. These points determine a curve of which any ordinate y is the distance from the center O of the projection of P upon the vertical diameter at the time t represented by the abscissa of the point.

It is evident that for the second and each successive revolution, the curve repeats, that is, it is a periodic curve.

Since the radius OP turns through 0.6283 radians per second,

angle $AOP = 0.6283t$ radians,

and $\qquad ON = OP \cdot \sin 0.6283t$,

or $\qquad y = 3 \sin 0.6283t$, the equation of the curve.

In general, then, it is readily seen that if a straight line of length r starts in a horizontal position when time, $t = 0$, and revolves in a vertical plane around one end at a uniform angular velocity ω per unit of time, the projection y of the moving end upon a vertical straight line has a motion represented by the equation

$$y = r \sin \omega t.$$

Similarly, the projection of the moving point upon the horizontal is given by the ordinates of the curve whose equation is

$$y = r \cos \omega t.$$

If the time is counted from some other instant than that from which the above is counted, then the motion is represented by

$$y = r \sin (\omega t + \alpha),$$

where α is the angle that OP makes with the line OA at the instant from which t is counted. As an illustration of this consider the following:

Example 2. A crank OP, Fig. 73, of length 2 ft. starts from a position making an angle $\alpha = 40° = \frac{2}{9}\pi$ radians with the horizontal line OA when $t = 0$. It rotates in the posi-

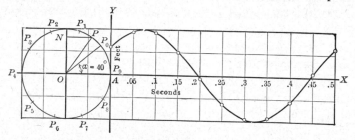

Fig. 73.

tive direction at the rate of 2 revolutions per second. Plot the curve showing the projection of P upon a vertical diameter, and write the equation.

Plotting. The axes are chosen as before, and points are found for each 0.05 sec. The curve is as shown in Fig. 73.

The equation is $y = 2 \sin (4\pi t + \frac{2}{9}\pi)$.

Definitions. The number of cycles of a periodic curve in a unit of time is called the **frequency.**

It is evident that

$$f = \frac{1}{T},$$

where f is the frequency and T is the period.

In $y = r \sin (\omega t + \alpha)$, $\quad f = \dfrac{\omega}{2\pi}$ and $T = \dfrac{2\pi}{\omega}$.

The angle α is called the **angle of lag**.

101. Summary.—In summary it may be noted again that the equation

$$y = a \sin (nx + \alpha)$$

gives a periodic curve. In this equation there are three arbitrary constants, a, n, and α. A change in any one of these constants will change the curve.

(1) If a is changed, the *amplitude* of the curve is changed.

(2) If n is changed, the *period* of the curve is changed.

(3) If α is changed, the curve is moved without change in shape from left to right or *vice versa*.

102. Simple harmonic motion.—If a point moves at a uniform rate around a circle and the point be projected on a straight line in the plane of the circle, the oscillating motion, that is, the back-and-forth motion, of the projected point is called **simple harmonic motion.** The name is abbreviated s.h.m. In **Art. 100,** the point N of Fig. 73 is the projection of the point P. As P moves around the circle the point N moves back-and-forth along the vertical diameter and performs a simple harmonic motion. It is readily seen that the point N moves most slowly near the ends of the diameter and most rapidly near the center. It thus changes its velocity or is accelerated.

It can be shown that many motions that one wishes to deal with are simple harmonic. Such is the motion of a swinging weight suspended by a string, a pendulum, a vibrating tuning fork, the particles of water in a wave, a coiled wire spring supporting a weight when the weight is pulled downward and released. Also many motions which are not simple harmonic may be treated as resulting from several such motions. Such motions occur in alternating electric currents, in sound waves, and in light waves.

103. Mathematical expression of simple harmonic motion.—It must not be thought that it is necessary to have a body moving in a circle in order to have simple harmonic motion. Making it depend upon the uniform motion in a circle is one of the simpler ways of treating it. When one is considering simple harmonic motion, the following questions among others may arise:

What is the *position* of the oscillating point at any time?

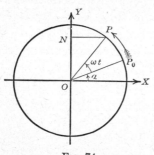

What is the *velocity* of the oscillating point at any time?

What is the *acceleration* of the oscillating point at any time?

In Fig. 74, P is the point moving uniformly in a circle of radius a, and N is its projection on the y-axis. If the point starts from P_0 when $t = 0$ and OP_0 makes an angle α with the x-axis, then, after time t with an angular velocity ω, the point will reach the position P. The position of the projection N at this instant is given by the equation

Fig. 74.

$$y = a \sin (\omega t + \alpha). \qquad (1)$$

The velocity of the oscillating point N is found by finding the derivative of y with respect to t. This gives

$$\frac{dy}{dt} = a\omega \cos (\omega t + \alpha). \qquad (2)$$

The acceleration of the oscillating point N is found by finding the derivative of the velocity with respect to t. This gives

$$\frac{d^2y}{dt^2} = -a\omega^2 \sin (\omega t + \alpha). \tag{3}$$

Since $a \sin (\omega t + \alpha) = y$, this may be written in the form

$$\frac{d^2y}{dt^2} = -\omega^2 y. \tag{4}$$

Equation (4) states that the acceleration of N is proportional to its distance from the origin, that is, proportional to its displacement.

Equation (1) may be written in a different form as follows:

$$y = a \sin (\omega t + \alpha) = a(\sin \omega t \cos \alpha + \cos \omega t \sin \alpha).$$
$$\therefore y = A \sin \omega t + B \cos \omega t, \tag{5}$$

where $A = a \cos \alpha$ and $B = a \sin \alpha$ are constants.

The above consideration could have been as readily carried out if the point had been projected on the x-axis.

In simple harmonic motion the quantity a is the **amplitude,** $\frac{2\pi}{\omega}$ is the **period,** and $-\frac{\alpha}{\omega}$ **is the phase,** of the vibration. It is readily seen that $\frac{2\pi}{\omega}$ is the time for one revolution of the point moving in the circle. Also, if $\frac{2\pi}{\omega}$ is substituted for t in the equation

$$y = a \sin (\omega t + \alpha),$$

the same value is obtained for y as when $t = 0$. This value is $y = a \sin \alpha$, the value of y at the start or at the instant from which the time is measured.

The sine curve showing the displacement in simple harmonic motion is that shown in Fig. 73.

EXERCISES

A point is moving around a circle in a counter-clockwise direction at a uniform rate. Its position at any time t is given by each pair of equations that follow. Find the horizontal and the vertical velocity for any instant.

1. $x = 3 \cos 2t$ and $y = 3 \sin 2t$.

2. $x = 8 \cos \omega t$ and $y = 8 \sin \omega t$.

In exercises 3–6, the functions given represent the displacements of a point moving in simple harmonic motion. In each find the velocity and the acceleration for any value of t.

3. $y = 3 \sin \frac{1}{2}t$.   **5.** $y = 3 \sin 3t + 4 \cos 3t$.

4. $y = 4 \sin (\frac{1}{3}t + \frac{1}{4}\pi)$.   **6.** $x = A \cos \omega t + B \sin \omega t$.

7. A flywheel 8 ft. in diameter makes one revolution a second. Find the horizontal and the vertical speed of a point on its rim 2 ft. above a horizontal line through its center. Note that there are two such points.

8. A crank 18 in. long starts from a horizontal position and rotates in the positive direction in a vertical plane at the rate of $\frac{1}{4}\pi$ radians per second. The projection of the moving end of the crank upon a vertical line oscillates with a simple harmonic motion. Construct a curve that represents this motion, and write its equation.

9. A crank 8 in. long starts from a position making an angle of 55° with the horizontal, and rotates in a vertical plane in the positive direction at the rate of one revolution in 3 sec. Construct a curve showing the projection of the moving end of the crank in a vertical line. Write the equation of the curve and give the period and the frequency.

10. Plot the curves that represent the following motions:

$$(1) \ y = 12 \sin (1.88t + 0.44),$$
$$(2) \ y = 2.5 \sin (\tfrac{1}{6}\pi t + \tfrac{1}{12}\pi).$$

Give the period and frequency of each.

11. Plot $y = r \sin \frac{1}{2}\pi t$ and $y = r \sin (\frac{1}{2}\pi t + \frac{1}{4}\pi)$ on the same set of axes. Notice that the highest points on each are separated by the constant angle $\frac{1}{4}\pi$. Such curves are said to be out of phase. The difference in phase is stated in time or as an angle. In the latter case it is called the **phase angle**.

12. Plot $y = r \sin \frac{1}{4}\pi t$, $y = r \sin (\frac{1}{4}\pi t - \frac{1}{4}\pi)$, and $y = r \cos \frac{1}{4}\pi t$ all on the same set of axes. What is the difference in phase between these?

13. What is the difference in phase between the curves of $y = \sin x$ and $y = \cos x$? Between $y = \cos x$ and $y = \sin (x + \frac{1}{2}\pi)$?

104. Damped vibrations.—A certain kind of retarded motion has already been discussed in **Art. 94,** and it is there shown that such a retarded motion is represented by the exponential function

$$y = ae^{-kx},$$

where a and k are constants. In the last few articles simple harmonic motion has been studied with reference to oscillations or vibrations. We now wish to find how to express a retarded or damped vibration by a function.

It is a matter of experience that when a body vibrates in a medium like a gas or a liquid, the amplitudes of the successive swings become less and less, or the motion slowly or rapidly dies out, or decays. If a pendulum vibrates in air, the rate of decay is comparatively slow as compared to its rate of decay when vibrating in water.

This damping effect is found in many oscillations arising in questions connected with alternating currents in electricity, in the damped oscillations of a galvanometer needle, in representing the oscillations of a stiff spring, or in the oscillations of a disk suspended in a liquid, such as is used to compare the viscosities of different liquids.

In all such damped vibrations, the amplitudes of the successive swings decreases by a constant factor, which gives rise to an exponential function (**Art. 91**) of which the logarithmic derivative is constant. (**Art. 82.**)

105. Exponential and periodic functions combined.—Damped vibrations can be represented by functions which combine the exponential function and the periodic function. A general form of this function is

$$y = be^{ax} \sin (nx + \alpha).$$

This may be classed as one of the most important functions in engineering.

The curve is most readily plotted by first plotting the curves represented by the exponential function and the periodic function separately on the same set of axes, and then finding the ordinates for various values of x by multiplying together the ordinates for various values of x in the exponential and periodic functions.

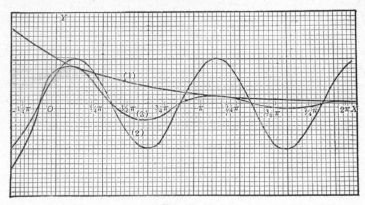

Fig. 75.

Since $\sin (nx + \alpha)$ is never greater than 1 nor less than -1, the value of the function is never greater than be^{ax} nor less than $-be^{ax}$. The curve then never passes above the curve $y = be^{ax}$ nor below the curve $y = -be^{ax}$. These curves are called the boundary curves. The curve touches the boundary curves whenever $\sin (nx + \alpha) = \pm 1$.

Example. Plot the curve showing the values of y for any value of x from $x = -\frac{7}{8}\pi$ to $x = 2\pi$ for the equation $y = e^{-0.5x} \sin (2x + \frac{1}{4}\pi)$.

The curve is readily plotted by first plotting $y_1 = e^{-0.5x}$ and $y_2 = \sin (2x + \frac{1}{4}\pi)$, and then finding various values of y from the relation $y = y_1 y_2$. In Fig. 75, (1) is the exponential curve, (2) the sine curve, and (3) the final curve. Note that (2) and (3) intersect the x-axis at the same points.

EXERCISES

In exercises 1 to 3 the equations represent damped harmonic motions. In each sketch a curve showing the "fading away" of the motion for values of t as indicated.

1. $y = e^t \sin t$ for t from 0 to 2π.

2. $i = e^{-\frac{1}{3}t} \sin (2t + \frac{1}{2}\pi)$ for t from -2 to 8.

3. $y = 3e^{-2t} \sin 3t$ for t from -1 to 4.

4. In an oscillatory discharge of a condenser under certain conditions, the charge q at any time t is represented by the equation, $q = 0.00224e^{-4000t} \sin (8000t + \tan^{-1} 2)$, where q is in coulombs and t in seconds. Plot the curve showing values of q for values of t from 0 to 0.0012 second   What is the period?

Suggestion. Choose 0.0001 second as a unit on the t-axis, and 0.001 coulomb as a unit on the q-axis; and let the length representing a unit on the q-axis be about twice that for the unit on the t-axis. Plot the exponential curve first, and then the sine curve choosing as a unit on the q-axis the length representing 0.001 coulomb.

CHAPTER XIII

CURVATURE, TANGENTS, NORMALS

106. The student who has followed the development of the subject as already given is probably willing to believe that there is hardly any limit to the applications of the calculus in the fields of human endeavor. In fact, many volumes could be written on the numerous uses of the subject; and all of these uses might be of interest to some readers. Here, however, the main stress must be placed on those topics which can be used most frequently in applications, and so be of greatest interest to the largest number of men who wish to use the calculus.

107. Meaning of curvature.—If a point moves in a straight line, the direction of its motion is the same at every point of its course; in fact, this is involved in the definition of a straight line. If, however, the path of a point is a curved line, there is a continual change of direction as the point moves along the curve. This change of direction, or deviation from a straight line, is called the **curvature of the curve.**

The question at once arises as to how the curvature of a curve can be dealt with mathematically. As always, before anything can be handled by mathematics, it must be *measured;* and before it can be measured, a *unit of measure* must be found.

Before discussing the unit of curvature, we will follow the idea further and endeavor to see some of its uses. The curves of which the curvature is to be found are divided into two classes; those of which the equations are not known, and those of which the equations are given. Under the first class would ordinarily fall such material curves as a curve in a railroad track, while the circle, ellipse, catenary, etc. would fall under the second class. Here, too, would fall the curves assumed by beams and struts under load.

108. Curvature, approximate measurement.—In the United States it is customary to express the curvature of railroad tracks in *degrees*. The number of degrees in the curvature of a track is determined by the number of degrees in the angle formed by the tangents drawn at the ends of a chord 100 ft. in length.

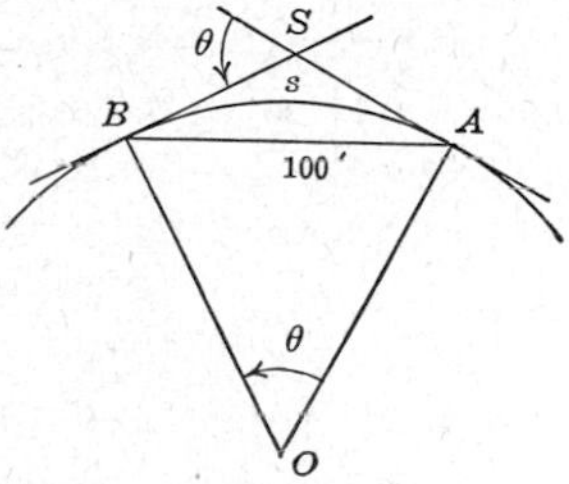

FIG. 76.

Thus, in going from A to B along the track AsB, Fig. 76, the direction in which the point is moving has changed by the angle θ shown at S, and the number of degrees in this angle is the number of degrees in the curvature of the track. A 5-deg. curve is one in which a 100-ft. chord gives an angle $\theta = 5°$.

It is evident that if AO and BO are drawn perpendicular to the tangents at A and B respectively, then the angle θ at O is also the measure of the curvature.   If, further, the track is an arc of a circle, it is evident that AO and BO are radii of this circle.   The radius of this circle is called the **radius of curvature** of this portion of the track.   It is hardly necessary to say that this scheme is entirely arbitrary, as any other length of chord could be chosen as well as that of 100 ft.   It is also quite evident that the method is best applied when the curve does not depart greatly from a straight line.

In curves commonly used in railroad tracks, the error is slight if the arc is taken in place of the chord.   Then assuming that 1 radian = 57.3°, the radius of a 1-degree curve is found by the formula of **P. M. IV, Art. 26; H. S., Art. 362,**

$$r = s \div \theta = 100 \div \frac{1}{57.3} = 5730.$$

Since the unit of length is 1 ft., 1 degree of curvature gives a radius of 5730 ft. It follows that 5730 divided by the number of degrees of curvature gives the radius of curvature, or the radius of the curve if considered the arc of a circle; and 5730 divided by the number of feet in the radius gives the number of degrees of curvature.

In many handbooks are found tables giving the radius corresponding to different degrees of curvature.

According to the agreements in the preceding, a circle having a radius of 5730 ft. has *unit* curvature.

In English practice the curvature, or the curve of the track, such as the curve in a street-car track when turning a corner, is given in feet and is the radius of curvature of the track. It is determined as follows: A straight edge AB, Fig. 77, 10 ft. long is laid against the rail on the inner side of the curve. The distance from the center of the straight-edge to the rail is measured. This is the height of the segment, or, as it is usually called, the "middle ordinate." The radius can then be found by simple geometry from the formula

Fig. 77.

$$r = \frac{(\frac{1}{2}w)^2 + h^2}{2h},$$

where r is the radius, w the length of the chord, and h the middle ordinate. (**P. M. III, Art. 40; H. S., Art. 148.**)

109. Curvature, accurate measurement.—As already stated the curvature of a curve is its deviation from a straight line.

The **total curvature** of an arc is defined to be its total change in direction.

Thus, the total curvature of the arc PQ, Fig. 78, is the difference in its directions at P and at Q, or it is $\Delta\theta = \theta_2 - \theta_1$, the change in the inclination of the tangent to the curve.

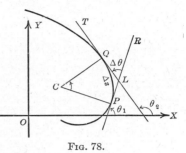

FIG. 78.

The **mean** or **average curvature** is the ratio of the total curvature to the length of arc. This is what the total curvature of each linear unit of arc would be if the curvature of the arc was *uniform*, that is, if the curvature was the same throughout.

Then the mean curvature of the arc PQ is $\dfrac{\Delta\theta}{\Delta s}$, where $\Delta\theta$ is in radians and Δs is in linear units.

The **actual curvature** K, or simply the **curvature,** of the curve at P is defined to be

$$K = \lim_{\Delta s \to 0}\left[\frac{\Delta\theta}{\Delta s}\right] = \frac{d\theta}{ds}.$$

If this is to be applied to a curve whose equation is given in rectangular coördinates it is necessary to express $\dfrac{d\theta}{ds}$ in terms of x and y.

110. Curvature in rectangular coördinates.—Since the derivative is always equal to the quotient of the differentials, we shall consider $\dfrac{d\theta}{ds}$ as $d\theta \div ds$.

Since θ is the inclination of the tangent line,

$$\theta = \tan^{-1}\frac{dy}{dx}.$$

Then $\quad d\theta = \dfrac{\dfrac{d^2y}{dx^2}}{1 + \left(\dfrac{dy}{dx}\right)^2} \cdot dx.$ $\hspace{2cm}$ By [29].

Since $\quad ds^2 = dx^2 + dy^2,$ $\hspace{3cm}$ **Art. 50.**

$$ds = \sqrt{dx^2 + dy^2} = \sqrt{1 + \left(\frac{dy}{dx}\right)^2} \cdot dx.$$

Therefore $\dfrac{d\theta}{ds} = \dfrac{\dfrac{\dfrac{d^2y}{dx^2}}{1 + \left(\dfrac{dy}{dx}\right)^2} \cdot dx}{\sqrt{1 + \left(\dfrac{dy}{dx}\right)^2} \cdot dx} = \dfrac{\dfrac{d^2y}{dx^2}}{\left[1 + \left(\dfrac{dy}{dx}\right)^2\right]^{\frac{3}{2}}}.$

[47] $\qquad \therefore \mathbf{K} = \dfrac{\dfrac{\mathbf{d^2y}}{\mathbf{dx^2}}}{\left[1 + \left(\dfrac{\mathbf{dy}}{\mathbf{dx}}\right)^2\right]^{\frac{3}{2}}}$

As there will be no occasion to distinguish between positive and negative curvature, the sign will be taken for $\sqrt{1 + \left(\dfrac{dy}{dx}\right)^2}$ which will make K positive, that is, the absolute value of K will always be taken. This is represented by $|K|$.

Example. Find the curvature for the circle $x^2 + y^2 = a^2$.

Solution. Given $x^2 + y^2 = a^2$.

Differentiating, $2x + 2y\dfrac{dy}{dx} = 0.$

Or $\hspace{3cm} \dfrac{dy}{dx} = -\dfrac{x}{y}.$

Differentiating again, $\dfrac{d^2y}{dx^2} = -\dfrac{y - x\dfrac{dy}{dx}}{y^2} = -\dfrac{y - x\left(-\dfrac{x}{y}\right)}{y^2}$

$$= -\frac{y^2 + x^2}{y^3} = -\frac{a^2}{y^3}.$$

Substituting these values in [**47**],

$$K = \dfrac{-\dfrac{a^2}{y^3}}{\left[1 + \left(-\dfrac{x}{y}\right)^2\right]^{\frac{3}{2}}} = \dfrac{-\dfrac{a^2}{y^3}}{\left[\dfrac{y^2 + x^2}{y^2}\right]^{\frac{3}{2}}} = \dfrac{-\dfrac{a^2}{y^3}}{\left(\dfrac{a^2}{y^2}\right)^{\frac{3}{2}}} = -\dfrac{1}{a}.$$

$$\therefore |K| = \dfrac{1}{a}.$$

It is to be noted that here for the circle the curvature of the circle is equal to the reciprocal of the radius.

111. Curvature of a circle.—In any circle the central angle in radians times the radius in linear units equals the intercepted arc in linear units. (**P. M. IV, Art. 26; H. S., Art. 362.**)

Thus, in Fig. 79, $s = r\theta$, or $\dfrac{\theta}{s} = \dfrac{1}{r}.$

Since the angle formed at the center by the radii is equal to the angle between the tangents drawn at the extremities of the radii; then, if the angle is $\Delta\theta$ and the arc Δs,

$$\frac{\Delta\theta}{\Delta s} = \frac{1}{r}.$$

Or, passing to the limit,

$$\frac{d\theta}{ds} = \frac{1}{r},$$

that is, the mean curvature of an arc of a circle is the same as the curvature at any point of that circle. This states that (1) the circle is a curve of constant, or uniform, curvature, and (2) the curvature is equal to the reciprocal of the radius.

Thus, in a circle, if $r = 5$, the curvature is $\frac{1}{5}$ radian for each unit length of arc.

If $r = 1$, the curvature is 1 radian for each unit length of arc, that is, *a circle of unit radius has unit curvature.*

112. Radius of curvature.—From what has been said in the previous articles, it is evident that the curvature of a curve can be computed for any given point P, and by drawing a circle having a radius equal to the reciprocal of the curvature, we shall have a circle that has the same curvature as the given curve at the point taken. If this circle is placed tangent to the curve at the point P, that is, so they have a common tangent, and is so placed that the center of the circle is on the concave side of the curve, it is called the **circle of curvature** of the curve for the point, or the **osculating circle**. Its center is called the **center of curvature** of the curve for the point, and its radius is called the **radius of curvature** of the curve for the point.

If R is the radius of curvature, then

[48]
$$R = \frac{\left[1 + \left(\frac{dy}{dx}\right)^2\right]^{\frac{3}{2}}}{\frac{d^2y}{dx^2}}.$$

Here as for K the value taken for R is always $|R|$.

Example. Compute the radius of curvature for the parabola $y^2 = 4x$ at the points $(0, 0)$ and $(4, 4)$. Draw the parabola and the circles of curvature at these points.

Solution. Given $y^2 = 4x$.

Differentiating, $2y\frac{dy}{dx} = 4$, or $\frac{dy}{dx} = \frac{2}{y}$.

$$\frac{d^2y}{dx^2} = -\frac{2\frac{dy}{dx}}{y^2} = -\frac{4}{y^3}.$$

$$R = \frac{\left(1 + \frac{4}{y^2}\right)^{\frac{3}{2}}}{-\frac{4}{y^3}} = -\frac{y^3\left(1 + \frac{4}{y^2}\right)^{\frac{3}{2}}}{4} = -\frac{(y^2 + 4)^{\frac{3}{2}}}{4}$$

$$= -\frac{(4x + 4)^{\frac{3}{2}}}{4} = -2(x + 1)^{\frac{3}{2}}.$$

$$\therefore |R| = |-2(x+1)^{\frac{3}{2}}|.$$

At point $(0, 0)$, $R = 2(1)^{\frac{3}{2}} = 2$.
At point $(4, 4)$, $R = 2(4+1)^{\frac{3}{2}} = 10\sqrt{5}$.

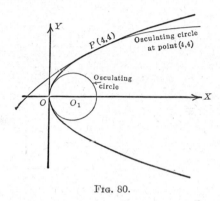

Fig. 80.

113. Approximate formulas for K and R.—When the curve deviates but slightly from a *horizontal* straight line, as in the elastic curve of a beam, the slope of the tangent line is near zero. Hence $\frac{dy}{dx}$ is small and $\left(\frac{dy}{dx}\right)^2$ is still smaller. Then the denominator in the formula for K differs but little from 1 and therefore the formula becomes approximately

$$K = \left|\frac{d^2y}{dx^2}\right|.$$

Likewise the approximate formula for R under the same conditions is

$$R = \left|\frac{1}{\dfrac{d^2y}{dx^2}}\right|.$$

These formulas are frequently used in mechanics in the study of the flexure of beams.

EXERCISES

1. Find the radius of curvature of $y = e^x$ at the point where $x = 0$.

2. Find the radius of curvature of the cubical parabola $y = x^3$ for any value of x.   Find the numerical value when $x = 2$.

Find K and R for each of the following:

3. $y = x^2$.

4. $y^2 = 2px$.

5. $xy = a^2$.

6. $y = ax^2 + bx + c$.

7. $y = \dfrac{e^x + e^{-x}}{2}$.

8. $y = \dfrac{a}{2} \left(e^{\frac{x}{a}} + e^{-\frac{x}{a}} \right)$.

9. $y = \sin x$.

10. $y = \cos x$.

11. $x = a \cos \theta,\ y = a \sin \theta$.

12. $y = b^x$.

13. $\dfrac{x^2}{a^2} + \dfrac{y^2}{b^2} = 1$.

14. $\dfrac{x^2}{a^2} - \dfrac{y^2}{b^2} = 1$.

15. Find the radius of curvature for the ellipse $\dfrac{x^2}{25} + \dfrac{y^2}{9} = 1$, at the points $(5, 0)$ and $(0, 3)$.   Draw the ellipse and the circles of curvature.

16. Find the radius of curvature for the sine curve $y = \sin x$ at a point of inflection.   What is always the radius of curvature at a point of inflection?

17. Find the radius of curvature for the cycloid $x = a(\theta - \sin \theta)$, $y = a(1 - \cos \theta)$ at the point $(a\pi, 2a)$.

Suggestion $\dfrac{dx}{d\theta} = a(1 - \cos \theta)$,

$\dfrac{dy}{d\theta} = a \sin \theta$.

Then $\dfrac{dy}{dx} = \dfrac{dy}{d\theta} \div \dfrac{dx}{d\theta} = \dfrac{\sin \theta}{1 - \cos \theta}$.

And $\dfrac{d^2y}{dx^2} = \dfrac{(1 - \cos \theta)\cos \theta - \sin^2 \theta}{(1 - \cos \theta)^2} \dfrac{d\theta}{dx}$

$= \dfrac{\cos \theta - 1}{(1 - \cos \theta)^2} \dfrac{1}{a(1 - \cos \theta)} = - \dfrac{1}{a(1 - \cos \theta)^2}$.

18. The equation for the shape of a beam supported at the ends and loaded uniformly is

$$y = \frac{w}{48EI} (3l^2x^2 - 2x^4),$$

where the origin is at the middle of the beam, l is the total length of the beam, w is the load per unit length, E is Young's modulus for the material, and I the moment of inertia of the cross section. If $l = 50$, $w = 20$, $E = 29 \times 10^6$, and $I = 80$, find the curvature when $x = 0$. Show that in this case where the slope of the curve is small the curvature for any value of x is represented very approximately by $\dfrac{d^2y}{dx^2}$.

114. Tangent, normal, subtangent, and subnormal.—

The method for finding the equations of a tangent and normal to a curve at any point on the curve was discussed in **Art. 17.** Here we are to determine the lengths of certain lines connected with the tangent and normal.

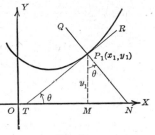

Let $y = f(x)$ be the equation of a curve which is shown in Fig. 81, plotted in rectangular coördinates. $P_1(x_1, y_1)$ is any point

FIG. 81.

on the curve at which TR is a tangent and NQ a normal. The tangent intersects the x-axis in T, and the normal intersects the x-axis in N. The line MP_1 is perpendicular to the x-axis, and hence $MP_1 = y_1$.

The segment TP_1 of the tangent line is called the **length of the tangent.**

The segment P_1N of the normal is called the **length of the normal.**

The segment TM, which is the projection of TP_1 on the x-axis, is called the **subtangent.**

The segment MN, which is the projection of P_1N on the x-axis, is called the **subnormal.**

Since the triangles TMP_1, NMP_1, and TP_1N are right triangles, and $\tan \theta = \dfrac{dy}{dx}\Big|_{x=x_1}$, the values of TP_1, P_1N, TM, and MN can be readily computed in any particular case.

Using $\dfrac{dy}{dx}$ for $\dfrac{dy}{dx}\Big|_{x\,=\,x_1}$ for convenience, we have the following by trigonometry:

$$TP_1 = MP_1 \csc \theta = y_1 . \frac{\sqrt{1 + \left(\dfrac{dy}{dx}\right)^2}}{\dfrac{dy}{dx}}$$

$$P_1N = MP_1 \sec \theta = y_1 \sqrt{1 + \left(\frac{dy}{dx}\right)^2}.$$

$$TM = MP_1 \cot \theta = \frac{y_1}{\dfrac{dy}{dx}}.$$

$$MN = MP_1 \tan \theta = y_1 \frac{dy}{dx}.$$

The lengths of the tangent and normal are usually considered positive.

If the subtangent starts from the point T and the subnormal from the point M, each will be positive or negative according as it extends to the right or to the left.

Example 1.   Find the lengths of the tangent and normal, and the subtangent and subnormal for the parabola $y^2 = 4x$ at the point in the first quadrant where $x = 1$.

Solution.   Given $y^2 = 4x$.

In the first quadrant when $x = 1$, $y = 2$.

Differentiating, $2y \dfrac{dy}{dx} = 4$, or $\dfrac{dy}{dx} = \dfrac{2}{y}$.

Then $\qquad \dfrac{dy}{dx}\Big|_{x\,=\,1} = \dfrac{2}{2} = 1.$

Length of tangent $= y_1 \dfrac{\sqrt{1 + \left(\dfrac{dy}{dx}\right)^2}}{\dfrac{dy}{dx}}$

$$= 2 \cdot \frac{\sqrt{1 + 1^2}}{1} = 2\sqrt{2}.$$

Length of normal $= y_1 \sqrt{1 + \left(\dfrac{dy}{dx}\right)^2}$

$$= 2\sqrt{1 + 1^2} = 2\sqrt{2}.$$

Subtangent $= \dfrac{y_1}{\dfrac{dy}{dx}} = \dfrac{2}{1} = 2.$

Subnormal $= y_1 \dfrac{dy}{dx} = 2 \cdot 1 = 2.$

Example 2.   Find the equation of a curve such that the subtangent is always equal to a.

Solution.   Here $\dfrac{y}{\dfrac{dy}{dx}} = a$, or $y = a\dfrac{dy}{dx}.$

Dividing by dy, $\dfrac{y}{dy} = \dfrac{a}{dx}.$

Taking the reciprocals, $\dfrac{dy}{y} = \dfrac{dx}{a}.$

Integrating, $\log y = \dfrac{x}{a} + c.$

Then $y = e^{\frac{x}{a}+c} = e^c e^{\frac{x}{a}}.$

Or $y = Ce^{\frac{x}{a}}.$

EXERCISES

Find the lengths of the tangent and normal, and the subtangent and subnormal for the following:

1. The parabola $y^2 = 2x$ at the point in the first quadrant where $x = 8$.

2. The hyperbola $xy = 4$ at the point in the first quadrant where $x = 4$.

3. The ellipse $\dfrac{x^2}{25} + \dfrac{y^2}{16} = 1$ at the point in the second quadrant where $x = -4$.

4. In the cycloid $x = a(\theta - \sin \theta)$, $y = a(1 - \cos \theta)$, find the subtangent and subnormal for $\theta = \frac{1}{2}\pi$.

5. Find the lengths of the tangent and normal for the curve

$$y = x^3 - 12x + 7$$

at the point where $x = 1$.

6. Find the equation of a curve of which the subnormal is always equal to the abscissa of the point in which the normal intersects the curve.

7. Find the equation of a curve of which the subtangent is n times the abscissa of the point of contact of the tangent.

CHAPTER XIV

METHODS OF INTEGRATION

115. From a study of the previous chapters it is evident that the derivative or the differential of any algebraic, trigonometric, exponential, or logarithmic function can be found; and the process is very simple and direct if one knows the formulas of differentiation. It might be assumed that the integral of any function could likewise be found; but unfortunately this is not the case, as functions are frequently found, especially in the applications of mathematics, that cannot be integrated.

Every differentiation that is performed gives a function of which the integral is at once known, for by definition integration is the inverse of differentiation. In this way a great number of integrals have been found. It is evident that a list of such forms could be used to advantage in finding the integral of a given function. All that would be necessary would be to find in the given list a form exactly like the given function. But because of the unlimited number of forms that arise for integration it is impracticable to form a list which will include all forms that can be integrated.

It was stated in **Art. 62** that, in general, an indefinite integral is found by one of the following methods:

(1) *By recognizing at once a function whose differential is the given differential.*

(2) *By reversing the rules of differentiation.*

(3) *By reference to a table of integrals.*

All of these schemes have been used in previous chapters, but more particularly the first two.   In the present chapter we propose to deal to a limited extent with methods making use of a table of integrals, first making use of a list called **fundamental formulas** and later using a more extended table.   The matter in this chapter then does not give new ideas of calculus, but it is rather a presentation of more or less mechanical schemes for arriving at integrals.   For this reason the reader who is not interested in this phase of the work can omit or touch lightly the following pages.

116. Fundamental formulas of integration.—A few formulas of integration have already been given in **Arts. 64, 71** and **83.**   These together with certain other formulas are given here, making a list of twenty of perhaps the most useful formulas of integration.   These are called the **fundamental formulas of integration,** but this should not be taken to mean that we could not get along without this complete list, in fact, only the first three are actually fundamental as all the others could be reduced to one of these.

In these formulas a and n are constants and u is a variable which, of course, may be a function of a variable.   For convenience the constant of integration is not printed but may be supplied at pleasure.

FUNDAMENTAL FORMULAS OF INTEGRATION

Algebraic functions.

I. $\int u^n du = \dfrac{u^{n+1}}{n+1}$, when n is not -1.

II. $\int u^{-1} du = \int \dfrac{du}{u} = \log u$.   The case when $n = -1$.

III. $\int \dfrac{du}{u^2 + a^2} = \dfrac{1}{a} \tan^{-1}\dfrac{u}{a}$, or $-\dfrac{1}{a}\cot^{-1}\dfrac{u}{a}$.

IV. $\int \dfrac{du}{u^2 - a^2} = \dfrac{1}{2a} \log \dfrac{u - a}{u + a}$, when $u^2 > a^2$.

$\qquad\qquad = \dfrac{1}{2a} \log \dfrac{a - u}{a + u}$, when $u^2 < a^2$.

V. $\int \dfrac{du}{\sqrt{a^2 - u^2}} = \sin^{-1}\dfrac{u}{a}$, or $- \cos^{-1}\dfrac{u}{a}$.

VI. $\int \dfrac{du}{\sqrt{u^2 \pm a^2}} = \log(u + \sqrt{u^2 \pm a^2})$.

VII. $\int \dfrac{du}{u\sqrt{u^2 - a^2}} = \dfrac{1}{a} \sec^{-1}\dfrac{u}{a}$, or $- \dfrac{1}{a} \csc^{-1}\dfrac{u}{a}$.

VIII. $\int \dfrac{du}{\sqrt{2au - u^2}} = \text{vers}^{-1}\dfrac{u}{a}$, or $\sin^{-1}\dfrac{u - a}{a}$.

Exponential functions.

IX. $\int a^u du = \dfrac{a^u}{\log a}$.

X. $\int e^u du = e^u$.

Trigonometric functions.

XI. $\int \sin u\, du = -\cos u$.

XII. $\int \cos u\, du = \sin u$.

XIII. $\int \tan u\, du = -\log \cos u = \log \sec u$.

XIV. $\int \cot u\, du = \log \sin u = -\log \csc u$.

XV. $\int \sec u\, du = \log \tan \left(\dfrac{u}{2} + \dfrac{\pi}{4}\right)$,

$\qquad\qquad$ or $\log (\sec u + \tan u)$.

XVI. $\int \csc u\, du = \log \tan \dfrac{u}{2}$, or $\log (\csc u - \cot u)$.

XVII. $\int \sec^2 u\, du = \tan u$.

XVIII. $\int \csc^2 u\, du = -\cot u$.

XIX. $\int \sec u \tan u\, du = \sec u$.

XX. $\int \csc u \cot u\, du = -\csc u$.

The above formulas can readily be established by differentiating the parts following the equality signs.

In several of the formulas the different forms given differ by constants.

117. How fundamental formulas are used.—When a function that is to be integrated is exactly of the form of one of the fundamental formulas, the integral is written at once by that formula.   When a function to be integrated is not exactly like any of these formulas, we endeavor, in some manner, to change it so that it shall be exactly like one or more of the fundamental integrals.   Often these transformations require considerable ability in handling algebra and trigonometry.

The two following theorems which have already been given in **Arts. 65** and **66,** are frequently used in transforming an integral to agree in form with one or more of the fundamental integrals.

THEOREM I.   *A constant factor can be transferred from one side of the integral sign to the other side without affecting the value of the integral.*

This theorem is stated in the formula

$$\int c \, du \,=\, c \int du,$$

and proved in **Art. 65**.

THEOREM II.   *The integral of the algebraic sum of a finite number of functions is equal to the algebraic sum of their integrals.*

This is stated in the formula

$$\int (du + dv + dw + \cdots) = \int du + \int dv + \int dw + \cdots,$$

and proved in **Art. 66**.

Some other schemes used in transforming integrals to fundamental forms follow and are treated in the succeeding articles.

(1) *Changing the form by substituting a new variable for the one given.*

(2) *Integration by parts.*

(3) *By separating fractions into partial fractions.*

118. Algebraic functions. Applications of formulas I–VIII.—The applications of the formulas and methods of integration can best be presented by giving examples that are worked out. The student should study these examples very carefully and then solve the exercises that follow them. Ability and freedom in integration can be gained only by doing many exercises.

Example 1.   Find $\int \dfrac{4x^4 + 13x^2 - 2x + 10}{x^2 + 2} \, dx.$

This can be made to agree with fundamental integrals by dividing the numerator by the denominator and using theorems I and II of the preceding article.

Then $\displaystyle\int \frac{4x^4 + 13x^2 - 2x + 10}{x^2 + 2} \, dx$

$$= \int \left(4x^2 + 5 - \frac{2x}{x^2 + 2} \right) dx$$

$$= 4\int x^2 dx + 5\int dx - \int \frac{2x \, dx}{x^2 + 2}$$

$$= \tfrac{4}{3}x^3 + 5x - \log(x^2 + 2). \qquad \text{By formulas I and II.}$$

The $\displaystyle\int \frac{2x \, dx}{x^2 + 2}$ agrees in form with formula II by making $u = x^2 + 2$ when $du = 2x \, dx.$

Note. In this chapter the constant of integration is omitted, but can be supplied if desired.

The same idea as here, that of separating an integral into simpler forms, is also illustrated in example 2, p. 113.

Example 2.   Find $\int (x^2 + 3)(x^2 - x + 1)\, dx$.

The same theorems are applied in this as in example 1, but the breaking up into simpler forms is accomplished by first multiplying together the two factors.

Then $\int (x^2 + 3)\,(x^2 - x + 1)\, dx$

$$= \int (x^4 - x^3 + 4x^2 - 3x + 3)\, dx$$

$$= \int x^4 dx - \int x^3 dx + 4\int x^2 dx - 3\int x\, dx + 3\int dx$$

$$= \tfrac{1}{5}x^5 - \tfrac{1}{4}x^4 + \tfrac{4}{3}x^3 - \tfrac{3}{2}x^2 + 3x. \qquad \text{By formula I.}$$

Example 3.   Find $\displaystyle\int \frac{dx}{x^2 + 4x + 13}$.

Such an integral, that is, where there appears in the denominator a form of the type $ax^2 + bx + c$, can be made to agree with a fundamental formula by completing the square in x.

Then $\displaystyle\int \frac{dx}{x^2 + 4x + 13} = \int \frac{dx}{x^2 + 4x + 4 + 9}$

$$= \int \frac{dx}{(x + 2)^2 + 3^2}.$$

This integral is like formula III where $u = x + 2$, $du = dx$, and $a = 3$.   Applying the formula,

$$\int \frac{dx}{(x + 2)^2 + 3^2} = \tfrac{1}{3} \tan^{-1} \frac{x + 2}{3}.$$

$$\therefore \int \frac{dx}{x^2 + 4x + 13} = \tfrac{1}{3} \tan^{-1} \frac{x + 2}{3}.$$

Example 4.   Find $\displaystyle\int \frac{dx}{\sqrt{2 + 3x - 2x^2}}$.

Here the coefficient of x^2 is not unity, and it is necessary to factor so as to make the coefficient unity which may be either plus or minus, but here is minus. The square is then completed to bring the integral to agree with a fundamental formula.

First factoring out the coefficient of x^2 and then completing the square in x,

$$\int \frac{dx}{\sqrt{2 + 3x - 2x^2}} = \frac{1}{\sqrt{2}} \int \frac{dx}{\sqrt{1 + \frac{3}{2}x - x^2}}$$

$$= \frac{1}{\sqrt{2}} \int \frac{dx}{\sqrt{1 + \frac{9}{16} - (x^2 - \frac{3}{2}x + \frac{9}{16})}}$$

$$= \frac{1}{\sqrt{2}} \int \frac{dx}{\sqrt{(\frac{5}{4})^2 - (x - \frac{3}{4})^2}} = \frac{1}{\sqrt{2}} \sin^{-1} \frac{x - \frac{3}{4}}{\frac{5}{4}}$$

$$= \frac{1}{\sqrt{2}} \sin^{-1} \frac{4x - 3}{5}. \qquad \text{By formula V.}$$

Example 5. Find $\displaystyle\int \frac{x \, dx}{\sqrt{6x - x^2}}$.

This can be made to come under I and VIII as follows:

$$\int \frac{x \, dx}{\sqrt{6x - x^2}} = \int \frac{[3 - (3 - x)]dx}{\sqrt{6x - x^2}}$$

$$= \int \frac{3dx}{\sqrt{6x - x^2}} - \int \frac{(3 - x)dx}{\sqrt{6x - x^2}}$$

$$= 3 \int \frac{dx}{\sqrt{6x - x^2}} - \tfrac{1}{2} \int (6x - x^2)^{-\frac{1}{2}}(6 - 2x)dx$$

$$= 3 \sin^{-1} \frac{x - 3}{3} - (6x - x^2)^{\frac{1}{2}}. \qquad \text{By VIII and I.}$$

EXERCISES

Find the indefinite integrals in the following, by using formulas
1 to VIII. Omit the constants of integration

1. $\int \dfrac{x^2 - 8}{x - 3}\, dx.$

2. $\int (1 + \tfrac{3}{2}x)^{\frac{1}{2}}dx.$

3. $\int (3 - x^3)x^2 dx.$

4. $\int \dfrac{x - 2}{\sqrt{4x - x^2}}\, dx.$

5. $\int \dfrac{x^3 - x^2 + 2}{x + 1}\, dx.$

6. $\int \dfrac{dx}{9x^2 + 25}.$

7. $\int \dfrac{dx}{9x^2 - 25}.$

8. $\int \dfrac{dx}{\sqrt{25 - 9x^2}}.$

9. $\int \dfrac{dx}{\sqrt{9x^2 + 25}}.$

10. $\int \dfrac{dx}{3x\sqrt{9x^2 - 25}}.$

11. $\int \dfrac{dx}{\sqrt{10x - 9x^2}}.$

12. $\int \dfrac{x\, dx}{\sqrt{9x^2 - 25}}.$

13. $\int \dfrac{x\, dx}{9x^2 - 25}.$

14. $\int \dfrac{dx}{x^2 - 4x + 5}.$

15. $\int \dfrac{dx}{5 - 4x - x^2}.$

16. $\int \dfrac{dx}{\sqrt{x^2 - 4x + 5}}.$

17. $\int \dfrac{dx}{\sqrt{5 - 4x - x^2}}.$

18. $\int \dfrac{(x - 2)dx}{x^2 - 4x + 5}.$

19. $\int \dfrac{(x - 2)\, dx}{\sqrt{x^2 - 4x + 5}}.$

20. $\int \dfrac{(x^2 - 4)dx}{x^2 - 4x + 5}.$

21. $\int \dfrac{dx}{2x^2 + 3x + 2}.$

22. $\int \dfrac{dx}{4 - 2x - 3x^2}.$

23. $\int \dfrac{(2 + 6x)dx}{4 - 2x - 3x^2}.$

24. $\int \dfrac{x^2\, dx}{3x + 1}.$

25. $\int \sqrt{1 + e^x}\, e^x dx.$

26. $\int (\log x)^3\, \dfrac{dx}{x}.$

27. $\int \dfrac{\tan^{-1} x\, dx}{1 + x^2}.$

28. $\int \dfrac{3x\, dx}{x^2 - 9}.$

29. $\int \dfrac{(3x - 1)dx}{x^2 - 9}.$

30. $\int \dfrac{(3x - 1)dx}{x^2 + 9}.$

31. $\int \dfrac{\sec^2 x dx}{\sqrt{1 - \tan^2 x}}.$ Use formula V. $u = \tan x.$

32. $\int \dfrac{\cos x\, dx}{4 + 3 \sin x}.$ Use formula II $u = 4 + 3 \sin x.$

33. $\displaystyle\int \frac{\sec^2 3x\ dx}{1 + \tan 3x}.$

34. $\displaystyle\int \frac{\sin 5x\ dx}{3 \cos 5x - 5}.$

35. $\displaystyle\int \frac{x\ dx}{\sqrt{4x - x^2}}.$ Follow solution of example 5.

36. $\displaystyle\int \frac{e^{2x}dx}{e^{2x} + 3}.$

37. $\displaystyle\int \frac{e^{2u} + 1}{e^{2u} + 2u}\ du.$

119. Exponential functions. Formulas IX and X.

Example 1. Find $\displaystyle\int \frac{e^{4x}dx}{e^x + 1}.$

Solution. Dividing e^{4x} by $e^x + 1$, the integral can be put in the form

$$\int\frac{e^{4x}\ dx}{e^x + 1} = \int\left(e^{3x} - e^{2x} + e^x - \frac{e^x}{e^x + 1}\right) dx$$

$$= \int e^{3x}dx - \int e^{2x}dx + \int e^x dx - \int \frac{e^x dx}{e^x + 1}$$

$$= \tfrac{1}{3}\int e^{3x}3dx - \tfrac{1}{2}\int e^{2x}2dx + \int e^x dx - \int \frac{e^x dx}{e^x + 1}$$

$$= \tfrac{1}{3}e^{3x} - \tfrac{1}{2}e^{2x} + e^x - \log(e^x + 1). \quad \text{By II and X.}$$

Example 2. Find $\int a^x b^x dx$, where a and b are constants.
Solution. $\quad \int a^x b^x dx = \int (ab)^x dx$

$$= \frac{(ab)^x}{\log(ab)} = \frac{a^x b^x}{\log a + \log b}. \qquad \text{By IX.}$$

EXERCISES

Find the indefinite integrals of the following, omitting the constants of integration.

1. $\int a^{5x}\ dx.$

2. $\int e^{x^3}x^2 dx.$

3. $\int e^{\cos x} \sin x\ dx.$ Use formula X, $u = \cos x$, $du = -\sin x\ dx.$

4. $\int e^{\tan x} \sec^2 x\ dx.$

5. $\int e^{\tan (2x+4)} \sec^2 (2x + 4)\ dx.$

6. $\int e^{\sin 3x} \cos 3x\ dx.$

7. $\int e^{x^2+6x-2} (x + 3)\ dx.$

8. $\int e^{\tan \frac{1}{3}x} \sec^2 \tfrac{1}{3}x\ dx.$

9. $\int e^{\cot 3x} \csc^2 3x\ dx.$

10. $\int a^{bx+c}\ dx.$

11. $\int (e^x - 1)^2\ dx.$

12. $\int (e^x - 1)^3\ e^x\ dx.$

13. $\int e^{-x^2}\ x\ dx.$

14. $\int (e^{\frac{x}{2}} + e^{-\frac{x}{2}})dx.$ **15.** $\int \dfrac{e^{\sqrt{x-2}}}{\sqrt{x-2}}\, dx.$

16 $\int \dfrac{du}{1 + e^u}$ Divide numerator by denominator.

120. Trigonometric functions.   Formulas XI–XX.

Example 1.   Find $\int \tan (3x + 1)dx.$

Solution.   Multiplying and dividing by 3,

$$\int \tan(3x + 1)dx = \tfrac{1}{3}\int \tan (3x + 1)3dx,$$

which is in the form of formula XIII where $u = 3x + 1$.

$$\therefore \int \tan (3x + 1)dx = -\tfrac{1}{3} \log \cos (3x + 1).$$

Example 2.   Find $\int \sin^2 x\, dx.$

Solution.   By trigonometry $\sin^2 x = \tfrac{1}{2}(1 - \cos 2x)$.

Then $\int \sin^2 x\, dx = \tfrac{1}{2}\int (1 - \cos 2x)dx$

$$= \tfrac{1}{2}\int dx - \tfrac{1}{2}\int \cos 2x\, dx$$
$$= \tfrac{1}{2}\int dx - \tfrac{1}{4}\int \cos 2x \cdot 2dx = \tfrac{1}{2}x - \tfrac{1}{4} \sin 2x.$$

This may also be written $\tfrac{1}{2}x - \tfrac{1}{2} \sin x \cos x$.

$\therefore \ \int \sin^2 x\, dx = \tfrac{1}{2}x - \tfrac{1}{4} \sin 2x = \tfrac{1}{2}x - \tfrac{1}{2} \sin x \cos x.$

This is an integral that occurs frequently.

EXERCISES

Find the indefinite integrals of the following, omitting the constants of integration.

1. $\int \sin (6x + 2)dx.$ **6.** $\int \csc 4\theta\, d\theta.$

2. $\int \cos (2x - 1)dx.$ **7.** $\int \sec^2 (2x - 1)dx.$

3. $\int \tan 3\theta\, d\theta.$ **8.** $\int \csc^2 (3x + 2)dx.$

4. $\int \cot 5\theta\, d\theta.$ **9.** $\int \sec 3x \tan 3x\, dx.$

5. $\int \sec 2\theta\, d\theta.$ **10.** $\int \csc 4\theta \cot 4\theta\, d\theta.$

11. $\int \tan^2 u\, du.$ By trigonometry, $\tan^2 u = \sec^2 u - 1$.

12. $\int \cot^2 u\, du.$ By trigonometry, $\cot^2 u = \csc^2 u - 1$.

13. $\int (2 \sin x - 2)^2 dx.$ Expand and use XI and example 2.

14. $\int \cos^2 x\, dx.$ Put $\cos^2 x = \tfrac{1}{2}(1 + \cos 2x)$ and follow example 2

15. $\int\sqrt{\sin x}\,\cos x\,dx$. Use formula I. $u = \sin x,\ n = \frac{1}{2}$.

16. $\int\sec^3 x\,\tan x\,dx$ Use formula I. $u = \sec x,\ n = 2$.

17. $\displaystyle\int\frac{\sin x\cos x\,dx}{3 + \sin^2 x}$. Use formula II. $u = 3 + \sin^2 x$.

18. $\int\cos^2 3x\,\sin 3x\,dx$.   **19.** $\int\csc^4 x\,\cot^4 x\,dx$.

20. $\int\sin^3 x\,\cos^2 x\,dx$.

Solution. All cases such as this of the product of the powers of sine and cosine where at least one of the exponents is a positive odd integer, can be brought to fundamental forms as illustrated here. First select one having an odd exponent, here it is $\sin^3 x$, which is changed as follows:

$$\sin^3 x = \sin^2 x\,\sin x = (1 - \cos^2 x)\sin x.$$

Then $\int\sin^3 x\,\cos^2 x\,dx = \int(1 - \cos^2 x)\,\cos^2 x\,\sin x\,dx$

$$
\begin{aligned}
&= \int\cos^2 x\,\sin x\,dx - \int\cos^4 x\,\sin x\,dx\\
&= -\int\cos^2 x(-\sin x\,dx) + \int\cos^4 x\,(-\sin x\,dx)\\
&= -\tfrac{1}{3}\cos^3 x + \tfrac{1}{5}\cos^5 x. \qquad\qquad\text{By I.}
\end{aligned}
$$

21. $\int\sin^2 x\,\cos^5 x\,dx$.

Suggestion. $\int\sin^2 x\,\cos^5 x\,dx = \int\sin^2 x(1 - \sin^2 x)^2\,\cos x\,dx$
$= \int\sin^2 x\,\cos x\,dx - 2\int\sin^4 x\,\cos x\,dx + \int\sin^6 x\,\cos x\,dx$.

22. $\int\sin^3 x\,\cos^3 x\,dx$.   **23.** $\int\sin^5 x\,\cos^2 x\,dx$.

24. $\int\sin^3 x\,dx$. Put $\sin^3 x = (1 - \cos^2 x)\sin x$.

25. $\int\sin^5\theta\,d\theta$.   **27.** $\int\sqrt{\sin x}\,\cos^3 x\,dx$.

26. $\int\cos^3\theta\,d\theta$.   **28.** $\displaystyle\int\frac{\cos^3\theta}{\sqrt{\sin\theta}}\,d\theta$.

29. $\int\sin^2 x\,\cos^2 x\,dx$.

Solution. When the powers of sine and cosine both have even exponents in a product such as this use the trigonometric relations,

$$
\begin{aligned}
\sin^2\theta &= \tfrac{1}{2}(1 - \cos 2\theta),\\
\cos^2\theta &= \tfrac{1}{2}(1 + \cos 2\theta),
\end{aligned}
$$
and
$$\sin\theta\cos\theta = \tfrac{1}{2}\sin 2\theta.$$

Then $\int\sin^2 x\,\cos^2 x\,dx = \int(\sin x\cos x)^2\,dx = \int(\tfrac{1}{2}\sin 2x)^2\,dx$
$$
\begin{aligned}
&= \tfrac{1}{4}\int\sin^2 2x\,dx = \tfrac{1}{8}\int(1 - \cos 4x)dx\\
&= \tfrac{1}{8}\int dx - \tfrac{1}{32}\int\cos 4x\,4dx\\
&= \tfrac{1}{8}x - \tfrac{1}{32}\sin 4x.
\end{aligned}
$$

30. $\int\sin^4 x\,dx$.   **32.** $\int\sin^4 x\,\cos^2 x\,dx$.

31. $\int\cos^4 x\,dx$.   **33.** $\int\cos^4 x\,\sin^2 x\,dx$.

121. Integration by substitution.—In many problems of integration the integral can be reduced to one of the fundamental forms by means of the substitution of a new variable. A few such problems will be illustrated by examples in this article. For convenience in referring to an integral the word **integrand** is used to refer to the function that is to be integrated. Thus, in $\int f(x)dx$, $f(x)$ is the integrand. That is, the integrand is the *rate function*, it is the derivative of the integral found when integrating.

In integrations already performed the student has made substitutions where u of the fundamental formula used stood for a more or less complicated form, but he did this substitution without much, if any, algebraic manipulation. All substitutions are not so simple as these, and often they require transformations in algebra and trigonometry. Here no attempt will be made to deal with any but the simpler cases.

(1) If the integrand is rational except for a radical of the form $\sqrt{ax + b}$ it can be rationalized by substituting a new variable for the radical. That is, substitute z for $\sqrt{ax + b}$, then
$$\sqrt{ax + b} = z \text{ or } ax + b = z^2.$$

Example 1. Find $\int x\sqrt{2x + 3}\, dx$.

Solution. Substituting z for $\sqrt{2x + 3}$,

$$2x + 3 = z^2, \ x = \frac{z^2 - 3}{2}, \text{ and } dx = z\, dz.$$

Then
$$\int x\sqrt{2x + 3}\, dx = \int \frac{z^2 - 3}{2} \cdot z \cdot z\, dz = \int \frac{z^4 - 3z^2}{2}\, dz$$

$$= \tfrac{1}{2}\int z^4 dz - \tfrac{3}{2}\int z^2 dz = \tfrac{1}{10}z^5 - \tfrac{1}{2}z^3$$

$$= \tfrac{1}{10}(2x + 3)^{\frac{5}{2}} - \tfrac{1}{2}(2x + 3)^{\frac{3}{2}}.$$

$$= \tfrac{1}{5}(x - 1)(2x + 3)^{\frac{3}{2}}.$$

The last step is made by reversing the substitution.

(2) If the integrand is rational except for fractional powers of x, it can be rationalized by substituting for x a new variable affected by an exponent equal to the least common multiple of the denominators of the exponents of x.

Example 2. Find $\int \dfrac{dx}{x^{\frac{1}{2}} - x^{\frac{1}{3}}}$.

Solution. Here the least common multiple of the denominators of $\frac{1}{2}$ and $\frac{1}{3}$ is 6. Then substitute z^6 for x and we have

$$x^{\frac{1}{2}} = z^3,\ x^{\frac{1}{3}} = z^2,\ \text{and}\ dx = 6z^5 dz$$

$$\int \frac{dx}{x^{\frac{1}{2}} - x^{\frac{1}{3}}} = \int \frac{6z^5 dz}{z^3 - z^2} = 6\int \frac{z^3 dz}{z - 1}$$

$$= 6\int \left(z^2 + z + 1 + \frac{1}{z - 1} \right) dz$$

$$= 6\int z^2 dz + 6\int z\, dz + 6\int dz + 6\int \frac{dz}{z - 1}$$

$$= 2z^3 + 3z^2 + 6z + 6 \log (z - 1)$$

$$= 2x^{\frac{1}{2}} + 3x^{\frac{1}{3}} + 6x^{\frac{1}{6}} + 6 \log (x^{\frac{1}{6}} - 1).$$

(3) The *reciprocal substitution* helps to transform an integral of the form $\int \dfrac{dx}{x\sqrt{ax^2 + bx + c}}$ to a fundamental form. The change is made by substituting $\dfrac{1}{z}$ for x.

Example 3. Find $\int \dfrac{dx}{x\sqrt{2x^2 + 3x - 2}}$.

Solution. Substituting $\dfrac{1}{z}$ for x, $x = \dfrac{1}{z}$ and $dx = -\dfrac{dz}{z^2}$.

$$\int \frac{dx}{x\sqrt{2x^2 + 3x - 2}} = \int \frac{-\dfrac{dz}{z^2}}{\dfrac{1}{z}\sqrt{\dfrac{2}{z^2} + \dfrac{3}{z} - 2}}$$

$$= -\int \frac{\dfrac{dz}{z^2}}{\dfrac{1}{z^2}\sqrt{2 + 3z - 2z^2}} = -\int \frac{dz}{\sqrt{2 + 3z - 2z^2}}.$$

This last form is like forms already handled and we can proceed by completing the square in z and applying formula V. It is carried through as in example 4, **Art. 118.**

EXERCISES

Integrate the following by substituting new variables.

1. $\int \dfrac{x \, dx}{\sqrt{2 - 7x}}$. Put $2 - 7x = z^2$.

2. $\int \dfrac{x \, dx}{\sqrt[3]{1 + x}}$. Put $1 + x = z^3$.

3. $\int \dfrac{x \, dx}{1 + x^{\frac{1}{3}}}$. Put $x = z^3$.

4. $\int \dfrac{dx}{x^{\frac{5}{8}} + x^{\frac{3}{4}}}$. Put $x = z^8$.

5. $\int \dfrac{(x^{\frac{1}{2}} + x^{\frac{1}{4}} + 4)dx}{x^{\frac{1}{2}} + 1}$. Put $x = z^4$.

6. $\int \dfrac{dx}{x\sqrt{ax + b}}$. Put $ax + b = z^2$.

7. $\int \dfrac{dx}{x\sqrt{x^2 - 3x + 7}}$. Put $x = \dfrac{1}{z}$.

8. $\int \sqrt{a^2 - x^2} \, dx$. Put $x = a \sin \theta$.
Then $dx = a \cos \theta \, d\theta$ and $\int \sqrt{a^2 - x^2} dx$
$= \int \sqrt{a^2 - a^2 \sin^2 \theta} \cdot a \cos \theta \, d\theta$.
$= a^2 \int \cos^2 \theta \, d\theta = \frac{1}{2}a^2 \int (1 + \cos 2\theta)d\theta$
$= \frac{1}{2}a^2 \int d\theta + \frac{1}{4}a^2 \int \cos 2\theta \, 2d\theta = \frac{1}{2}a^2\theta + \frac{1}{4}a^2 \sin 2\theta$
$= \frac{1}{2}a^2\theta + \frac{1}{2}a^2 \sin \theta \cos \theta = \frac{1}{2}a^2 \sin^{-1}\dfrac{x}{a} + \frac{1}{2}x\sqrt{a^2 - x^2}$.

9. $\int \dfrac{\sqrt{a^2 + x^2}}{x} \, dx$. Put $x = a \tan \theta$

10. $\int \dfrac{\sqrt{x^2 - a^2}}{x^3} \, dx$. Put $x = a \sec \theta$

11. $\int \dfrac{dx}{\sqrt{x^2 - a^2}}$.

12. $\int \dfrac{\sqrt{x^2 - a^2}}{x} \, dx$.

13. $\int \dfrac{dx}{x\sqrt{a^2 - x^2}}$

14. $\int \dfrac{dx}{x\sqrt{a^2 + x^2}}$

15. $\int \dfrac{(x-3)^{\frac{2}{3}}dx}{(x-3)^{\frac{1}{3}}+4}.$ Put $(x-3)^{\frac{1}{3}} = z.$

16. $\int \dfrac{\sqrt{e^x}\,dx}{e^x+1}.$ Put $e^x = z^2.$

17. $\int \dfrac{dx}{1-\sqrt{x}}.$ Put $x = z^2.$

18. $\int \dfrac{dx}{x+2+\sqrt{x+2}}.$ Put $x+2 = z^2.$

122. Integration by parts.—In this article is given one of the most useful methods for bringing certain integrals to forms that can be evaluated by the fundamental formulas. It is particularly useful in integrating the products of two or more functions, and is used in expressing the integrals of logarithmic, exponential, and inverse trigonometric functions in terms of fundamental integrals.

If u and v are functions of the same independent variable,

$$d(uv) = u\,dv + v\,du. \qquad \text{By [7].}$$

Transposing, $u\,dv = d(uv) - v\,du.$

Integrating both members of the equation we obtain

[49] $$\int u\,dv = uv - \int v\,du.$$

This equation is known as the formula for **integration by parts.** By means of it the integral $\int u\,dv$ is made to depend upon the integral $\int v\,du$, and it is evident that a gain has been made if the second integral is simpler than the first.

No general directions can be given for the use of the formula for integration by parts, but its application is illustrated in the following examples.

Example 1.   Find $\int xe^x dx$.

Solution.   Put $u = x$ and $dv = e^x dx$.

Differentiating $u = x$, and integrating $dv = e^x dx$, we have

$$du = dx \text{ and } v = e^x.$$

Substituting in [**49**], $\int xe^x dx = xe^x - \int e^x dx$.

In this the integral to be evaluated is $\int e^x dx$, which is integrated by formula X.

$$\therefore \int xe^x dx = xe^x - e^x = e^x(x - 1).$$

Note. In this example the product of functions $xe^x dx$ was such that we might have chosen

$$u = e^x \text{ and } dv = x \, dx.$$

Then $du = e^x dx$ and $v = \frac{1}{2}x^2$.

Substituting these in [**49**], $\int xe^x dx = \frac{1}{2}x^2 e^x - \frac{1}{2}\int x^2 e^x dx$.

The integral given in the example would then depend upon $\int x^2 e^x dx$, which is evidently a more difficult integral to evaluate than the original integral $\int xe^x dx$. So we have lost rather than gained by this choice. Whenever a choice is made that results in a more difficult integral, another choice for u and dv should be made. It frequently happens that there are many choices, and several trials may be necessary before a suitable choice is found.

Example 2.   Find $\int x^2 \sin x \, dx$.

Solution.   Put $u = x^2$ and $dv = \sin x \, dx$.

Then $du = 2x \, dx$ and $v = -\cos x$.

Substituting in [**49**],

(1) $\int x^2 \sin x \, dx = -x^2 \cos x + 2\int x \cos x \, dx$.

We now have to find $\int x \cos x \, dx$, which is evidently simpler than the original integral $\int x^2 \sin x \, dx$, but is not a fundamental integral. The method of integrating by parts will now be applied to this.

Put $u = x$ and $dv = \cos x \, dx$.

Then $du = dx$ and $v = \sin x$.

Substituting in [**49**], $\int x \cos x \, dx = x \sin x - \int \sin x \, dx$
$$= x \sin x + \cos x.$$

Substituting in (1),

$$\int x^2 \sin x \, dx = -x^2 \cos x + 2 \, (x \sin x + \cos x)$$
$$= (2 - x^2) \cos x + 2x \sin x.$$

Note. In this example there were five choices for u and dv.

$$u = x^2 \sin x \text{ and } dv = dx,$$
$$u = x \sin x \text{ and } dv = x \, dx,$$
$$u = \sin x \text{ and } dv = x^2 dx,$$
$$u = x^2 \text{ and } dv = \sin x \, dx,$$
$$u = x \text{ and } dv = x \sin x \, dx.$$

The choice should be so made that after formula [**49**] is applied the integral $\int v \, du$ will be simpler, if possible, and, at least, not any more difficult than the original integral $\int u \, dv$.

Example 3. Find $\int e^{ax} \sin nx \, dx$.

First solution. Put $u = e^{ax}$ and $dv = \sin nx \, dx$.

Then $du = ae^{ax} dx$ and $v = -\dfrac{1}{n} \cos nx$.

Substituting in [**49**],

(1) $\int e^{ax} \sin nx \, dx = -\dfrac{1}{n} e^{ax} \cos nx + \dfrac{a}{n} \int e^{ax} \cos nx \, dx.$

Applying integration by parts to $\int e^{ax} \cos nx \, dx$, and putting $u = e^{ax}$ and $dv = \cos nx \, dx$,

$$du = ae^{ax} dx \text{ and } v = \frac{1}{n} \sin nx.$$

Substituting in [**49**],

$$\int e^{ax} \cos nx \, dx = \frac{1}{n} e^{ax} \sin nx - \frac{a}{n} \int e^{ax} \sin nx \, dx.$$

Substituting these values in (1),

$$\int e^{ax} \sin nx \, dx$$

$$= -\frac{1}{n} e^{ax} \cos nx + \frac{a}{n} \left[\frac{1}{n} e^{ax} \sin nx - \frac{a}{n} \int e^{ax} \sin nx \, dx \right]$$

$$= -\frac{1}{n} e^{ax} \cos nx + \frac{a}{n^2} e^{ax} \sin nx - \frac{a^2}{n^2} \int e^{ax} \sin nx \, dx.$$

Transposing $- \dfrac{a^2}{n^2}\int e^{ax} \sin nx \, dx$ to the first member and uniting,

$$\left(1 + \frac{a^2}{n^2}\right)\int e^{ax} \sin nx \, dx = -\frac{1}{n}e^{ax} \cos nx + \frac{a}{n^2}e^{ax} \sin nx.$$

Dividing by $1 + \dfrac{a^2}{n^2}$ and simplifying,

$$\int e^{ax} \sin nx \, dx = \frac{e^{ax}(a \sin nx - n \cos nx)}{a^2 + n^2}.$$

Note.   Such an integral as this occurs frequently in applications.   The integral $\int v\,du$ was no simpler than the integral $\int u \, dv$, but after two applications of integration by parts an integral exactly like the original integral appeared. Whenever this happens the integral is found by transposing and dividing by the coefficient of the original integral.

In this example, of the two choices:

$$u = e^{ax} \text{ and } dv = \sin nx \, dx,$$

and $\qquad\qquad u = \sin nx \text{ and } dv = e^{ax}dx,$

either could be chosen as will be seen by making the choice of the second.

Second solution.   Put $u = \sin nx$ and $dv = e^{ax}dx$.

Then $\qquad\qquad du = n \cos nx \, dx$ and $v = \dfrac{1}{a} e^{ax}.$

Substituting in [**49**],

(1) $\qquad\int e^{ax} \sin nx \, dx = \dfrac{1}{a} e^{ax} \sin nx - \dfrac{n}{a}\int e^{ax} \cos nx \, dx.$

Applying integration by parts to $\int e^{ax} \cos nx \, dx$ and putting $\qquad u = \cos nx$ and $dv = e^{ax}dx,$

$$du = -n \sin nx \, dx \text{ and } v = \frac{1}{a} e^{ax}.$$

Substituting in formula [**49**],

$$\int e^{ax} \cos nx \, dx = \frac{1}{a} e^{ax} \cos nx + \frac{n}{a}\int e^{ax} \sin nx \, dx.$$

Substituting these values in (1),

$$\int e^{ax} \sin nx \, dx$$

$$= \frac{1}{a} e^{ax} \sin nx - \frac{n}{a}\left[\frac{1}{a} e^{ax} \cos nx + \frac{n}{a}\int e^{ax} \sin nx \, dx \right]$$

$$= \frac{1}{a} e^{ax} \sin nx - \frac{n}{a^2} e^{ax} \cos nx - \frac{n^2}{a^2}\int e^{ax} \sin nx \, dx.$$

Transposing, uniting, and dividing by $1 + \dfrac{n^2}{a^2}$,

$$\int e^{ax} \sin nx \, dx = \frac{e^{ax}(a \sin nx - n \cos nx)}{a^2 + n^2}.$$

EXERCISES

Apply integration by parts in integrating the following exercises.

1. $\int x^2 e^x \, dx$.

2. $\int \log x \, dx$.

3. $\int x \log x \, dx$.

4. $\int x \sin x \, dx$.

5. $\int x \cos x \, dx$.

6. $\int x^2 \cos x \, dx$.

7. $\int x^2 \log x \, dx$.

8. $\int e^x \sin x \, dx$.

9. $\int e^x \cos x \, dx$.

10. $\int e^{ax} \cos nx \, dx$.

11. $\int e^{-x} \sin 4x \, dx$.

12. $\int \sin^{-1} x \, dx$.

13. $\int \cos^{-1} x \, dx$.

14. $\int \tan^{-1} x \, dx$.

15. $\int x \sin 2x \, dx$.

16. $\int x^2 \sin 2x \, dx$.

17. $\int x^2 \sin x \cos x \, dx$.

   Put $\sin x \cos x = \frac{1}{2} \sin 2x$.

18. $\int e^{-0.5t} \sin 4t \, dt$.

19. $\int e^{-0.4t} \cos 5t \, dt$.

INTEGRATION OF RATIONAL FRACTIONS

123. Rational fractions.—A fraction that has rational integral algebraic expressions for both numerator and denominator is called a **rational fraction**. This implies that the exponents are positive integers.

Thus, $\dfrac{2x^3 - 3x^2 + 7x - 2}{x^4 - 1}$ and $\dfrac{x^5 - x + 2}{3x^2 + 6}$ are rational fractions. The first of these is a **proper fraction** since the numerator is of lower degree than the denominator, and the second is an **improper fraction** since its numerator is not of lower degree than the denominator.

A rational fraction sometimes occurs in the integrand, and so it is necessary to devise methods for reducing integrals containing such fractions to forms that can be integrated, that is, to forms that are like the fundamental integrals.

124. Partial fractions.—If simpler fractions can be found that when added together give a certain rational fraction, then the rational fraction is said to be separated into partial fractions. The simpler fractions are the **partial fractions** that go to make up the given fraction. It is evident that the process of separating a rational fraction into partial fractions is the inverse of adding fractions. It follows then that the work can be checked by adding the partial fractions and obtaining the given fraction.

Thus, $\dfrac{4 - 2x}{x^3 - x} = \dfrac{1}{x - 1} + \dfrac{3}{x + 1} - \dfrac{4}{x}$, as can be proved by adding the three fractions on the right and obtaining as their sum the fraction $\dfrac{4 - 2x}{x^3 - x}$. The fraction $\dfrac{4 - 2x}{x^3 - x}$ is then separated into the three partial fractions $\dfrac{1}{x - 1}$, $\dfrac{3}{x + 1}$, and $-\dfrac{4}{x}$; and these three simpler fractions may be used in place of the fraction $\dfrac{4 - 2x}{x^3 - x}$.

Here we shall make no effort to prove that the methods given are correct. It will be considered sufficient if the partial fractions when added produce the given fraction. Proper fractions only will be separated into partial fractions, and then only when the denominators can be separated into factors of the first or second degree. An improper rational fraction can always by actual division be put equal to an integral expression plus a proper fraction.

The work of separating a fraction into partial fractions will be carried out under three headings:

(1) *When the denominator consists of a single first or second degree factor that is repeated.*

(2) *When the denominator consists of first or second degree factors that are not repeated.*

(3) *When the denominator consists of first or second degree factors one or more of which are repeated.*

125. Denominator consisting of single factor repeated.— *A proper rational fraction whose denominator consists of a repeated factor and whose numerator is of degree not less than the degree of that factor, can be broken up into partial fractions by ordinary division by using the factor to the first power as a divisor.*

Example 1.   Separate $\dfrac{5x + 3}{(x + 2)^2}$ into partial fractions, and find $\displaystyle\int\dfrac{5x + 3x}{(x + 2)^2}dx$.

Solution. By actual division $\dfrac{5x + 3}{x + 2} = 5 - \dfrac{7}{x + 2}$.

Then $\dfrac{5x + 3}{(x + 2)^2} = \dfrac{5}{x + 2} - \dfrac{7}{(x + 2)^2}$.

$$\int\frac{5x + 3}{(x + 2)^2}dx = \int\frac{5dx}{x + 2} - \int\frac{7dx}{(x + 2)^2}$$

$$= 5\int\frac{dx}{x + 2} - 7\int (x + 2)^{-2}\,dx.$$

$$= 5\log (x + 2) + 7(x + 2)^{-1}. \text{ By I and II.}$$

Example 2.   Separate $\dfrac{2x^4 + 3x^3 - 4x + 2}{(x^2 + 1)^3}$ into partial fractions, and find $\displaystyle\int\dfrac{2x^4 + 3x^3 - 4x + 2}{(x^2 + 1)^3}dx$ so far as it can be done by methods already given.

Solution.   By actual division

$$\frac{2x^4 + 3x^3 - 4x + 2}{x^2 + 1} = 2x^2 + 3x - 2 - \frac{7x - 4}{x^2 + 1}.$$

Then $\dfrac{2x^4 + 3x^3 - 4x + 2}{(x^2 + 1)^3} = \dfrac{2x^2 + 3x - 2}{(x^2 + 1)^2} - \dfrac{7x - 4}{(x^2 + 1)^3}.$

Here the fraction $\dfrac{2x^2 + 3x - 2}{(x^2 + 1)^2}$ can be separated into simpler fractions by actual division.

$$\frac{2x^2 + 3x - 2}{x^2 + 1} = 2 + \frac{3x - 4}{x^2 + 1}.$$

Then $\dfrac{2x^2 + 3x - 2}{(x^2 + 1)^2} = \dfrac{2}{x^2 + 1} + \dfrac{3x - 4}{(x^2 + 1)^2}.$

$\therefore \dfrac{2x^4 + 3x^3 - 4x + 2}{(x^2 + 1)^3} = \dfrac{2}{x^2 + 1} + \dfrac{3x - 4}{(x^2 + 1)^2} - \dfrac{7x - 4}{(x^2 + 1)^3}.$

Then $\displaystyle\int \frac{2x^4 + 3x^3 - 4x + 2}{(x^2 + 1)^3} dx$

$$= \int \frac{2dx}{x^2 + 1} + \int \frac{3x - 4}{(x^2 + 1)^2} dx - \int \frac{7x - 4}{(x^2 + 1)^3} dx.$$

Considering each of these integrals separately:

$$\int \frac{2dx}{x^2 + 1} = 2\int \frac{dx}{x^2 + 1} = 2 \tan^{-1} x. \qquad \text{By III.}$$

$$\int \frac{3x - 4}{(x^2 + 1)^2} dx = \tfrac{3}{2}\int (x^2 + 1)^{-2} 2x \, dx - 4\int \frac{dx}{(x^2 + 1)^2}$$

$$= -\tfrac{3}{2}(x^2 + 1)^{-1} - 4\int \frac{dx}{(x^2 + 1)^2}. \quad \text{By I.}$$

$$\int \frac{7x - 4}{(x^2 + 1)^3} dx = \tfrac{7}{2}\int (x^2 + 1)^{-3} 2x \, dx - 4\int \frac{dx}{(x^2 + 1)^3}$$

$$= -\tfrac{7}{4}(x^2 + 1)^{-2} - 4\int \frac{dx}{(x^2 + 1)^3}. \quad \text{By I.}$$

$$\int \frac{2x^4 + 3x^3 - 4x + 2}{(x^2 + 1)^3} dx = 2 \tan^{-1} x - \frac{3}{2(x^2 + 1)}$$

$$+ \frac{7}{4(x^2 + 1)^2} - 4\int \frac{dx}{(x^2 + 1^2)} + 4\int \frac{dx}{(x^2 + 1)^3},$$

The two integrals, $\int \dfrac{dx}{(x^2 + 1)^2}$ and $\int \dfrac{dx}{(x^2 + 1)^3}$ are forms that cannot be easily integrated by methods already given. (See **Art. 129.**)

EXERCISES

Separate the following rational fractions into partial fractions by actual division as illustrated in the preceding examples, and find the integrals if they can be found by the methods of this chapter.

1. $\int \dfrac{x - 5}{(x - 3)^2} dx.$

2. $\int \dfrac{2x - 5}{(x - 2)^3} dx.$

3. $\int \dfrac{x^2 + 4x - 2}{(x^2 + 1)^2} dx.$

4. $\int \dfrac{3x^2 - 5x + 4}{(x - 1)^3} dx.$

5. $\int \dfrac{x^3}{(x^2 + 1)^2} dx.$

6. $\int \dfrac{x^3 + 2x^2 + 2}{x^4 + 2x^2 + 1} dx.$

7. $\int \dfrac{3x^3 - 2x^2 + 4x + 2}{x^2 - 2x + 1} dx.$ First divide numerator by denominator to express as an integral expression and a proper fraction.

126. Denominator consisting of factors not repeated.—
If a proper rational fraction has a denominator consisting only of factors of the first or second degree none of which are repeated, the fraction can be separated into just as many proper partial fractions as there are factors, and each of these fractions will have one of the factors as a denominator.

A careful study of the solutions and discussions of the following examples should make clear the method of separating such a fraction into partial fractions.

Example 1.   Separate the fraction into partial fractions and integrate $\int \dfrac{5x - 3}{(x - 3)(x + 1)} dx.$

Solution. The partial fractions that enter into this fraction will have as denominators $x - 3$ and $x + 1$. Since these are to be proper fractions, the degree of each numerator is zero, that is, each numerator is a single term not containing x.   We will use A and B to stand for these numerators, and find such values for A and B as will make the sum of the partial fractions equal to the given fraction. We will then put

(1) $$\frac{5x - 3}{(x - 3)(x + 1)} = \frac{A}{x - 3} + \frac{B}{x + 1}.$$

Clearing of fractions by multiplying by $(x - 3)(x + 1)$,

(2) $$5x - 3 = A(x + 1) + B(x - 3).$$

Now this is an identity, that is, an equation that is true for all values that may be given to x. The question now is, how can A and B be found. We know from algebra that two equations are needed to find two unknowns. These equations can be found by giving two different values to x.

Put $x = 3$ in (2) and $5 \cdot 3 - 3 = A(3 + 1) + B(3 - 3)$.

Or $$12 = 4A.$$

Put $x = -1$ in (2) and

$$5(-1) - 3 = A(-1 + 1) + B(-1 - 3).$$

Or $$-8 = -4B.$$

From these $A = 3$ and $B = 2$.

Substituting these values of A and B in (1),

$$\frac{5x - 3}{(x - 3)(x + 1)} = \frac{3}{x - 3} + \frac{2}{x + 1}.$$

Since by addition $\dfrac{3}{x - 3} + \dfrac{2}{x + 1} = \dfrac{5x - 3}{(x - 3)(x + 1)}$, the given fraction is separated into partial fractions.

Remark. The question naturally arises as to why the two values 3 and -1 were chosen for x in finding the values of A and B. Any other values for x could have been chosen, but these values gave the simplest equations for finding A and B. For, as is seen, when $x = 3$, the coefficient of B is zero; and when $x = 1$, the coefficient of A is zero. Suppose two other values are chosen, say, 2 and 4.

Put $x = 2$ and $5 \cdot 2 - 3 = A (2 + 1) + B(2 - 3)$.
Or $\qquad\qquad 7 = 3A - B$.
Put $x = 4$ and $5 \cdot 4 - 3 = A(4 + 1) + B(4 - 3)$.
Or $\qquad\qquad 17 = 5A + B$.

Solving these equations, $A = 3$ and $B = 2$ as before, but there is more labor involved in the solution.

$$\int \frac{5x - 3}{(x - 3)(x + 1)}\, dx = \int \frac{3dx}{x - 3} + \int \frac{2dx}{x + 1}$$

$$= 3 \int \frac{dx}{x - 3} + 2 \int \frac{dx}{x + 1}$$

$$= 3 \log (x - 3) + 2 \log (x + 1). \quad \text{By II.}$$

Example 2. Separate the fraction into partial fractions and integrate $\int \dfrac{x^3 + 6x^2 - 3x + 8}{x^4 - 1}\, dx$.

Solution. The denominator $x^4 - 1$ can be separated into the factors $(x - 1)\ (x + 1)\ (x^2 + 1)$. The partial fractions will then have as denominators $x - 1$, $x + 1$, and $x^2 + 1$. The first two will have single numbers as numerators, and the third may have a numerator having a term in x and a term without x. We will then put

(1) $\qquad \dfrac{x^3 + 6x^2 - 3x + 8}{x^4 - 1} = \dfrac{A}{x - 1} + \dfrac{B}{x + 1} + \dfrac{Cx + D}{x^2 + 1}.$

Clearing of fractions,

(2) $\quad x^3 + 6x^2 - 3x + 8 = A(x + 1)\ (x^2 + 1) + B(x - 1)$
$$(x^2 + 1) + (Cx + D)\ (x - 1)\ (x + 1)$$

Here four equations are needed to find the four unknowns $A, B, C,$ and D.

Put $x = 1,$ $\qquad 12 = 4A$.
Put $x = -1,$ $\quad 16 = -4B$.
Put $x = 0,$ $\qquad 8 = A - B - D$.
Put $x = 2,$ $\qquad 34 = 15A + 5B + 6C + 3D$.

Solving these equations for A, B, C, and D,
$$A = 3, B = -4, C = 2, D = -1.$$

Substituting these values in (1),
$$\frac{x^3 + 6x^2 - 3x + 8}{x^4 - 1} = \frac{3}{x - 1} - \frac{4}{x + 1} + \frac{2x - 1}{x^2 + 1}.$$

The work can be checked by uniting the partial fractions and obtaining the given fraction.

It is to be noted that we always provide numerators that are one less in degree than their denominators.

$$\int \frac{x^3 + 6x^2 - 3x + 8}{x^4 - 1} dx = \int \frac{3dx}{x - 1} - \int \frac{4dx}{x^2 + 1} + \int \frac{2x - 1}{x^2 + 1} dx$$

$$= 3 \int \frac{dx}{x - 1} - 4 \int \frac{dx}{x + 1} + \int \frac{2x \, dx}{x^2 + 1} - \int \frac{dx}{x^2 + 1}$$

$$= 3 \log (x - 1) - 4 \log (x + 1) + \log (x^2 + 1) - \tan^{-1}x.$$
$$\text{By II and III.}$$

EXERCISES

Separate the following rational fractions into partial fractions by methods illustrated in the preceding examples, and find the integrals.

1. $\int \dfrac{3x - 7}{(x - 2)(x - 3)} \, dx.$

2. $\int \dfrac{5x + 1}{x^2 + x - 2} \, dx.$

3. $\int \dfrac{4x^2 - 3x - 2}{x(x^2 - 4)} \, dx.$

4. $\int \dfrac{x^2 - 3}{(x + 2)(x^2 + 1)} \, dx.$

5. $\int \dfrac{x \, dx}{(x + 1)(x^2 + 2x + 3)}$

6. $\int \dfrac{x \, dx}{(x + 1)(x^3 - 1)}.$

7. $\int \dfrac{x^4}{x^3 + 1} dx.$ Divide to obtain a proper fraction.

127. Denominator consisting of different factors one or more repeated.—*If a proper rational fraction has a denominator consisting of factors of the first or second degree one or more of which are repeated, the fraction can be separated into as many partial fractions as there are different factors in the* *denominator.* *Each of the factors that are not repeated will be a denominator, and also each factor that is repeated affected with an exponent that is the number of times it is repeated will be a denominator. Finally, the partial fractions having repeated factors as denominators may be further separated by the method of* **Art. 125.**

Example 1. Separate the fraction into partial fractions and integrate so far as the methods have been given

$$\int \frac{x^3 + 2x^2 + 5x + 8}{x(x^2 + 4)^2} \, dx.$$

Solution. First separate into fractions having as denominators x and $(x^2 + 4)^2$. Since x is of the first degree, the numerator of the fraction having x for denominator will be a single number. Since $(x^2 + 4)^2$ is of the fourth degree, we will provide a numerator of the third degree, that is, we always provide a numerator of one less degree than the denominator. We will then put

(1) $\quad \dfrac{x^3 + 2x^2 + 5x + 8}{x(x^2 + 4)^2} = \dfrac{A}{x} + \dfrac{Bx^3 + Cx^2 + Dx + E}{(x^2 + 4)^2}.$

Clearing of fractions,

(2) $\quad x^3 + 2x^2 + 5x + 8 = A(x^2 + 4)^2 + (Bx^3 + Cx^2 + Dx + E)x.$

Here the five equations for finding the values of A, B, C, D, and E will be found by equating the coefficients of like powers of x from the two members of the equation. That this is permissible is proved in algebra. This method is often shorter than the one used heretofore. Either method, however, could be used.

Equating coefficients of x^4, $\quad 0 = A + B$.

Equating coefficients of x^3, $\quad 1 = C$.

Equating coefficients of x^2, $\quad 2 = 8A + D$.

Equating coefficients of x, $\quad 5 = E$.

Equating coefficients of x^0, $\quad 8 = 16A$.

Solving these five equations for A, B, C, D, and E,

$A = \frac{1}{2}$, $B = -\frac{1}{2}$, $C = 1$, $D = -2$, $E = 5$.

Substituting these values in (1),

$$\frac{x^3 + 2x^2 + 5x + 8}{x(x^2 + 4)^2} = \frac{\frac{1}{2}}{x} + \frac{-\frac{1}{2}x^3 + x^2 - 2x + 5}{(x^2 + 4)^2}.$$

By factoring out $\frac{1}{2}$ in the right-hand member this can be put equal to

$$\frac{1}{2}\left[\frac{1}{x} - \frac{x^3 - 2x^2 + 4x - 10}{(x^2 + 4)^2}\right].$$

By actual division as in **Art. 125,**

$$\frac{x^3 - 2x^2 + 4x - 10}{x^2 + 4} = x - 2 - \frac{2}{x^2 + 4}.$$

Then $\dfrac{x^3 - 2x^2 + 4x - 10}{(x^2 + 4)^2} = \dfrac{x - 2}{x^2 + 4} - \dfrac{2}{(x^2 + 4)^2}.$

$\therefore \dfrac{x^3 + 2x^2 + 5x + 8}{x(x^2 + 4)^2} = \dfrac{1}{2}\left[\dfrac{1}{x} - \dfrac{x - 2}{x^2 + 4} + \dfrac{2}{(x^2 + 4)^2}\right]$

$$= \frac{1}{2x} - \frac{x - 2}{2(x^2 + 4)} + \frac{1}{(x^2 + 4)^2}.$$

$\displaystyle\int \frac{x^3 + 2x^2 + 5x + 8}{x(x^2 + 4)^2} = \int \frac{dx}{2x} - \int \frac{x - 2}{2(x^2 + 4)}\,dx + \int \frac{dx}{(x^2 + 4)^2}$

$\displaystyle = \frac{1}{2}\int \frac{dx}{x} - \frac{1}{4}\int \frac{2x\,dx}{x^2 + 4} + \int \frac{dx}{x^2 + 4} + \int \frac{dx}{(x^2 + 4)^2}$

$\displaystyle = \frac{1}{2}\log x - \frac{1}{4}\log(x^2 + 4) + \frac{1}{2}\tan^{-1}\frac{x}{2} + \int \frac{dx}{(x^2 + 4)^2}.$

By II and III.

Example 2. Separate the fraction into partial fractions and integrate $\displaystyle\int \frac{x^2 + x}{(x - 1)^2(x^2 + 4)}\,dx.$

Solution. Put $\dfrac{x^2 + x}{(x - 1)^2(x^2 + 4)} = \dfrac{Ax + B}{(x - 1)^2} + \dfrac{Cx + D}{x^2 + 4}.$

Clearing of fractions,

$$x^2 + x = (Ax + B)(x^2 + 4) + (Cx + D)(x - 1)^2.$$

Put $x = 1$, $\qquad\qquad 2 = 5A + 5B$.

Put $x = 0$, $\qquad\qquad 0 = 4B + D$.

Equating coefficients of x^3, $0 = A + C$.

Equating coefficients of x, $1 = 4A + C - 2D$.

Solving these four equations for A, B, C, and D,

$$A = \tfrac{11}{25},\ B = -\tfrac{1}{25},\ C = -\tfrac{11}{25},\ D = \tfrac{4}{25}.$$

Substituting these values,

$$\frac{x^2 + x}{(x-1)^2(x^2+4)} = \frac{\tfrac{11}{25}x - \tfrac{1}{25}}{(x-1)^2} + \frac{-\tfrac{11}{25}x + \tfrac{4}{25}}{x^2+4}$$

$$= \tfrac{1}{25}\left[\frac{11x - 1}{(x-1)^2} - \frac{11x - 4}{x^2+4}\right]$$

By actual division, $\dfrac{11x - 1}{x - 1} = 11 + \dfrac{10}{x - 1}$.

Then $\qquad \dfrac{11x - 1}{(x-1)^2} = \dfrac{11}{x-1} + \dfrac{10}{(x-1)^2}$.

$$\therefore \frac{x^2 + x}{(x-1)^2(x^2+4)} = \tfrac{1}{25}\left[\frac{11}{x-1} + \frac{10}{(x-1)^2} - \frac{11x - 4}{x^2+4}\right].$$

$$\int \frac{x^2 + x}{(x-1)^2(x^2+4)}\,dx$$

$$= \tfrac{11}{25}\int \frac{dx}{x-1} + \tfrac{2}{5}\int (x-1)^{-2}\,dx - \tfrac{11}{50}\int \frac{2x\,dx}{x^2+4} + \tfrac{4}{25}\int \frac{dx}{x^2+4}$$

$$= \tfrac{11}{25}\log(x-1) - \frac{2}{5(x-1)} - \tfrac{11}{50}\log(x^2+4) + \tfrac{2}{25}\tan^{-1}\frac{x}{2}.$$

$$\text{By I, II, III.}$$

EXERCISES

Separate the following rational fractions into partial fractions by the methods illustrated in the preceding examples, and find the integrals where it can be done by methods already given.

1. $\displaystyle\int \frac{x\,dx}{(x+1)^2(x-1)}$.

2. $\displaystyle\int \frac{dx}{x^2(x^2+3)}$.

3. $\displaystyle\int \frac{2x^2 - 1}{(x+1)^2(x^2+x+1)}\,dx$.

4. $\displaystyle\int \frac{dx}{(x-1)^2(x^2+1)^2}$

INTEGRATION BY A MORE EXTENDED TABLE

128. Explanation of the table.—In the table, page 388, are arranged a list of the more common forms in integration that arise in applications of the calculus. Larger tables can be obtained if desired,[1] but the use of all such tables is the same. Search is made in the table until an integrand is found which is exactly of the form of that given, and then the integral can be written at once from the integral found in the table.

To use a table of integrals intelligently one should study the classification of the integrals in the table, noting that they are arranged in a systematic order. Then too it must not be presumed that any form one may wish to integrate will be found in the table, for, as has been said, forms arise that cannot be integrated and many of those that can be integrated may require some transformation before they will agree exactly in form with those found in the table. To become proficient in using a table of integrals requires systematic intelligent practice and considerable knowledge of algebra and trigonometry in order that the necessary transformations can be made.

129. Integration by means of a table of integrals.—The process of integration by means of a table of integrals is a more or less purely mechanical process of substituting in a formula. The process is illustrated in the following examples.

Example 1.   Find $\int \dfrac{dx}{5 + 3x^2}$.

Formula 21, page 389 is

$$\int \frac{dx}{a + bx^2} = \frac{1}{\sqrt{ab}} \tan^{-1} x \sqrt{\frac{b}{a}}, \text{ when } a > 0 \text{ and } b > 0, \text{ and}$$

$\int \dfrac{dx}{5 + 3x^2}$ is exactly of this form where $a = 5$ and $b = 3$.

Therefore the integration can be performed by substituting in formula 21.

---

[1] A very good larger table is *"A Short Table of Integrals"* by B. O. PEIRCE, published by Ginn and Company.

$$\therefore \int \frac{dx}{5 + 3x^2} = \frac{1}{\sqrt{15}} \tan^{-1} x\sqrt{\tfrac{3}{5}}.$$

Example 2. Find $\displaystyle\int \frac{dx}{\sqrt{3x^2 - 2x + 5}}.$

This is exactly of the form of formula 113, which is

$$\int \frac{dx}{\sqrt{ax^2 + bx + c}} =$$
$$\frac{1}{\sqrt{a}} \log (2ax + b + 2\sqrt{a}\ \sqrt{ax^2 + bx + c}), \text{ when } a > 0.$$

Substituting in this formula,

$$\int \frac{dx}{\sqrt{3x^2 - 2x + 5}} =$$
$$\frac{1}{\sqrt{3}} \log (6x - 2 + 2\sqrt{3}\sqrt{3x^2 - 2x + 5}).$$

Example 3. Find $\int e^{2x} \sin x\, dx.$

This is exactly of the form of formula 198.

Substituting in this formula,

$$\int e^{2x} \sin x\, dx = \frac{e^{2x}(2 \sin x - \cos x)}{5}.$$

Example 4. Find $\displaystyle\int \frac{dx}{x^2\sqrt{2 + 3x}}.$

Substituting in formula 39,

$$\int \frac{dx}{x^2\sqrt{2 + 3x}} = -\frac{\sqrt{2 + 3x}}{2x} - \frac{3}{4}\int \frac{dx}{x\sqrt{2 + 3x}}.$$

Substituting in formula 37,

$$\int \frac{dx}{x\sqrt{2 + 3x}} = \frac{1}{\sqrt{2}} \log \frac{\sqrt{2 + 3x} - \sqrt{2}}{\sqrt{2 + 3x} + \sqrt{2}}.$$
$$\therefore \int \frac{dx}{x^2\sqrt{2 + 3x}} = -\frac{\sqrt{2+3x}}{2x} - \frac{3}{4\sqrt{2}}\log\frac{\sqrt{2 + 3x} - \sqrt{2}}{\sqrt{2 + 3x} + \sqrt{2}}.$$

130. Reduction formulas.—The formulas 28, 29, 30, and 31 on page 390 are applicable to a class of integrals having integrands of the form

$$x^m(a + bx^n)^p,$$

where *m*, *n*, *p*, *a*, and *b* are constants either positive or negative, integral or fractional. By these formulas the exponents *m* and *p* may be either increased or decreased.

Formula 28 decreases the exponent *m* by *n*, that is, it makes $\int x^m(a + bx^n)^p dx$ depend upon $\int x^{m-n}(a + bx^n)^p dx$.

Formula 29 decreases the exponent *p* by 1, that is, it makes $\int x^m(a + bx^n)^p dx$ depend upon $\int x^m(a + bx^n)^{p-1} dx$.

Formula 30 increases the exponent *m* by *n*, that is, it makes $\int x^m(a + bx^n)^p dx$ depend upon $\int x^{m+n}(a + bx^n)^p dx$.

Formula 31 increases the exponent *p* by 1, that is, it makes $\int x^m(a + bx^n)^p dx$ depend upon $\int x^m(a + bx^n)^{p+1} dx$.

Several applications of one or more of these formulas is often necessary to change an integral into a form that exactly fits a formula of the table.

Example 1.   Find $\int \dfrac{x^7 dx}{(5x^4 - 2)^{\frac{3}{4}}}$.

This integral can be written in the form $\int x^7 (5x^4 - 2)^{-\frac{3}{4}} dx$, which is $\int x^m(a + bx^n)^p dx$, where $m = 7$, $n = 4$, $p = -\frac{3}{4}$, $a = -2$, and $b = 5$.

It is seen that the integral could be made to fit formula I, page 202 if *m* were 3 instead of 7.   This leads to the application of formula 28 of the reduction formulas, which gives

$$\int x^7(5x^4 - 2)^{-\frac{3}{4}} dx = \frac{x^4(5x^4 - 2)^{\frac{1}{4}}}{25} + \tfrac{8}{25}\int x^3(5x^4 - 2)^{-\frac{3}{4}} dx.$$

Now $\int x^3(5x^4 - 2)^{-\frac{3}{4}} dx = \tfrac{1}{20}\int (5x^4 - 2)^{-\frac{3}{4}} 20x^3 dx$, which is of the form $\int u^n du$.

Then $\tfrac{1}{20}\int (5x^4 - 2)^{-\frac{3}{4}} 20x^3 dx = \tfrac{1}{5}(5x^4 - 2)^{\frac{1}{4}}$.

$$\therefore \int \frac{x^7 dx}{(5x^4 - 2)^{\frac{3}{4}}} = \tfrac{1}{25}x^4(5x^4 - 2)^{\frac{1}{4}} + \tfrac{8}{25}[\tfrac{1}{5}(5x^4 - 2)^{\frac{1}{4}}]$$

$$= \tfrac{1}{125}(5x^4 + 8)(5x^4 - 2)^{\frac{1}{4}}.$$

Example 2.   Find $\int \dfrac{dx}{x^3\sqrt{a + bx}}$.

This integral can be written in the form $\int x^{-3}(a + bx)^{-\frac{1}{2}} dx$. One application of formula 30 will express this in the form of formula 39.

EXERCISES

In integrating the following integrals use the table, pages 388 to 401, or any other table of integrals.

1. $\int x\sqrt{1 + 3x}\, dx$.

2. $\int \dfrac{x\, dx}{3 - 4x}$.

3. $\int \dfrac{x^2 dx}{\sqrt{3x + 5}}$.

4. $\int \dfrac{dx}{x\sqrt{x - a}}$.

5. $\int x^2\sqrt{5 - 2x}\, dx$.

6. $\int \sqrt{3 - 4x^2}\, dx$.

7. $\int \dfrac{(x + 1)dx}{2x^2 + 3x + 1}$.

8. $\int \sqrt{\dfrac{1 + x}{1 - x}}\, dx$.

9. $\int \dfrac{(5x - 1)dx}{\sqrt{3 - 2x^2}}$.

10. $\int (x^2 - a^2)^{\frac{3}{2}} dx$.

11. $\int \dfrac{dx}{\sqrt{x^2 + 5x + 6}}$.

12. $\int \dfrac{dx}{\sqrt{-x^2 + 5x - 6}}$.

13. $\int \dfrac{x\, dx}{\sqrt{-x^2 + 6x - 5}}$.

14. $\int \dfrac{dx}{3x^2 - 4x + 3}$.

15. $\int \dfrac{(x + 2)dx}{2x^2 + 3x + 1}$.

16. $\int \dfrac{dx}{x\sqrt{-x^2 + 5x - 6}}$.

17. $\int \dfrac{x^2 dx}{\sqrt{x^2 + a^2}}$.

18. $\int \dfrac{x^2 dx}{\sqrt{x^2 - a^2}}$.

19. $\int \dfrac{dx}{x^2\sqrt{x^2 + a^2}}$.

20. $\int \dfrac{dx}{x^3\sqrt{a^2 - x^2}}$.

21. $\int \dfrac{dx}{9x^2 - 4}$.

22. $\int \dfrac{dx}{16x^2 + 9}$.

23. $\int \dfrac{x\, dx}{x^4 + a^4}$.

24. $\int \dfrac{x^2 dx}{x^6 - a^6}$.

25. $\int \dfrac{(1 + x^2)dx}{\sqrt{4 - x^2}}$.

26. $\int \dfrac{d\theta}{4 + 3\cos\theta}$.

27. $\int \dfrac{d\theta}{2 + 5\sin\theta}$.

28. $\int \dfrac{d\theta}{1 - \sin\theta}$.

29. $\int \dfrac{3x\, dx}{\sqrt[3]{x + 1}}$.

30. $\int \dfrac{(x^3 + x)dx}{x^4 + 9}$.

31. $\int \sin x \sec^2 x \, dx$.

32. $\int \sin 2x \cos x \, dx$.

33. $\int \sqrt{\sin x} \cos x \, dx$

34. $\int \sin^2 \theta \cos^4 \theta \, d\theta$.

35. $\int (\sin \theta)^{\frac{3}{2}} \cos^3 \theta \, d\theta$.

36. $\int \sin^3 \theta \cos^2 \theta \, d\theta$.

37. $\int \tan^5 \theta \sec^2 \theta \, d\theta$.

38. $\int \cot^2 \theta \csc^4 \theta \, d\theta$.

39. $\int \cot^3 \theta \sin \theta \, d\theta$.

40. $\int \cot^2 \theta \sec^4 \theta \, d\theta$.

41. $\int x^2 e^{-x} \, dx$.

42. $\int x \tan^2 x \, dx$.

43. $\int x^2 \sin^{-1} x \, dx$.

44. $\int 4x^2 \sin 2x \, dx$.

45. $\int e^{0.4x} \cos 2x \, dx$.

46. $\int e^{-3x} \sin 5x \, dx$.

47. $\int e^{-0.5x} \sin 3x \, dx$.

48. $\int e^{-0.3x} \sin 2x \, dx$.

49. $\int e^{-0.2t} \sin \omega t \, dt$.

50. $\int 3x^3 \log x \, dx$.

CHAPTER XV

PLANE AREAS. DEFINITE INTEGRALS. INTEGRAL LIMIT OF SUM

131. In the present chapter the area between a curve, the x-axis, and two ordinates will be considered somewhat differently than has already been done. Before proceeding the student should review the method already used in finding areas, and he should think through again very carefully the ideas connected with the differentials.

While the endeavor to find the areas of plane figures bounded by curves was the main incentive for the invention of integral calculus, integration is applied to finding lengths of curves, areas of surfaces, and volumes of solids, as well as to answering many other questions.

132. Plane areas by indefinite integrals.—*Example* 1. Let it be required to find the area between the parabola $y = \frac{1}{4}x^2$, the x-axis, and the two ordinates corresponding to $x = 1$ and $x = 5$.

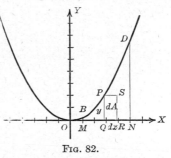

First, plot the curve as shown in Fig. 82 and indicate the area $MNDB$ that is to be found. Now think of this area as being generated by a

FIG. 82.

line starting at MB and moving toward the right so that x will increase uniformly. Then the area will be increasing more and more rapidly.

235

To determine the differential of the area, think of the moving line at some certain position as QP and consider *what the change in the area would be* if its change *became* uniform at the instant the generating line was in the position QP, and *remained* uniform while x changed by the length $QR = dx$. The change in the area would evidently be the rectangle $QRSP = dA$.

Since the height of this rectangle is y,

$$dA = y\, dx.$$

But $y = \frac{1}{4}x^2$.   Hence $dA = \frac{1}{4}x^2 dx$.

The variables in this equation are the independent variable x and the dependent variable A, and a relation is expressed between their differentials, or between their changes considered as uniform. Integration of the members of the equation gives a relation between the variables themselves.

Then $\int dA = \int \frac{1}{4}x^2 dx.$

Integrating, $A = \frac{1}{12}x^3 + C.$

To determine the constant C we know that the generating line starts at MB where $x = 1$. Then $A = 0$ when $x = 1$. Substituting these values for A and x,

$$0 = \tfrac{1}{12}\cdot 1^3 + C.\quad \therefore\ C = -\tfrac{1}{12}.$$

For whatever value of x the generating line reaches, the value of A is expressed by

$$A = \tfrac{1}{12}x^3 - \tfrac{1}{12}.$$

Then when the generating line reaches the position ND where $x = 5$, the value of A is given by

$$A = \tfrac{1}{12}\cdot 5^3 - \tfrac{1}{12} = 10\tfrac{1}{3}.$$

Therefore the area of $MNDB$ is $10\frac{1}{3}$ square units of such size as determined by the linear units on the x-axis and y-axis.

Example 2. As another illustration let it be required to find the area in the first quadrant between the same curve $y = \frac{1}{4}x^2$, the y-axis, and the two lines $y = 1$ and $y = 6$.

As before plot the curve, Fig. 83, and locate the area $MBDN$ that is to be found. This area is generated by a line moving from the position MB to the position ND. Consider this line in any particular position in its movement as QP, and think of the rate that the area is being generated. If the change in the area *became* uniform at this instant and *remained* so while y increased by dy, the differential of the area would be the rectangle $QRSP$.

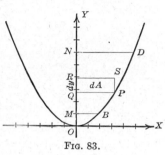

FIG. 83.

Then $\qquad dA = x\, dy$.

But since $y = \frac{1}{4}x^2$, $\quad x = 2\sqrt{y}$.

Hence $\qquad dA = 2\sqrt{y}\, dy$.

Integrating, $\qquad A = \frac{4}{3}y^{\frac{3}{2}} + C$.

To find the constant C, we know that $A = 0$ when $y = 1$. Substituting these values,

$$0 = \frac{4}{3} \cdot 1^{\frac{3}{2}} + C. \quad \therefore C = -\frac{4}{3}.$$

When the generating line has moved to the position ND where $y = 6$, the area is given by

$$A = \frac{4}{3} \cdot 6^{\frac{3}{2}} - \frac{4}{3} = 18.26.$$

133. Interpretation of $\int f(x)dx$.—It is of importance to note that $\int f(x)dx$ can be represented by an area whatever unit x may be in, and a proper interpretation of its meaning can be made.

Let $y = f(x)$ be a continuous single valued function of x. Let the curve in Fig. 84 be the graph of this equation. Then for any value of x as OQ, $f(x)dx$ is represented by the rectangle $QRSP$, which is the differential of the area under the curve when thought of as generated by an ordinate

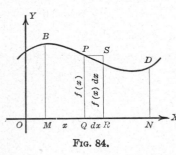

FIG. 84.

moving toward the right. Hence $\int y\, dx$, or $\int f(x)dx$, can be represented by the area generated by an ordinate moving toward the right, and it will have a determinate value if it is known where the ordinate starts and where it stops. We have then

$$dA = y\, dx = f(x)dx,$$
and
$$A = \int y\, dx = \int f(x)dx.$$

It is evident that the interpretation as to the meaning of A, will be determined by the nature of the quantities that are represented on the x-axis and y-axis. If these quantities are both lengths, then $y\, dx$ evidently is the number of square units in an area. If time is represented on the x-axis and a rate of motion on the y-axis, then $y\, dx$ is interpreted as distance. In this way integrals that may be represented by areas may be interpreted as areas, lenghts, volumes weights, velocities, etc.; and the interpretation made will depend upon the nature of the quantities that enter into $y\, dx$.

134. Definite integral.—In the first example of **Art. 132**,

$$A = \tfrac{1}{12}x^3 + C.$$

The area to be found was generated while x was changing from $x = 1$ to $x = 5$. These values are called the **end values** of x. It is noted that C is found by substituting the lower value of x, and that finally A is found by substituting the upper value of x. This leads to shortening to some extent the labor in solving such examples, and brings in a form known as the *definite integral*. This will now be discussed in a more general manner.

Let $y = f(x)$ be a single valued continuous function of x.

Let $$\int f(x)dx = F(x) + C.$$

Let x change from a lower value a to an upper value b, where $a < b$.

Then the actual change, or the *increment*, of $\int f(x)dx$ when x changes from $x = a$ to $x = b$ is

$$F(b) + C - [F(a) + C] = F(b) - F(a).$$

This increment of $\int f(x)dx$ as x changes from $x = a$ to $x = b$ is called the **definite integral** from $x = a$ to $x = b$ of $f(x)dx$, and it is written $\int_a^b f(x)dx$. This is stated in the form

[50] $$\int_a^b \mathbf{f(x)dx = F(b) - F(a)},$$

where $$\int f(x)dx = F(x) + C.$$

The numbers a and b are called the **end values** of the variable x, or the **lower limit** and the **upper limit**, respectively, of x.

The work can be carried out by the following:

RULE. *To find the definite integral from $x = a$ to $x = b$ of $f(x)dx$, (1) find the indefinite integral of $f(x)dx$, (2) substitute b for x in the integral, (3) substitute a for x in the integral, (4) subtract the result found in (3) from the result found in (2).*

The notation frequently used is

$$\int_a^b f(x)dx = F(x)]_a^b.$$

Then $$F(x)]_a^b = F(b) - F(a).$$

The formula of **Art. 133** for area can now be written

[51] $$\mathbf{A} = \int_a^b \mathbf{f(x)dx}.$$

Example 1.   Evaluate $\int_0^8 x^{\frac{2}{3}} dx$.

Solution. $\int_0^8 x^{\frac{2}{3}} dx = \frac{3}{5} x^{\frac{5}{3}} \big]_0^8 = \frac{3}{5}(8)^{\frac{5}{3}} - \frac{3}{5}(0)^{\frac{5}{3}}$

$\qquad\qquad\qquad = \frac{3}{5} \cdot 32 - \frac{3}{5} \cdot 0 = 19\frac{1}{5} \cdot$

Example 2.   Evaluate $\int_{\frac{1}{3}\pi}^{\pi} \sin x \, dx$.

Solution. $\int_{\frac{1}{3}\pi}^{\pi} \sin x \, dx = -\cos x \big]_{\frac{1}{3}\pi}^{\pi}$

$\qquad\qquad\qquad = -\cos \pi - (-\cos \frac{1}{3}\pi)$

$\qquad\qquad\qquad = -(-1) - (-\frac{1}{2}) = 1\frac{1}{2}.$

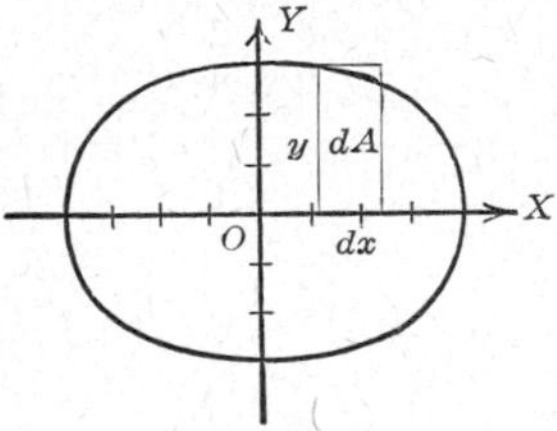

Example 3.   Find the area of the ellipse $\dfrac{x^2}{16} + \dfrac{y^2}{9} = 1$.

Fig. 85.

Solution.   The ellipse is plotted as shown in Fig. 85. It is symmetrical with respect to both axes. The area can then be found by taking four times the area of the part that is in the first quadrant.

Solving the equation $\dfrac{x^2}{16} + \dfrac{y^2}{9} = 1$ for y,

$$y = \pm \frac{3}{4}\sqrt{16 - x^2}.$$

This is a double valued function, but if y is taken positive it represents the part of the curve above the x-axis and is single valued.

Then $dA = \frac{3}{4}\sqrt{16 - x^2} \, dx.$

In generating the area in the first quadrant x changes from 0 to 4.

Hence $A = 4\int_0^4 \frac{3}{4}\sqrt{16 - x^2} \, dx = 3\int_0^4 \sqrt{4^2 - x^2} \, dx.$

Integrating by formula 55, which is

$\int \sqrt{a^2 - x^2} \, dx = \frac{1}{2}\Big(x\sqrt{a^2 - x^2} + a^2 \sin^{-1}\dfrac{x}{a}\Big)$, gives

$3\int_0^4 \sqrt{4^2 - x^2} \, dx = 3\left\{ \frac{1}{2}\Big(x\sqrt{16 - x^2} + 16 \sin^{-1}\dfrac{x}{4}\Big) \right\} \Big]_0^4$

$= 3[\frac{1}{2}(4\sqrt{16 - 16} + 16 \sin^{-1}\frac{4}{4}) - \frac{1}{2}(0\sqrt{16 - 0} + 16\sin^{-1}\frac{0}{4})]$

$= 3[\frac{1}{2}(0 + 16 \cdot \frac{1}{2}\pi) - \frac{1}{2}(0 + 0)] = 12\pi.$

∴ the area of the ellipse is 12π square units.

Note. If we had taken the general equation of the ellipse $\dfrac{x^2}{a^2} + \dfrac{y^2}{b^2} = 1$, the formula for the area of any ellipse would have been found. This formula is

$$A = \pi ab,$$

where a and b are the semimajor axis and semiminor axis, respectively, of the ellipse.

135. Area when f(x) is negative.—When the area lies below the x-axis, it is evident, since $f(x)$ is negative, that $f(x)dx$ is negative. But an area is necessarily a positive quantity and therefore

$$dA = -f(x)dx.$$

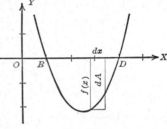

FIG. 86.

Example 1. Find the area lying between the curve $y = x^2 - 5x + 4$ and the x-axis.

Solution. The curve is plotted in Fig. 86. To find where it intersects the x-axis we put $y = 0$ and solve the resulting equation

$$x^2 - 5x + 4 = 0.$$

This gives $x = 1$ and $x = 4$, which are the end values of x.

$$\therefore A = -\int_1^4 (x^2 - 5x + 4)dx$$
$$= -(\tfrac{1}{3}x^3 - \tfrac{5}{2}x^2 + 4x)]_1^4$$
$$= -[(\tfrac{1}{3} \cdot 4^3 - \tfrac{5}{2} \cdot 4^2 + 4 \cdot 4) - (\tfrac{1}{3} \cdot 1^3 - \tfrac{5}{2} \cdot 1^2 + 4 \cdot 1)] = 4\tfrac{1}{2}.$$

∴ the area below the x-axis is $4\tfrac{1}{2}$ square units.

If the area to be found is partly above the x-axis and partly below each of the portions above and below are computed separately and then these are added to find the total area.

Example 2.   Find the area between the curve $y = \cos x$ and the x-axis from where $x = \frac{1}{6}\pi$ to where $x = \frac{3}{2}\pi$.

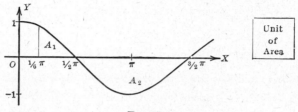

FIG. 87.

Solution.   The curve is plotted in Fig. 87.   The areas to be found are A_1 and A_2.

$$A_1 = \int_{\frac{1}{6}\pi}^{\frac{1}{2}\pi} \cos x \, dx = \sin x]_{\frac{1}{6}\pi}^{\frac{1}{2}\pi}$$
$$= \sin \tfrac{1}{2}\pi - \sin \tfrac{1}{6}\pi = 1 - \tfrac{1}{2} = \tfrac{1}{2}.$$
$$A_2 = -\int_{\frac{1}{2}\pi}^{\frac{3}{2}\pi} \cos x \, dx = -\sin x]_{\frac{1}{2}\pi}^{\frac{3}{2}\pi}$$
$$= -(\sin \tfrac{3}{2}\pi - \sin \tfrac{1}{2}\pi) = -(-1 - 1) = 2.$$

Then $A = A_1 + A_2 = \tfrac{1}{2} + 2 = 2\tfrac{1}{2}.$

$\therefore$ the area to be found is $2\tfrac{1}{2}$ square units.

EXERCISES

Evaluate the definite integrals in exercises 1 to 10.

1. $\int_1^3 7x^2 \, dx.$

2. $\int_{\frac{1}{4}\pi}^{\pi} \cos x \, dx$

3. $\int_{-2}^2 3x^4 dx.$

4. $\int_1^{10} \frac{dx}{x}.$

5. $\int_0^1 \frac{x \, dx}{4 + x^2}.$

6. $\int_{\frac{1}{3}\pi}^{\frac{1}{2}\pi} \sin^2 x \cos x \, dx.$

7. $\int_0^1 \frac{x \, dx}{\sqrt{2 - x^2}}.$

8. $\int_0^1 xe^{x^2} \, dx.$

9. $\int_0^2 \sqrt{4 - x^2} \, dx.$

10. $\int_1^3 \frac{1 + 2x}{x + x^2} dx.$

11. Find the area bounded by the curve $xy = 6$, the x-axis, and the ordinates corresponding to $x = \frac{1}{2}$ and $x = 8$.

12. Find the area described as in exercise 11 except that the ordinates correspond to $x = -4$ and $x = -\frac{1}{2}$.

13. Find the area between the curve $y = \sin x$ and the x-axis from the ordinate at $x = 1$ radian to the ordinate at $x = 5$ radians.

14. Use the calculus method and find the area of the circle

$$x^2 + y^2 = r^2.$$

15. Find the area of the ellipse $\dfrac{x^2}{36} + \dfrac{y^2}{16} = 1.$

16. Find the area in the first quadrant bounded by the hyperbola $\dfrac{x^2}{16} - \dfrac{y^2}{9} = 1$, the x-axis, and the ordinate corresponding to $x = 8$.

17. Find the area between the parabola $y = 4 - x^2$ and the x-axis.

18. Find the area bounded by the lines $y = 3x$, $y = 15 - 3x$, and the x-axis.

Suggestion. Solve the first two equations as simultaneous to find the point of intersection. The area to be found is under the first line to this point, and under the second line from this point on.

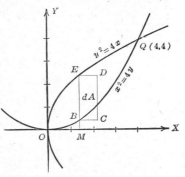

Fig. 88.

19. Find the area bounded by the curve $y = x^3 + 3x^2 + 2x$, the x-axis, and the ordinates corresponding to $x = -3$ and $x = 3$.

20. Find the area included between the parabolas $y^2 = 4x$ and $x^2 = 4y$.

Suggestion. The two parabolas are shown in Fig. 88. By solving the equations as simultaneous the coördinates of the points of intersection O and Q are found to be $(0, 0)$ and $(4, 4)$, respectively.

The area $OBQE$ may be thought of as generated by a line moving to the right from O, with its lower end on the curve $x^2 = 4y$ and its upper end on the curve $y^2 = 4x$.

Then $BCDE$ represents the differential of the area.

The height of this rectangle $BE = ME - MB$.

But MB is an ordinate of $x^2 = 4y$. From which $y = \frac{1}{4}x^2$.

And ME is an ordinate of $y^2 = 4x$. From which $y = 2\sqrt{x}$.

Then $ME - MB = 2\sqrt{x} - \frac{1}{4}x^2$, which gives $dA = (2\sqrt{x} - \frac{1}{4}x^2)dx$

Or $\qquad A = \displaystyle\int_0^4 (2\sqrt{x} - \frac{1}{4}x^2)dx.$

136. Polar coördinates.—If the area is bounded by a curve whose equation is given in polar coördinates, the differential of the area is a sector of a circle, and is deter-

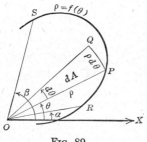

FIG. 89.

mined as follows: In Fig. 89, the curve has the equation $\rho = f(\theta)$, OX is the polar axis, and O is the pole. The area to be found is $ORPS$, beginning with the radius vector OR and ending with OS.

This area is thought of as generated by the radius vector rotating from OR where $\theta = \alpha$ to OS where $\theta = \beta$. Here θ is the independent variable and has the end values of α and β. The dependent variable in $\rho = f(\theta)$ is ρ.

As the radius vector turns we think of the differential of the area at any position as OP. If in this position the change becomes and remains uniform while θ changes by $d\theta$, the sector of a circle OPQ is generated. Now the area of the sector of a circle is equal to half the radius times the arc, and the arc equals the angle in radians times the radius.

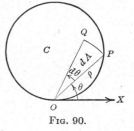

FIG. 90.

Then $dA = $ sector $OPQ = \frac{1}{2}\rho^2 d\theta$.
But $\rho = f(\theta)$, which gives
$$dA = \frac{1}{2}[f(\theta)]^2 d\theta.$$

[52] $\therefore \mathbf{A} = \int_\alpha^\beta \frac{1}{2}[\mathbf{f(\theta)}]^2 \mathbf{d\theta}.$

Example 1.   Find the area which is bounded by the curve $\rho = \sin \theta$.

Solution.   The curve is shown in Fig. 90, and is generated while θ changes from 0 to π radians.

$$dA = \frac{1}{2} \sin^2 \theta \ d\theta.$$

$$A = \int_0^\pi \tfrac{1}{2} \sin^2 \theta \, d\theta = \tfrac{1}{2}(\tfrac{1}{2}\theta - \tfrac{1}{2}\cos\theta\sin\theta)\big]_0^\pi$$
$$= \tfrac{1}{2}[(\tfrac{1}{2}\pi - \tfrac{1}{2}\cos\pi\sin\pi) - (\tfrac{1}{2}\cdot 0 - \tfrac{1}{2}\cos 0\sin 0)]$$
$$= \tfrac{1}{2}[(\tfrac{1}{2}\pi - 0) - (0 - 0)] = \tfrac{1}{4}\pi = 0.7854.$$

Therefore the area is 0.7854 square units. This is evidently true when it is noted that the curve is a circle whose radius is $\tfrac{1}{2}$.

Example 2. Find the area bounded by the cardioid

$$\rho = a(1 - \cos\theta).$$

Solution. The curve is shown in Fig. 91, and is symmetrical with respect to the polar axis. For this reason the area is twice the area above the line OX, and can be

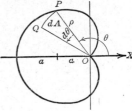

Fig. 91.

found by finding this area and multiplying by 2. In generating the area above OX, θ varies from 0 to π radians.

$$dA = \tfrac{1}{2}\rho^2 d\theta = \tfrac{1}{2}[a(1 - \cos\theta)]^2 d\theta.$$
$$A = a^2 \int_0^\pi (1 - \cos\theta)^2 d\theta$$
$$= a^2\left(\int_0^\pi d\theta - 2\int_0^\pi \cos\theta\, d\theta + \int_0^\pi \cos^2\theta\, d\theta\right)$$
$$= a^2(\theta - 2\sin\theta + \tfrac{1}{2}\theta + \tfrac{1}{2}\sin\theta\cos\theta)\Big]_0^\pi$$
$$= \tfrac{3}{2}a^2\pi.$$

EXERCISES

1. Find the area bounded by the curve $\rho = 4\cos\theta$ and between the radii vectores where $\theta = 0$ and where $\theta = \tfrac{1}{4}\pi$.

2. Find the area bounded by the curve $\rho = 6\sin\theta$.

3. Find the area bounded by the cardioid $\rho = a(1 + \cos\theta)$.

4. Find the area of one loop of the curve $\rho = 4\sin 2\theta$.

Suggestion. The curve has a loop between the values $\theta = 0$ and $\theta = \tfrac{1}{2}\pi$.

5. Find the area generated by one revolution of the radius vector of the spiral of Archimedes, $\rho = a\theta$, starting from $\theta = 0$.

SUMMATION

137. The problem of integration from another viewpoint.
As has been stated the problem in differential calculus is
to find the rate at which some quantity will change
compared with some other quantity upon which it depends;
and the methods developed can be applied to a great variety
of questions. By integration we determine the value of a
varying quantity at any instant, knowing its value at a
given instant and its rate of change at all times.

Heretofore the problems in integration have been
solved by finding a differential and then applying the rules
for integrating. Now we are to consider problems in a
manner that finally leads us to use the same rules for
integrating, but the analysis approaches the problem from
a quite different viewpoint. This **method by summation,**
as it is known, is essentially the method used by Leibniz,
one of the inventors of the calculus. It is given here not
because it is considered superior to the method by differentials; but because it is a very useful method and one
that many find more convenient and easier to follow.
It may be stated however, that the establishing of the
summation method with mathematical rigor is tedious,
and, in many cases, difficult and will not be attempted here.

The method by differentials always considers the area or
other quantity as being generated in some manner, and
thus finding a differential expression for the area or other
quantity. The method by summation considers the area
or other quantity as cut in some manner into a large number
of parts, and then the endeavor is made to find the limit of
the sum of these parts as their number increases without
limit. While this method as well as that of differentials can
be applied to questions concerning a great variety of quantities, such as areas, arc lengths, volumes, and work, we will
discuss it by means of areas. *First,* the approximate area

will be found by dividing the area sought into a small number of parts and finding their sum. *Second*, the exact area will be found by finding the limit of the sum of the parts as the number of parts increases without limit.

138. Approximate area by summation.—Let us choose again the curve $y = \frac{1}{4}x^2$ used in **Art. 132**, and find the approximate area between this curve, the x-axis, and the ordinates at $x = 1$ and $x = 5$.

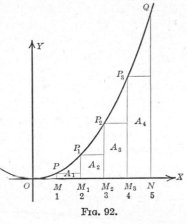

Plot the curve as shown in Fig. 92, and divide the x-axis between M where $x = 1$ and N where $x = 5$ into four equal parts as indicated by the points M_1, M_2, and M_3. At these points erect perpendiculars to the x-axis to meet the curve at P_1, P_2, and P_3, respectively, and draw lines through these points parallel to the x-axis, forming the rectangles A_1, A_2, A_3, and A_4.

FIG. 92.

Now the sum of the areas of these rectangles is approximately the area between the curve, the x-axis, and the ordinates at $x = 1$ and $x = 5$.

The base of each rectangle is 1, and their heights are $MP = \frac{1}{4}$, $M_1P_1 = 1$, $M_2P_2 = 2\frac{1}{4}$, $M_3P_3 = 4$. The sum of the areas of the rectangles is

$$A_1 + A_2 + A_3 + A_4 = 1 \cdot \tfrac{1}{4} + 1 \cdot 1 + 1 \cdot 2\tfrac{1}{4} + 1 \cdot 4 = 7\tfrac{1}{2}.$$

Since we have not taken into account the four areas between the respective rectangles and the curve we should not expect the result to be the true area under the curve. By comparing the result with the true area which is $10\frac{1}{3}$ as found in **Art. 132**, it is seen to be less than 75 per cent of the correct value, a result that could hardly be of practical use.

Next let us divide the x-axis between M and N into eight

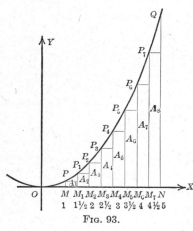

FIG. 93.

equal parts as shown in Fig. 93, and by computing the areas of the rectangles see if we arrive at a value more nearly the true area. The bases of the rectangles are each $\frac{1}{2}$, and the heights are $MP = \frac{1}{4}$, $M_1P_1 = \frac{9}{16}$, $M_2P_2 = 1$, $M_3P_3 = 1\frac{9}{16}$, $M_4P_4 = 2\frac{1}{4}$, $M_5P_5 = 3\frac{1}{16}$, $M_6P_6 = 4$, $M_7P_7 = 5\frac{1}{16}$. The sum of the areas of the rectangles is

$$A_1 + A_2 + A_3 + A_4 + A_5 + A_6 + A_7 + A_8 = \frac{1}{2}\cdot\frac{1}{4}$$
$$+ \frac{1}{2}\cdot\frac{9}{16} + \frac{1}{2}\cdot 1 + \frac{1}{2}\cdot 1\frac{9}{16} + \frac{1}{2}\cdot 2\frac{1}{4} + \frac{1}{2}\cdot 3\frac{1}{16} + \frac{1}{2}\cdot 4 + \frac{1}{2}\cdot 5\frac{1}{16} = \frac{1}{8}$$
$$+ \frac{9}{32} + \frac{1}{2} + \frac{25}{32} + \frac{9}{8} + \frac{49}{32} + 2 + \frac{81}{32} = 8\frac{7}{8}.$$

This value is nearer to the true value, but is only about 86 per cent of it, that is, while there are twice as many small areas disregarded above the rectangles, their sum is less than the sum of the four areas disregarded in the first computation.

As a third trial at approximating the area under the curve, the x-axis between M and N is divided into 16 equal parts, and 16 rectangles formed. The area then found is $9\frac{19}{32}$, which is about 92.8 per cent of the correct value.

139. Observations and conclusions.—It is evident then, that, at least in the case in the preceding article, the larger number of parts we divide the x-axis between M and N into, the more nearly is the sum of the rectangles equal to the true area under the curve. It can be proved that the *limit* of the sum of these rectangles as their number increases without limit is *exactly* the true area. The proof of this will not be attempted here, but other statements that will be given later may make it a little more evident.

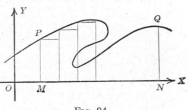

Fɪɢ. 94.

If the curve is not single valued the method used would not apply as can be seen by inspecting the area under the curve in Fig. 94. If the curve extends to infinity, there would certainly be doubt about the application of the method. Also, if there was a break in the curve, the method would not apply.

The safe thing to do then is to apply the method only when the curve is *single valued* and *continuous*.

It may be noted further that if the curve is *above* the *x*-axis and *rising* as it passes toward the right, the sum of the rectangles is always less than the true area; while if the curve is *above* the *x*-axis and *falling*, the area is always greater than the true area. How should these statements be changed so that they would apply when the curve is below the *x*-axis?

If the curve bounding the area was both rising and falling the effect would be to make the sum of the areas of the rectangles more nearly equal to the true area than it would otherwise be.

EXERCISES

1. Find the approximate area between the curve $y = x^2$, the *x*-axis, and the ordinates at $x = 0$ and $x = 4$. First, divide the interval from $x = 0$ to $x = 4$ into four equal parts, and, second, divide it into eight equal parts. In each case draw the figure. Also find the exact area and the per cent of error in each of the approximate results

2. Sketch the figure and find the approximate area between the curve $y = 9 - x^2$ and the x-axis, by dividing the interval into six equal parts.

3. Sketch the figure and find the approximate area between the curve $y = \sin x$, the x-axis, and the ordinates at $x = \frac{1}{6}\pi$ and $x = \pi$, dividing the interval into five equal parts.

Suggestion. The rectangles formed have the areas $A_1 = \frac{1}{6}\pi \cdot \sin \frac{1}{6}\pi$, $A_2 = \frac{1}{6}\pi \cdot \sin \frac{1}{3}\pi$, $A_3 = \frac{1}{6}\pi \cdot \sin \frac{1}{2}\pi$, $A_4 = \frac{1}{6}\pi \cdot \sin \frac{2}{3}\pi$, $A_5 = \frac{1}{6}\pi \cdot \sin \frac{5}{6}\pi$.

140. Summation stated in general terms.—We should now be able to understand the meaning of the following problem, which could be stated as a theorem if one so desired. Here it is stated as a problem because no attempt is made to prove the theorem.

Let $y = f(x)$ be a continuous single valued function of x between and including the values $x = a$ and $x = b$. Let the interval between a and b be divided into n equal parts each of which is Δx. Let $y_1, y_2, y_3, \cdots y_n$ be the values of y at the beginnings of these smaller intervals. It is required to find the limit of

$$y_1\Delta x + y_2\Delta x + y_3\Delta x + \cdots y_n\Delta x$$

as n increases without limit and as Δx approaches zero as a limit.

As explained in **Art. 133,** no matter what magnitudes are represented by x and y, $y = f(x)$ can be represented by a curve, and $y_1\Delta x$, $y_2\Delta x$, $\cdots$ $y_n\Delta x$ can be represented as areas of rectangles, and, further, a proper interpretation of the meaning can be made.

At first consider a curve that does not extend below the x-axis, then, as in the simple case discussed in **Art. 138** the sum of

$$y_1\Delta x + y_2\Delta x + y_3\Delta x + \cdots y_n\Delta x$$

is more and more nearly equal to the area between the curve $y = f(x)$, the x-axis, and the ordinates at $x = a$ and $x = b$, the larger n becomes. And, as stated before, it can be proved that the limit of this sum as n becomes infinite and Δx approaches zero is *exactly* equal to the area.

This is stated in the form

$$[53_1] \qquad A = \lim_{n \to \infty} \sum_{x=a}^{x=b} y \, \Delta x,$$

and since $y = f(x)$ it can as well be stated in the form

$$[53_2] \qquad A = \lim_{n \to \infty} \sum_{x=a}^{x=b} f(x) \Delta x.$$

The first of these is read "A equals the limit of the sum as n becomes infinite of such terms as $y \, \Delta x$ from $x = a$ to $x = b$." The Greek letter Σ (sigma) indicates a summation and is frequently used in mathematics.

The task before us now is to devise a scheme for finding the value of $A = \lim\limits_{n \to \infty} \sum\limits_{x=a}^{x=b} y \Delta x = \lim\limits_{n \to \infty} \sum\limits_{x=a}^{x=b} f(x) \Delta x$.

141. The evaluation of $\lim\limits_{n \to \infty} \sum\limits_{x=a}^{x=b} f(x) \Delta x$.—In Art. **134** the area between a curve $y = f(x)$, the x-axis, and two ordinates corresponding to $x = a$ and $x = b$ was represented by the definite integral $\int_a^b f(x) dx$. In the preceding article the same area is given by $\lim\limits_{n \to \infty} \sum\limits_{x=a}^{x=b} f(x) \Delta x$. Therefore

$$[54] \qquad \lim_{n \to \infty} \sum_{x=a}^{x=b} f(x) \Delta x = \int_a^b f(x) \, dx.$$

The evaluation of the summation can then be made by methods of integration. This is one of the remarkable discoveries in mathematics. Leibniz used the method long before he understood why it gave the proper results.

142. Areas below the x-axis.—When the area lies below the x-axis between the curve $y - f(x)$, the x-axis, and the ordinates at $x = a$ and $x = b$, evidently the area is the limit of the sum of

$$(-y_1\Delta x) + (-y_2\Delta x) + (-y_3\Delta x) + \cdots (-y_n\Delta x),$$

or is represented by

$$A = - \lim_{n \to \infty} \sum_{x=a}^{x=b} y\,\Delta x = - \lim_{n \to \infty} \sum_{x=a}^{x=b} f(x)\Delta x = - \int_a^b f(x)dx.$$

Further, when we are to find the area between the curve $y = f(x)$, the x-axis, and the ordinates at $x = a$ and $x = b$, and the curve is both above and below the x-axis, we will find the areas of the parts above the x-axis and the parts below the x-axis separately, and then find their sum.

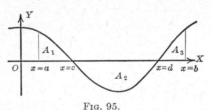

Fig. 95.

Thus, in Fig. 95, let the curve $y = f(x)$ cross the x-axis at points where $x = c$ and $x = d$, then the total area between the curve, the x-axis, and the ordinates at $x = a$ and $x = b$ is equal to $A_1 + A_2 + A_3$.

But
$$A_1 = \lim_{n \to \infty} \sum_{x=a}^{x=c} f(x)\,\Delta x = \int_a^c f(x)dx,$$

$$A_2 = - \lim_{n \to \infty} \sum_{x=c}^{x=d} f(x)\,\Delta x = - \int_c^d f(x)dx,$$

and
$$A_3 = \lim_{n \to \infty} \sum_{x=d}^{x=b} f(x)\,\Delta x = \int_d^b f(x)dx.$$

143. Remarks and suggestions.—It is well to note that historically the definite integral was first used as the limit of a sum, and for this reason the definite integral $\int_a^b f(x)dx$ is usually defined as $\lim\limits_{n \to \infty} \sum\limits_{x=a}^{x=b} f(x)\Delta x$.

It was this idea of the integral that gave the symbol, $\int$, which is an elongated S, the first letter of the word *summa* meaning sum.

The summation method can be applied to areas, volumes, arc lengths, velocities, pressures, centers of gravity, and many other magnitudes. It thus gives in many cases a simple method of finding a desired differential, and should be used whenever it seems to be easier than the method of differentials. In the examples given later in finding surfaces, volumes, etc., both methods will frequently be used, and in this way the advantages of each over the other will appear. It will usually be found, however, that the method of differentials is the more direct.

A suggestion as how to prove that the area between a curve $y = f(x)$, the x-axis, and the ordinates at $x = a$ and $x = b$ is equal to $\lim\limits_{n \to \infty} \sum\limits_{x=a}^{x=b} f(x)\Delta x$ will now be given.

Suppose that the curve $y = f(x)$ is rising in passing toward the right and that the area $MNQP$, Fig. 96, is to be found.

$$MNQP = A_1 + A_2 + A_3 + A_4 + A_5 + (a_1 + a_2 + a_3 + a_4 + a_5)$$
$$= \sum_{x=a}^{x=b} A_n + \sum_{x=a}^{x=b} a_n.$$

At the right of the figure is a rectangle with a base Δx and a height equal to $RS = f(b) - f(a)$, and is the sum of the rectangles a_1', a_2', a_3', a_4', and a_5', constructed as shown in the figure. Then

$$(a_1 + a_2 + a_3 + a_4 + a_5) < (a_1' + a_2' + a_3' + a_4' + a_5').$$

Or

$$\sum_{x=a}^{x=b} a_n < \sum_{x=a}^{x=b} a_n'.$$

But

$$\sum_{x=a}^{x=b} a_n' = RS \cdot \Delta x.$$

As the number of rectangles formed becomes infinite, Δx approaches zero as a limit and $RS \cdot \Delta x$ approaches zero as a limit.

Then $MNQP = \lim\limits_{n \to \infty} \sum\limits_{x=a}^{x=b} A_n = \lim\limits_{n \to \infty} \sum\limits_{x=a}^{x=b} f(x)\,\Delta x.$

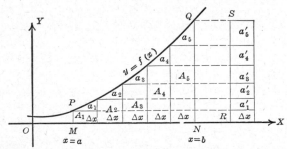

Fig. 96.

144. Illustrative examples. *Example 1.* Find $\displaystyle\sum_{x=1}^{x=2} 2x^2 \Delta x$

when $\Delta x = 0.1$, then find $\displaystyle\lim_{n \to \infty} \sum_{x=1}^{x=2} 2x^2 \Delta x$.

Solution. When $\Delta x = 0.1$,

$$\sum_{x=1}^{x=2} 2x^2 \Delta x = 2(1^2 + 1.1^2 + 1.2^2 + 1.3^2 + \cdots 1.9^2)0.1 = 4.37$$

$$\lim_{n \to \infty} \sum_{x=1}^{x=2} 2x^2 \Delta x = 2 \int_1^2 x^2 dx = 2(\tfrac{1}{3}x^3)\Big]_1^2 = \tfrac{2}{3}(2^3 - 1^3) = 4\tfrac{2}{3}.$$

Example 2. Find the area between the curve $y = \cos x$, the x-axis, and the ordinates at $x = \frac{1}{6}\pi$ and $x = \frac{4}{3}\pi$.

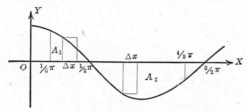

Fig. 97.

Solution. The curve is shown in Fig. 97, and crosses the x-axis at $x = \frac{1}{2}\pi$. The area to be found is then equal to $A_1 + A_2$.

$$A_1 = \lim_{n \to \infty} \sum_{x=\frac{1}{6}\pi}^{x=\frac{1}{2}\pi} \cos x \, \Delta x = \int_{\frac{1}{6}\pi}^{\frac{1}{2}\pi} \cos x \, dx$$

$$= \sin x \Big]_{\frac{1}{6}\pi}^{\frac{1}{2}\pi} = \sin \frac{1}{2}\pi - \sin \frac{1}{6}\pi = 1 - \frac{1}{2} = 0.5.$$

$$A_2 = - \lim_{n \to \infty} \sum_{x=\frac{1}{2}\pi}^{x=\frac{4}{3}\pi} \cos x \, \Delta x = - \int_{\frac{1}{2}\pi}^{\frac{4}{3}\pi} \cos x \, dx$$

$$= -\sin x \Big]_{\frac{1}{2}\pi}^{\frac{4}{3}\pi} = - (\sin \frac{4}{3}\pi - \sin \frac{1}{2}\pi)$$

$$= - (-\frac{1}{2}\sqrt{3} - 1) = 1.866.$$

$\therefore$ total area $= 0.5 + 1.866 = 2.366.$

EXERCISES

1. Find $\displaystyle\sum_{x=1}^{x=3} (x^2 + 3)\Delta x$ when $\Delta x = 0.2$, or $n = 10$.

2. Find $\displaystyle\lim_{n \to \infty} \sum_{x=1}^{x=3} (x^2 + 3)\Delta x$.

3. Find $\displaystyle\lim_{n \to \infty} \sum_{x=0}^{x=2} 3x^3 \Delta x$.

4. Find the area between the curve $y = \cos x$, the x-axis, and the ordinates at $x = 0$, and $x = \frac{3}{2}\pi$.

5. Find the area bounded by the curve $y = \sin^2 x$, the x-axis, and the ordinates at $x = \frac{1}{3}\pi$ and $x = 2\pi$.

6. Find the area bounded by the curve $y = 5 + 4x - x^2$ and the x-axis.

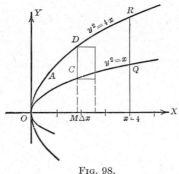

FIG. 98.

7. Find the area bounded by the curve $y = 4 - x^2$, the x-axis, and between the limits $x = -1$ and $x = 2$.

8. Find the area bounded by the hyperbola $xy = 6$, the x-axis, and the ordinates at $x = 1$ and $x = 6$.

9. Find the area bounded by the curve $xy^{1.37} = 6$, the x-axis, and the ordinates at $x = \frac{1}{2}$ and $x = 10$.

10. Find the area in the first quadrant and bounded by the parabolas $y^2 = x$ and $y^2 = 4x$, and the line $x = 4$.

Suggestion. The area $A = OQR$ of Fig. 98 is to be found.

One of the rectangles that are to be summed is shown and has a height $CD = MD - MC$.

But $MD = 2\sqrt{x}$ and $MC = \sqrt{x}$.

$$\therefore \quad A = \lim_{n \to \infty} \sum_{x=0}^{x=4} (2\sqrt{x} - \sqrt{x})\Delta x = \lim_{n \to \infty} \sum_{x=0}^{x=4} \sqrt{x}\,\Delta x = \int_0^4 x^{\frac{1}{2}} dx.$$

11. Solve exercise 10 by method of differentials noting carefully the difference of thought in the two methods.

Suggestion. By differentials the area is thought of as generated by a line moving from O to QR and remaining parallel to the y-axis. CD is a position of this moving line.

12. Find the area in the first quadrant and bounded by the curves $y = \sin x$ and $y = \cos x$, and the y-axis.

13. By integration find the distance passed over by a falling body from 2 sec. to 6 sec. after it starts, if $v = gt$, where g is the constant acceleration, v is velocity, and t is time.

Suggestion. If $v = gt$ is plotted the area under the curve will represent the distance s, since $v \, \Delta t$ represents approximately the distance passed over in time Δt. Then the approximate total distance can be found by finding the sum of such terms as $v \, \Delta t$ for different values of v as t changes from 2 to 6.

The actual value of s is

$$s = \lim_{\Delta t \to 0} \sum_{t=2}^{t=6} gt \, \Delta t = g \int_2^6 t \, dt.$$

Not using the summation method we can say, since velocity is $\dfrac{ds}{dt}$,

$$\frac{ds}{dt} = gt.$$
$$ds = gt \, dt.$$
$$\therefore s = g \int_2^6 t \, dt$$

CHAPTER XVI

ARC LENGTHS. AREAS OF SURFACES

145. Length of arc of curve.—To measure a length we usually think of applying to it a unit of length; but when the length to be measured is a curved line, the unit of length which is a straight line cannot be applied, and the method does not work. For this reason some other method will have to be used.

In plane geometry the length of a circle was found as the limit of the perimeter of an inscribed or circumscribed regular polygon. A similar method by limits could be used on any curve, but the work necessary to develop it would be difficult and tedious. For simplicity then the method of differentials will be used in developing the formulas for finding the length of the arc of a curve.

146. Length of arc, rectangular coördinates.—Let $y = f(x)$ be a curve that is single valued and continuous between and including the values $x = a$ and $x = b$. Further it is to be a curve such that at all points considered $\dfrac{dy}{dx}$ is continuous. The last condition makes it impossible for the curve to have cusp points at which the tangent line would be perpendicular to the x-axis.

Given such a curve it is required to find the arc length from $x = a$ to $x = b$. That is, it is required to find the distance a point will move in travelling from $x = a$ to $x = b$ along the curve.

Let $y = f(x)$ be the curve as shown in Fig. 99. Consider the point starting at Q where $x = a$ and moving toward R where $x = b$. Let s be the distance it has moved when it has reached any point as P. Then as shown in **Art. 50,**

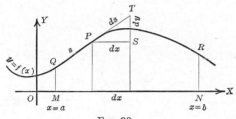

Fig. 99.

(1) $$ds^2 = dx^2 + dy^2.$$

Dividing by dx^2, $$\frac{ds^2}{dx^2} = 1 + \frac{dy^2}{dx^2}.$$

Taking square root, $$\frac{ds}{dx} = \sqrt{1 + \left(\frac{dy}{dx}\right)^2}.$$

Multiplying by dx, $$ds = \sqrt{1 + \left(\frac{dy}{dx}\right)^2}\, dx.$$

Integrating and using the definite integral,

[**55₁**] $$s = \int_a^b \sqrt{1 + \left(\frac{dy}{dx}\right)^2}\, dx.$$

In this formula $\frac{dy}{dx}$ appears as the quotient of differentials, but its value can always be found by getting the derivative of y with respect to x.

Again, if the function is single valued when x is considered as a function of y, starting with (1) and dividing by dy^2,

$$\frac{ds^2}{dy^2} = \frac{dx^2}{dy^2} + 1.$$

Taking square root, $$\frac{ds}{dy} = \sqrt{1 + \left(\frac{dx}{dy}\right)^2}.$$

Multiplying by dy, $ds = \sqrt{1 + \left(\dfrac{dx}{dy}\right)^2}\,dy$.

Integrating and using $y = c$ when $x = a$, and $y = d$ when $x = b$, as the limits,

[55₂] $$s = \int_c^d \sqrt{1 + \left(\frac{dx}{dy}\right)^2}\,dy.$$

In any problem the one of the two formulas should be used that will give the simpler integral.

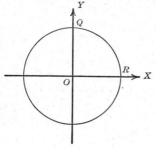

FIG. 100.

Example 1. Find the length of the circle $x^2 + y^2 = r^2$.

Solution. In $x^2 + y^2 = r^2$, y is a double valued function of x, for solving for y,

$$y = \pm\sqrt{r^2 - x^2}.$$

If we find the length of the arc in the first quadrant, we can use $y = +\sqrt{r^2 - x^2}$ as the equation of the curve. Then four times this length is the length of the circle.

Differentiating, $\dfrac{dy}{dx} = -\dfrac{x}{\sqrt{r^2 - x^2}}$.

Substituting in [55₁] and noting that the point moves from Q to R and so makes the limits on x from 0 to r,

$$s = \int_0^r \sqrt{1 + \frac{x^2}{r^2 - x^2}}\,dx = \int_0^r \sqrt{\frac{r^2}{r^2 - x^2}}\,dx$$

$$= r\int_0^r \frac{dx}{\sqrt{r^2 - x^2}} = r\sin^{-1}\frac{x}{r}\bigg]_0^r \qquad \text{By V.}$$

$$= r(\sin^{-1} 1 - \sin^{-1} 0) = \tfrac{1}{2}\pi r.$$

$\therefore$ total length of circle $= 2\pi r$.

Example 2. A telegraph wire stretched between two poles hangs approximately in the form of a parabola if the sag is small compared with the length. If the poles are 100 ft. apart and the sag in the wire is 4 ft., find the length of the wire.

Solution. It is necessary to find the equation of the curve along which the wire hangs. In Fig. 101, QOR is the wire. If the origin of axes is taken at the lowest point of the wire and the x-axis horizontal, the general equation of such a parabola is of the form

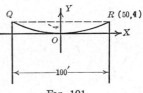

Fig. 101.

$$x^2 = 2py,$$

where p is to be found so that the curve will pass through the point $R(50, 4)$. Substituting these values for x and y in $x^2 = 2py$, we have

$$50^2 = 2p \cdot 4. \quad \therefore \ p = 312\tfrac{1}{2}.$$

Substituting this value for p in $x^2 = 2py$,

$$x^2 = 625y, \text{ the equation of the curve.}$$

Solving for y, $y = \dfrac{x^2}{625}$.

Substituting in [**55**₁] and noting that the total length is twice that between the limits 0 and 50,

$$s = 2\int_0^{50} \sqrt{1 + \frac{4x^2}{(625)^2}}dx = \tfrac{2}{625}\int_0^{50} \sqrt{(625)^2 + 4x^2}dx$$

$$= \tfrac{4}{625}\int_0^{50} \sqrt{(312\tfrac{1}{2})^2 + x^2} \ dx$$

$$= \tfrac{4}{625}\left\{\tfrac{1}{2}x\sqrt{(312\tfrac{1}{2})^2 + x^2}\right.$$

$$\left. +\tfrac{1}{2}(312\tfrac{1}{2})^2 \log\left(x + \sqrt{(312\tfrac{1}{2})^2 + x^2}\right)\right\}\Big]_0^{50}$$

$$= \tfrac{4}{625}[\{25\sqrt{(312\tfrac{1}{2})^2 + 50^2} + \tfrac{1}{2}(312\tfrac{1}{2})^2$$
$$\log (50 + \sqrt{(312\tfrac{1}{2})^2 + 50^2)}\} - \tfrac{1}{2}(312\tfrac{1}{2})^2 \log \sqrt{(312\tfrac{1}{2})^2}]$$
$$= \tfrac{4}{625}[7911.87 + 288,276 - 280,498] = 100.42 -.$$

$$\therefore \text{ length is about 100 ft. 5 in.}$$

Example 3.   Find the length of one arch of the cycloid, using the parametric equations

$$x = a(\varphi - \sin \varphi), \; y = a(1 - \cos \varphi).$$

(For the meaning of these equations see **Art. 204.**)
Solution.   Given $x = a(\varphi - \sin \varphi)$, $y = a(1 - \cos \varphi)$.
Differentiating, $dx = a(1 - \cos \varphi)d\varphi$, $dy = a \sin \varphi \, d\varphi$.
Substituting in [**55₁**] and noting that the limits on φ are 0 and 2π,

$$s = \int_0^{2\pi} \sqrt{1 + \frac{\sin^2 \varphi}{(1 - \cos \varphi)^2}}a(1 - \cos \varphi)d\varphi$$

$$= a\int_0^{2\pi} \sqrt{2 - 2\cos \varphi}\, d\varphi = 2a\int_0^{2\pi} \sqrt{\frac{1 - \cos \varphi}{2}}d\varphi$$

$$= 2a\int_0^{2\pi} \sin \tfrac{1}{2}\varphi \, d\varphi \qquad\qquad \text{By trigonometry.}$$

$$= 4a\int_0^{2\pi} \sin \tfrac{1}{2}\varphi \, \tfrac{1}{2}d\varphi = -4a \cos \tfrac{1}{2}\varphi\Big]_0^{2\pi}$$

$$= -4a(-1 - 1) = 8a.$$

This states that the length of an arch of the cycloid is eight times the radius of the revolving circle.

Remark.   It will be noted that the integrations and computations when finding arc lengths are apt to be difficult and tedious.   In fact, integrals frequently arise that are impossible to handle by methods we have given.   Such integrals are encountered when finding the length of an arc of an ellipse or an hyperbola.

EXERCISES

1. Find the length of the circle $x^2 + y^2 = 36$.

2. Find the length of the arc of the parabola $4y = x^2$ from $x = 0$ to $x = 4$.

3. Find the length of the arc of the catenary $y = \frac{1}{2}a(e^{\frac{x}{a}} + e^{-\frac{x}{a}})$ from $-x$ to x. Suppose that the catenary is formed by a wire, weighing 0.1 lb. per foot of length, suspended between two points 50 ft. apart on a horizontal line with a horizontal tension of 10 lb. at each end. Find the length of the wire and find the sag.

Suggestion. $\dfrac{dy}{dx} = \frac{1}{2}(e^{\frac{x}{a}} - e^{-\frac{x}{a}})$.

$$s = \int_{-x}^{x} \sqrt{1 + \tfrac{1}{4}(e^{\frac{x}{a}} - e^{-\frac{x}{a}})^2}\, dx = \frac{1}{2}\int_{-x}^{x}(e^{\frac{x}{a}} + e^{-\frac{x}{a}})dx$$

$$= \tfrac{1}{2}a(e^{\frac{x}{a}} - e^{-\frac{x}{a}})\bigg]_{-x}^{x} = a(e^{\frac{x}{a}} - e^{-\frac{x}{a}}).$$

By Art. 97, Ex. 2, $a = 10 \div 0.1 = 100$, and it is given that the points of suspension are 50 ft. apart, so the limits on x are -25 and 25.

$\therefore s = 100(e^{\frac{1}{4}} - e^{-\frac{1}{4}}) = 50.52 =$ length in feet.

To find the sag, we note that the lowest point is $a = 100$ ft. above the origin. And the points of support are at a height of

$$y = 50(e^{\frac{1}{4}} + e^{-\frac{1}{4}}) = 103.14 \text{ ft.}$$

$$\therefore \text{sag} = 3.14 \text{ ft.}$$

A catenary with as small a sag as here could be very closely approximated by a parabola, as was done in example 2.

4. Solve the same as in the preceding using wire weighing 0.2 lb. per foot of length and having a horizontal tension of 5 lb. at each supporting end.

5. Find the total length of the four cusped hypocycloid $x^{\frac{2}{3}} + y^{\frac{2}{3}} = a^{\frac{2}{3}}$. Note that $\dfrac{dy}{dx} = \infty$ when $x = 0$.

6. The cables of a suspension bridge hang in the form of a parabola. If the distance between the tops of the supports for the cables is 1000 ft., and the lowest point of the cables is 100 ft. below this level, find the length of the cables between the supports.

147. Length of arc, polar coördinates.—Let $\rho = f(\theta)$ be the equation of a curve in polar coördinates, of which the length of an arc is desired. A formula will now be derived for finding the length of such an arc from a point on the curve where $\theta = \alpha$ to another point where $\theta = \beta$. Such a curve is shown in Fig. 102. The length to be found is from

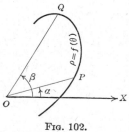

P where $\theta = \alpha$ to Q where $\theta = \beta$. Here θ is the independent variable and its limits are α and β.

The formula will be derived, first, by transforming the formula already found for rectangular coördinates to polar coördinates; and, second, the formula will be derived directly by using the definition of a differential.

Fig. 102.

148. Derivation from rectangular coördinate formula for arc length.—If the equation of the curve is given in rectangular coördinates, the differential of the arc is

(1) $$ds = \sqrt{dx^2 + dy^2}.$$

To transform from rectangular coördinates to polar coördinates we use the relations, (See **Art. 205**).

$$x = \rho \cos \theta,$$
$$y = \rho \sin \theta.$$

Differentiating each of these,

$$dx = \cos \theta \, d\rho - \rho \sin \theta \, d\theta,$$
$$dy = \sin \theta \, d\rho + \rho \cos \theta \, d\theta.$$

Substituting these values in (1),

$$\begin{aligned}
ds &= \sqrt{(\cos \theta \, d\rho - \rho \sin \theta \, d\theta)^2 + (\sin \theta \, d\rho + \rho \cos \theta \, d\theta)^2} \\
&= \sqrt{(\sin^2 \theta + \cos^2 \theta)d\rho^2 + (\sin^2 \theta + \cos^2 \theta)\rho^2 d\theta^2} \\
&= \sqrt{\rho^2 d\theta^2 + d\rho^2}.
\end{aligned}$$

Dividing and multiplying by $d\theta$,

$$ds = \sqrt{\rho^2 + \left(\frac{d\rho}{d\theta}\right)^2}\, d\theta.$$

The length of the arc from the point where $\theta = \alpha$ to the point where $\theta = \beta$ is then

[56]
$$s = \int_{\alpha}^{\beta} \sqrt{\varrho^2 + \left(\frac{d\varrho}{d\theta}\right)^2}\,d\theta.$$

149. Formula derived directly by differentials.—Let the equation of the curve, Fig. 103, be $\rho = f(\theta)$ in polar coördinates. If s is the length of the curve generated by the moving point, then if the changes in ρ and s become and remain uniform with respect to θ at any point P, the differential of the arc, ds, is along the tangent line PT; the differential of the radius vector, $d\rho$, is along the radius vector OP; and the differential of the motion perpendicular to the radius vector is $\rho\ d\theta$ along PR tangent to the circle having OP for a radius.   Then it follows that when θ takes an increment $d\theta$,

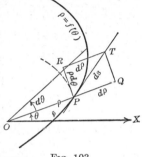

Fig. 103.

$$ds = PT,\ d\rho = PQ = RT,\text{ and }\rho\ d\theta = PR.$$

Hence in the right triangle PRT,

$$ds = \sqrt{(\rho\ d\theta)^2 + d\rho^2}.$$

Dividing and multiplying by $d\theta$,

$$ds = \sqrt{\rho^2 + \left(\frac{d\rho}{d\theta}\right)^2}\,d\theta.$$

The length of the arc from the point where $\theta = \alpha$ to the point where $\theta = \beta$ is then

[56]
$$s = \int_{\alpha}^{\beta} \sqrt{\varrho^2 + \left(\frac{d\varrho}{d\theta}\right)^2}\,d\theta.$$

Example 1.   Find the length of the circle $\rho = r$.

Solution.   Here the equation of the circle is in polar coördinates with its center at the pole and a radius r.   To generate this circle θ will change from 0 to 2π radians, that is, the radius vector will make one revolution.

Given $\rho = r$,

Differentiating with respect to θ, $\dfrac{d\rho}{d\theta} = 0$.

Substituting in [**56**],

$$s = \int_0^{2\pi} \sqrt{\rho^2 + 0^2}\, d\theta = \int_0^{2\pi} \rho\, d\theta.$$

Putting for ρ its value r, a constant,

$$s = r\int_0^{2\pi} d\theta = r\theta\big]_0^{2\pi} = 2\pi r.$$

Example 2.   Find the entire length of the arc of the cardioid $\rho = a(1 - \cos \theta)$.

Solution.   The curve is shown in Fig. 104, and is traced by a point starting at O and moving in the direction

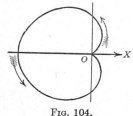

shown by the arrows.   Since the curve is symmetrical with respect to the polar axis OX, one-half of the curve is generated while θ is changing from 0 to π radians. The length of the curve can then be found by taking twice the integral between the limits 0 and π.

Fig. 104.

Given $\qquad\qquad \rho = a(1 - \cos \theta).$

Differentiating, $\dfrac{d\rho}{d\theta} = a \sin \theta.$

Substituting in [**56**],

$$\begin{aligned}
s &= 2\int_0^{\pi} \sqrt{a^2(1 - \cos \theta)^2 + a^2 \sin^2 \theta}\ d\theta \\
&= 2a\int_0^{\pi} \sqrt{2(1 - \cos \theta)}\, d\theta = 4a\int_0^{\pi} \sin \tfrac{1}{2}\theta\ d\theta \\
&= -8a \cos \tfrac{1}{2}\theta\big]_0^{\pi} = -8a(0 - 1) = 8a.
\end{aligned}$$

EXERCISES

1. Find the length of the curve $\rho = 2a \cos \theta$ that is generated while θ changes from 0 to π radians. Note that the curve is a circle of radius a.

2. Find the length of the curve $\rho = 2a \sin \theta$ that is generated while θ changes from 0 to π radians.

3. Find the length of the spiral of Archimedes $\rho = a\theta$ contained between the points on the curve where $\theta = 0$ and $\theta = 2\pi$ radians, respectively.

AREAS OF SURFACES

150. Kinds of surfaces considered.—Here we will consider areas of surfaces that can be thought of as generated by a straight line or a curve moving in such a manner that the differential of the area can be expressed in a form that can be integrated. Surfaces that were generated by an ordinate or a radius vector have already been studied, and these were necessarily plane surfaces; but the methods given for finding these plane areas cannot be applied to finding the surface of a cone, a sphere, a paraboloid, or other such surfaces that may be called **curved surfaces.**

A large class of these surfaces may be thought of as generated by a straight line or a curve revolving about an axis. They are called **surfaces of revolution.**

Thus, the right circular cone, shown in Fig. 105, may be thought of as generated by the line OQ revolving about OX as an axis. It may also be thought of as generated by a variable circle starting as a point at O and moving toward the right as it continually becomes larger.

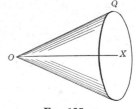

FIG. 105.

The sphere, shown in Fig. 106, may be generated by the circle revolving about its diameter BC as an axis. It may

also be thought of as generated by a variable circle starting
as a point at B and moving toward the right as it becomes
larger until it reaches the center O, and then decreasing in
size becoming a point at C.

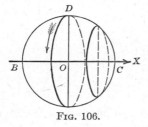

FIG. 106.

Whatever surface of revolution
is taken it may always be thought
of as generated by a circle moving
in a position perpendicular to the
axis of revolution. It is when
thought of as generated in this
manner that the differential of the
area is most readily written. It
is always necessary to know just how the generating
circle is varying in size as it moves, and this is known, in
most cases, from the equation of the curve which revolves
about the axis to generate the surface.

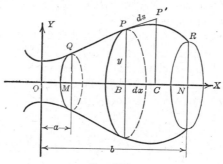

FIG. 107.

151. Area of surface of revolution.—In Fig. 107, let the
curve QPR, whose equation is $y = f(x)$, revolve about the
x-axis and generate a surface of revolution. It is understood that $y = f(x)$ is a curve of which the arc length can
be found. The area of the surface from where $x = a$
at M to where $x = b$ at N is to be found.

To find the differential of the surface, consider it as generated by a circle starting at M and moving toward N, while varying in size as guided by the curve $y = f(x)$. The center of the circle is moving along the x-axis uniformly, that is, x is the independent variable and increases uniformly. To find an expression for dS, the differential of the surface S, one must be able to decide as to the change in S for a change dx in x when the circle has reached some point P of the curve, provided the change in S *becomes* and *remains* uniform.

Evidently the rate at which the surface is being generated when the circle reaches P is equal to the length of the circle times the rate at which P is moving at that instant. Right here is the idea that the student is most liable to miss, and it is the fact that *the point P is moving in a direction along the tangent to the curve $y = f(x)$* at such a rate that it will cover the distance $PP' = ds$ while x increases by dx, or B reaches C.

Since the rate of change in S must *become* and *remain* constant while x changes by dx, the circumference of the circle must be thought of as constant. The change in S under these conditions would then be the surface of a cylinder of radius $BP = y$ and altitude $PP' = ds$. This gives

$$dS = 2\pi y \, ds = 2\pi y \sqrt{1 + \left(\frac{dy}{dx}\right)^2} dx.$$

[57] $$\therefore \mathbf{S} = 2\pi \int_a^b \mathbf{y} \sqrt{1 + \left(\frac{\mathbf{dy}}{\mathbf{dx}}\right)^2} \mathbf{dx}.$$

This is a formula that can be used in finding any surface of revolution generated by a curve $y = f(x)$ revolving about the x-axis, provided $y = f(x)$ is positive, that is, the curve is above the x-axis, single valued, continuous, and has no cusp points in the portion used. If the curve is below the x-axis it is only necessary to use $-y$.

Example 1. Find the area of the surface of revolution formed by revolving the circle $x^2 + y^2 = r^2$ about the x-axis.

Solution. Given $x^2 + y^2 = r^2$.

Differentiating, $2x + 2y\dfrac{dy}{dx} = 0$. $\therefore \dfrac{dy}{dx} = -\dfrac{x}{y}.$

Substituting in [**57**], noting that from the equation of the circle $y = \sqrt{r^2 + x^2}$ for the upper half of the circle, and that the area is twice that generated when x varies from 0 to r,

$$S = 4\pi \int_0^r \sqrt{r^2 - x^2}\sqrt{1 + \frac{x^2}{r^2 - x^2}}\,dx$$

$$= 4\pi \int_0^r r\,dx = 4\pi rx\Big]_0^r = 4\pi r^2.$$

This is the well known formula for the area of the surface of a sphere. The problem was solved by substituting in

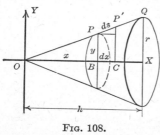

the formula in a mechanical manner. It might have been done by thinking the solution out and finding the expression for dS and then integrating.

Example 2. Find the area of the lateral surface of the right circular cone shown in Fig. 108, if the radius of the base is r

FIG. 108.

and the altitude is h.

Solution. Consider the surface as generated by a circle starting at O and moving toward the right keeping perpendicular to the x-axis. The differential of the surface can then be readily thought out.

In any position of the moving circle as when it reaches the point P, the circumference, if its rate of motion remained as at that instant, would move a distance $PP' = ds$ while x increased by $BC = dx$.

Then $dS = 2\pi y \, ds = 2\pi y \sqrt{1 + \left(\dfrac{dy}{dx}\right)^2} dx.$

But y must be expressed in terms of x before the expression can be integrated. This can be done by making use of the similar triangles OBP and OXQ.

Then $OB : BP = OX : XQ.$ Or $x : y = h : r.$

$$\therefore y = \frac{r}{h}x.$$

Differentiating, $\dfrac{dy}{dx} = \dfrac{r}{h}.$

Substituting, $dS = 2\pi \cdot \dfrac{r}{h} x \sqrt{1 + \dfrac{r^2}{h^2}} dx$

$$= 2\pi \frac{r}{h^2} x \sqrt{h^2 + r^2} \, dx.$$

Since x varies from 0 to h while the conical surface is generated, the limits are 0 and h.

$$\therefore S = 2\pi \frac{r}{h^2}\sqrt{h^2 + r^2} \int_0^h x \, dx = 2\pi \frac{r}{h^2}\sqrt{h^2 + r^2} \cdot \tfrac{1}{2}x^2 \Big]_0^h$$

$$= \pi r \sqrt{h^2 + r^2}.$$

Noting that $\sqrt{h^2 + r^2}$ is the slant height s of the cone, the formula becomes the one that is well known from geometry.

$$S = \pi r s.$$

Example 3. Find the area from the origin to $x = 16$ of the paraboloid of revolution formed by revolving the parabola $y^2 = 16x$ about the x-axis.

Solution. Given $y^2 = 16x$, or $y = \pm 4\sqrt{x}$. When this is plotted it is seen that $y = 4\sqrt{x}$ is the part above the x-axis and is single valued. It also generates the complete surface when revolved.

Differentiating, $\dfrac{dy}{dx} = 2x^{-\frac{1}{2}}.$

Substituting in [**57**],

$$S = 2\pi \int_0^{16} 4\sqrt{x}\sqrt{1 + \frac{4}{x}}\,dx$$

$$= 8\pi \int_0^{16} \sqrt{x + 4}\,dx = \tfrac{16}{3}\pi\,(x + 4)^{\frac{3}{2}}\Big]_0^{16}$$

$$= \tfrac{16}{3}\pi(20^{\frac{3}{2}} - 4^{\frac{3}{2}}) = 1364.6.$$

152. Area bounded by involute of circle.—A problem of interest because it is frequently asked as a puzzling question involves the finding of the area bounded by the involute

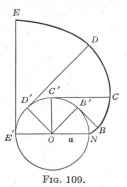

Fig. 109.

of a circle. The involute of a circle is the curve traced in the plane of a circle by the end of a string as the string is unwound from the circle.

In Fig. 109, let O be the center of a circle of radius a. Suppose that a string is wound around the circle in such a manner that it ends at N. If a pencil is fastened to the end of the string at N, as the string is unwound the pencil can be made to trace the curve $NBCDE$. While unwinding, the string is kept taut, and it will therefore always be tangent to the circle. It will then always be perpendicular to the radius drawn to the point of tangency. In the figure, $C'C$ is the string when unwound from one-quarter of the circle. It is then perpendicular to the radius OC'. The tracing point reaches E when the string has been unwound from one-half of the circle. The curve thus traced is the **involute of the circle.**

The area generated by the string as it is unwound can readily be found by the method of differentials.

Example. Find the area bounded by a circle of radius a, its involute, and the string when unwound from one-quarter of the circle.

Solution. In Fig. 110, the area A to be found is bounded by the involute NPQ, the string in the position RQ, and the quadrant of the circle NTR.

The variables are the angle φ through which the radius drawn to the point of tangency of the string turns, and the area A. To find the expression for dA we notice that the string turns through the same angle that the radius turns through, and that the length of the string unwound is always equal to the arc of the circle, having φ as the angle at the center.

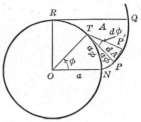

FIG. 110.

When the string is unwound to any point T, the rate at which the area is being generated is determined by the length of the string TP and the rate it is turning. By the definition of a differential, in order to find dA, the rate of change of A must remain as it is when the string is in the position TP, while φ takes a change of $d\varphi$.

Then dA equals sector TPP' of circle of radius $TP = a\varphi$. The angle of the sector is $d\varphi$, and its arc $PP' = a\varphi d\varphi$. Since the area of a sector of a circle equals one-half the arc length times the radius

$$dA = \tfrac{1}{2}a^2\varphi^2 d\varphi.$$

When the string has been unwound from one-quarter of the circle φ has become $\tfrac{1}{2}\pi$.

$$\therefore A = \tfrac{1}{2}a^2\int_0^{\frac{1}{2}\pi}\varphi^2 d\varphi = \tfrac{1}{6}a^2\varphi^3\Big]_0^{\frac{1}{2}\pi} = \tfrac{1}{48}a^2\pi^3.$$

EXERCISES

Using the calculus method find the lateral area of each of the following:

1. A right circular cone, altitude 10 ft. and radius of base 4 ft.

2. A regular-pyramid, altitude 10 ft. and square base 10 ft. on a side.

3. A regular-pyramid, altitude 10 ft. and equilateral triangle 6 ft. on a side for base.

4. A sphere with radius 10 ft..

5. Find the area formed by revolving the parabola $y^2 = 4x$ about the x-axis, from the origin to where $x = 4$.

6. Find the area formed by revolving the parabola $x^2 = 4y$ about the x-axis, from the origin to where $x = 4$.

7. Find area generated by revolving the hypocycloid $x^{\frac{2}{3}} + y^{\frac{2}{3}} = a^{\frac{2}{3}}$ about the x-axis.

8. A circular garden having a diameter of 50 ft. is enclosed by a stone wall. A horse is tied on the outside of the garden to the wall by a rope 50 ft. long. Find the area of the ground the horse can graze over.

Suggestion. The surface grazed over is a semicircle of 50-ft. radius, and two equal areas bounded by the rope, an involute of a circle, and the wall. The angle φ changes from 0 to 2 radians.

CHAPTER XVII

VOLUMES

153. Retrospect.—For one who is trying to master a subject in mathematics and is studying without a teacher, the great danger is that he will not be contented to make progress slowly. He is apt to push on too rapidly and find that his ideas are vague, and that he cannot apply the methods given. It is necessary then to consider again and again the fundamental ideas and the general plan of procedure.

For this reason we again raise the question as to what is the problem of integral calculus. The student must frequently ask this question and answer it clearly in his own mind. He should then fit into this general idea each new phase of the subject and each new application as it occurs.

As has been stated before in somewhat different words, the problem of integral calculus is: Given the relation at all times between the *changes* in two related variables and the exact value of these variables at some particular instant, to find a relation true at all times between the variables themselves. The question now is: Do the problems in finding areas and arc lengths fall under the general class as stated above? They do if one thinks of the relation between the variables as it is expressed before the limits are substituted. After the limits are substituted the result obtained is the value of the *increment* of the dependent variable due to an increment of the independent variable equal to the difference between the limits.

Thus, when we are finding the area between a curve, the x-axis, and two ordinates corresponding to $x = a$ and $x = b$, the independent variable is x and the dependent variable is the area A. As x changes the value of A changes. The area found is really the increment of A when x takes an increment equal to $b - a$.

154. Volume of revolution by means of differentials.— The problem of finding the volume of a solid, in a great variety of cases, falls under the general problem of integral calculus. Whenever a solid can be thought of as generated by a moving surface, and the rate with respect to the

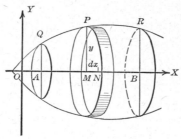

Fig. 111.

independent variable at which the volume is generated can be expressed as a function of that variable, we have a problem in integral calculus.

Many solids, or volumes, can be generated by revolving an area about an axis. Such volumes are called **volumes of revolution.** Thus, a sphere may be generated by the area of a circle being revolved about one of its diameters as an axis. A right circular cone is formed when a right triangular area is revolved about one of the sides, not the hypotenuse, of the triangle.

In all cases a volume of revolution may be thought of as generated by the area of a variable circle moving with its plane

perpendicular to the axis of revolution. **It is from this consideration that the differential of the volume is readily found.**

In Fig. 111, let the curve QPR be represented by $y = f(x)$
a single valued and continuous function of x. Let the area
$ABRQ$ be revolved about OX as an axis generating the
volume as shown.

The volume can be thought of as generated by the area of
a variable circle perpendicular to the x-axis moving toward
the right from the position at A. When it has reached any
position, as M, the rate at which the volume is being generated is determined by its area at that instant together with
the rate at which it is moving.

To find the differential of the volume V, the rate of
change must *become* constant at a particular instant and
remain so while x increases by dx. In this manner the
changes in V and x become and remain uniform. It is
evident then that the differential of the volume is the
volume of a right circular cylinder of radius $MP = y$ and
height $MN = dx$.

$$\therefore \ dV = \pi y^2 dx.$$

The total volume is the volume generated while the circle
is moving from A to B, that is, while x is changing from
$x = OA = a$ to $x = OB = b$. A volume of revolution
formed by revolving an area about the x-axis can therefore
be found by the formula

[58] $$V = \pi \int_a^b y^2 dx.$$

Example 1. Find the volume generated by revolving
the area of the upper half of the circle $x^2 + y^2 = r^2$ about
the x-axis. Check by geometry.

Solution. Given $x^2 + y^2 = r^2$.
Solving for y, $\qquad y = \pm \sqrt{r^2 - x^2}$.

This is a double valued function, but $y = + \sqrt{r^2 - x^2}$ represents the upper half of the circle, Fig. 112, and is

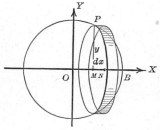

single valued.

The volume formed is twice the volume generated by a circle starting at O and moving toward the right to B. The differential of the volume is represented in the figure when the moving circle has reached M, and is

$$dV = \pi y^2 dx.$$

But $y = \sqrt{r^2 - x^2}$, which must be substituted for y before we can integrate. Also for half the volume x changes from $x = 0$ to $x = r$. Then the total volume is given by

$$V = 2\pi \int_0^r (r^2 - x^2)dx$$
$$= 2\pi (r^2 x - \tfrac{1}{3}x^3)\big]_0^r$$
$$= 2\pi (r^3 - \tfrac{1}{3}r^3) = \tfrac{4}{3}\pi r^3.$$

This is the well-known formula in geometry for the volume of a sphere.

Example 2. A right circular cone has a base with radius r, and an altitude h. Find its volume when thought of as generated by the area of a variable circle moving from its apex to its base.

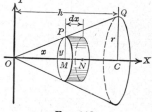

Fig. 113.

Solution. Consider the cone placed with its apex at the origin and its axis on the x-axis extending toward the right as shown in Fig. 113.

The cone is generated by a variable circle moving from O toward C. When the circle has reached some point M

at a distance x from O its radius is y, and the differential of the volume is

$$dV = \pi y^2 dx.$$

Before integrating y must be expressed in terms of x. This can be done from the similar triangles OMP and OCQ.

$$x:y = h:r. \quad \therefore y = \frac{rx}{h}.$$

Substituting this value for y,

$$dV = \pi \frac{r^2 x^2}{h^2} dx.$$

Then $V = \dfrac{\pi r^2}{h^2} \displaystyle\int_0^h x^2 dx$

$$= \frac{\pi r^2}{h^2} \cdot \tfrac{1}{3}x^3\Big]_0^h = \tfrac{1}{3}\pi r^2 h.$$

This agrees with the formula in geometry for finding the volume of a right circular cone.

Example 3. Find the volume generated by revolving about the x-axis the area under the curve $y = \sin x$ from where $x = 0$ to where $x = \pi$.

Solution. The volume generated is shown in Fig. 114.

$$dV = \pi y^2 dx.$$

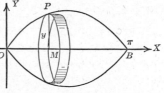

FIG. 114.

But $y = \sin x$, and the limits on x are 0 and π. Then

$$V = \pi \int_0^\pi \sin^2 x \, dx$$
$$= \pi(\tfrac{1}{2}x - \tfrac{1}{2}\cos x \sin x)\Big]_0^\pi$$
$$= \pi(\tfrac{1}{2}\pi - 0) = \tfrac{1}{2}\pi^2.$$

The result $\tfrac{1}{2}\pi^2$ is the number of cubic units in the volume, the unit of volume being a cube OQ on an edge, providing the unit on the x-axis to represent one radian is the length OQ.

155. Volume of revolution by summation.—The volume of a solid formed by revolving an area about an axis can also be found as the limit of a sum. In considering the volume from this viewpoint, we think of the volume as cut into a number of slices by planes perpendicular to the axis of revolution, Fig. 115. Each of these slices is considered a cylinder, and the limit of the sum of the volumes of these cylinders is found as their number increases without limit.

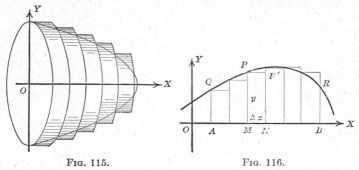

FIG. 115. FIG. 116.

In Fig. 116, let the curve QPR be represented by $y = f(x)$, a single valued continuous function of x. Let the volume be generated by revolving the area $ABRQ$ about the x-axis. Divide the length AB into n equal parts each Δx, and form the rectangles as shown. When revolved about the x-axis each of these rectangles generates a right circular cylinder of altitude Δx, and each having as radius the ordinate at the beginning of that interval.

Consider any one of these rectangles as $MNP'P$. The cylinder generated by it has an altitude Δx and a radius $MP = y$. Its volume is then $\pi y^2 \Delta x$. Of course y is different for the different cylinders, but is always equal to $f(x)$ where x is the abscissa of the point P, that is, $x = OM$.

It is evident that the sum of the volumes of all such cylinders will approximate the volume generated by revolving the area $ABRQ$, and it can be proved that the *limit* of this sum as the number of the cylinders becomes infinite is exactly the volume required.

Letting V = the volume required, $a = OA$, and $b = OB$, and noting that $\Delta x \to 0$ as $n \to \infty$, we have

$$V = \lim_{\Delta x \to 0} \sum_{x=a}^{x=b} \pi y^2 \Delta x.$$

But the limit of a sum can be put equal to a definite integral using the proper limits.

[58] $$\therefore V = \pi \int_a^b y^2 dx.$$

This is simply another means of thinking through the problem of finding a volume of revolution. In the end we use a differential form and find the value of a definite integral. The method has been given because it may be found an easier method than is the method by differentials.

Example. Find the volume formed when the area under the hyperbola $xy = 8$ from $x = 1$ to $x = 8$ is revolved about the x-axis. Think the process through as a summation.

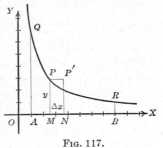

Fig. 117.

Solution. The curve is as shown in Fig. 117, and the volume is generated by revolving $ABRQ$ about OX. One of the cylinders thought of is generated by the rectangle $MNP'P$, and its volume is $\pi y^2 \Delta x$. The volume to be found is given by

$$V = \lim_{\Delta x \to 0} \sum_{x=1}^{x=8} \pi y^2 \Delta x = \pi \int_1^8 y^2 dx.$$

In order to integrate, y must be expressed in terms of x This is done by using the relation given in the equation $xy = 8$. Solving this for y, $y = \dfrac{8}{x}$.

$$\therefore V = \pi \int_1^8 \frac{64}{x^2} dx = 64\pi \int_1^8 x^{-2} dx$$

$$= -64\pi x^{-1}\Big]_1^8 = -64\pi(\tfrac{1}{8} - 1) = 56\pi.$$

Therefore the volume required is 56π cubic units.

EXERCISES

Use the method of differentials or that of summation in solving the following exercises.

1. Find the volume of the sphere generated by revolving the area of the upper half of the circle $x^2 + y^2 = 25$ about the x-axis.

2. Find the volume of a right circular cone with radius of base 4 in., and altitude 12 in. when thought of as generated by a variable circle moving from the vertex to the base.

3. Find the volume generated by revolving the area under one arch of the curve $y = \cos x$ about the x-axis.

4. Find the volume generated by revolving the area under the upper half of the parabola $y^2 = 4x$ from $x = 0$ to $x = 8$, about the x-axis. This is a paraboloid of revolution. Also find the volume when the area between the curve, the y-axis, and from $y = 0$ to $y = 4$, is revolved about the y-axis.

5. Find the volume generated by revolving the area under the catenary $y = \frac{1}{2}a(e^{\frac{x}{a}} + e^{-\frac{x}{a}})$ from $x = -a$ to $x = a$, about the x-axis.

6. Find the volume generated by revolving the area under the parabola $x^2 = 4y$ from $x = 0$ to $x = 4$, about the x-axis.

7. Find the volume generated by revolving the area under one arch of the cycloid $x = a(\theta - \sin \theta)$, $y = a(1 - \cos \theta)$ about the x-axis.

Suggestion. Here $dx = a(1 - \cos \theta)d\theta$, $y = a(1 - \cos \theta)$, and the limits must be taken on θ. At the beginning of the arch $\theta = 0$ and at the end $\theta = 2\pi$.

$$\therefore V = \pi a^3 \int_0^{2\pi} (1 - \cos \theta)^3 \, d\theta.$$

8. A solid ring, called a torus, is generated by revolving the area of the circle $x^2 + (y - b)^2 = a^2$, where $b > a$, about the x-axis. Find the volume of the ring.

Suggestion. The circle is shown in Fig. 118. Its center is on the y-axis where $y = b$, and its radius is a. The volume to be found is equal to the volume generated by the area under the upper half of the circle minus the volume generated by the area under the lower half of the circle.

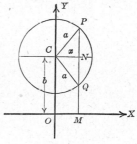

For the upper half of the circle
$$y = MP = MN + NP = b + \sqrt{a^2 - x^2}.$$

For the lower half of the circle

Fig. 118.

$$y = MQ = MN - QN = b - \sqrt{a^2 - x^2}.$$
$$\therefore V = \pi \int_{-a}^{a} (b + \sqrt{a^2 - x^2})^2 \, dx - \pi \int_{-a}^{a} (b - \sqrt{a^2 - x^2})^2 \, dx.$$

9. Find the volume generated by revolving the area of the upper half of the ellipse $\dfrac{x^2}{a^2} + \dfrac{y^2}{b^2} = 1$ about the x-axis. This is an ellipsoid of revolution.

Suggestion. Solving the equation of the ellipse for y,
$$y = +\frac{b}{a}\sqrt{a^2 - x^2}.$$
The limits on x are $-a$ and a.

10. A sphere 24 in. in diameter has a segment cut off by a plane 4 in. from the center. Find the volume of the segment.

156. Volumes not of revolution.—Other solids than those of revolution can often be supposed cut into slices in such a manner that their volumes can be found by taking the limit of the sum of the slices as the number of slices increases without limit.

If the solid represented in Fig. 119 is cut into slices by parallel planes drawn at intervals of Δx, and if the variable A stands for the area of the section of the solid forming the base, as MNP, of any one of the slices, the volume of one of the slices is approximately
$$\Delta V = A \, \Delta x.$$

The total volume of the solid can be approximated by dividing it into a number of such slices, computing the volume of each, and finding their sum.

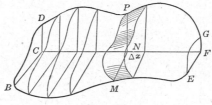

Fig. 119.

The *exact* volume is equal to the limit of the sum of these slices as the number increases without limit. For any solid that can be cut up in this manner the volume is expressed by the formula

$$V = \lim_{n \to \infty} \sum A \Delta x,$$

where the summation is to cover the entire volume.

To actually find the value of this summation it is necessary to determine limiting values for x, and also to express A in terms of x. When this is done the summation can be expressed as a definite integral that can be evaluated.

The definite integral is of the form

$$V = \int_a^b A \, dx,$$

where a and b are the limits on x.

If we had thought through the problem by the method of differentials, exactly the same results would have been found. Thus, the solid shown in Fig. 119 may be thought of as generated by a variable area A starting at BCD and moving toward EFG. At any instant the differential of the volume is $A \, dx$. If $x = a$ at the start and $x = b$ at the finish, the volume is given by

$$V = \int_a^b A \, dx.$$

Here, as before, the integration cannot be performed until A is expressed as a function of x.

157. Applications.—In applying the methods of the preceding article in finding volumes, do not be in too great haste to express the volume in the form of an integral, but try and select the most efficient way for solving the problem. Go about the work in a systematic manner.

First, visualize the solid clearly and make a careful drawing.

Second, consider the different ways in which the solid can be cut into slices, and select the one that seems to be the most easily used.

Third, select an origin from which to measure the variable distance to the slices, and write the area of any slice in terms of this variable distance.

Fourth, express the volume as the limit of a summation and then express as a definite integral.

Fifth, evaluate the integral.

If one solves the problem by differentials, the steps can be carried out in the same order.

A number of particular examples follow and these should be studied very carefully, noting the different methods used and suggested.

Example 1. A right pyramid has an altitude of 12 ft. and a square base 8 ft. on a side. Find its volume by methods of calculus.

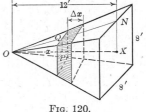

Fig. 120.

Solution by summation. Consider the pyramid cut into slices by planes equally spaced and drawn perpendicular to the altitude, that is, parallel to the base of the pyramid, one slice being shown in Fig. 120. Then the volume is the limit of the sum of these slices as their number increases without limit.

The slice shown in the figure, which may be any slice, has a square face through P. This face has an area equal to $(2PQ)^2$. If the distance of P from the vertex O is x and the thickness of the slice is Δx, the volume of this slice is approximately $(2PQ)^2\Delta x$.

But $PQ : XN = OP : OX$.

Or $PQ : 4 = x : 12$
              $\therefore PQ = \tfrac{1}{3}x$.

Then $V = \displaystyle\lim_{n \to \infty} \sum_{x=0}^{x=12} (\tfrac{2}{3}x)^2\Delta x$

              $= \int_0^{12}(\tfrac{2}{3}x)^2dx = \tfrac{4}{9}\int_0^{12}x^2dx$

              $= \tfrac{4}{27}x^3\Big]_0^{12} = 256.$

Therefore the volume is 256 cu. ft.

This result is readily checked by geometry.

Solution by differentials.   Suppose that the volume of the pyramid is generated by a square starting at O, Fig. 121, and moving toward X keeping perpendicular to OX. At the instant the moving square has reached the point P at a distance x from O, the differential of the volume is the area at that instant times dx. The area is found as in the previous solution and is $(\tfrac{2}{3}x)^2$.

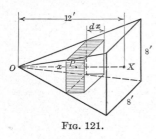

FIG. 121.

Then $dV = (\tfrac{2}{3}x)^2dx$.

        $V = \int_0^{12}(\tfrac{2}{3}x)^2dx = \tfrac{4}{27}x^3\Big]_0^{12} = 256.$

Example 2.   A tree circular in cross section and 36 in. in diameter has a notch made by two planes intersecting at the center. Find the volume removed in cutting the notch

if one of the planes is perpendicular to the axis of the tree
and the other is at an angle of 45° with the first.

First solution. Think of the volume of the notch, shown
in Fig. 122, as generated by the area of a triangle moving
and always being perpendicular to the edge NM. Suppose
that the triangle starts at the center O and moves toward N.
This triangle varies in size but is always a 45° right triangle.
When it has reached any position, as PQR in the figure,

$$PQ = \sqrt{\overline{OQ}^2 - \overline{OP}^2} = \sqrt{18^2 - x^2}.$$

But $\qquad QR = PQ = \sqrt{18^2 - x^2}.$

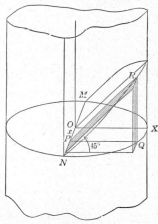

Fig. 122.

Then the area of $PQR = \frac{1}{2}(18^2 - x^2)$.

$$\therefore dV = \frac{1}{2}(18^2 - x^2)dx.$$

The total volume is twice the volume generated while x
is changing from 0 to 18.

$$\therefore V = 2 \int^{18} \frac{1}{2}(18^2 - x^2)dx$$
$$= 324 \int_0^{18} dx - \int_0^{18} x^2 dx$$
$$= (324x - \tfrac{1}{3}x^3)\,\Big]_0^{18} = 3888.$$

Therefore the volume is 3888 cu. in.

Second solution. Think of the volume as generated by a rectangle starting at the line NM and moving toward X, Fig. 123. Then in any position, as $PQRS$ at distance x from O, the area of the rectangle is $PQ \times PS$.

But $PQ = 2PB = 2\sqrt{\overline{OP}^2 - \overline{OB}^2} = 2\sqrt{18^2 - x^2}$.

And $PS = TP = x$.

Then area of $PQRS = 2x\sqrt{18^2 - x^2}$.

$\therefore dV = 2x\sqrt{18^2 - x^2}\,dx.$

$$V = \int_0^{18} 2x\sqrt{18^2 - x^2}\,dx = -\int_0^{18}(18^2 - x^2)^{\frac{1}{2}}(-2x)\,dx$$

$$= -\tfrac{2}{3}(18^2 - x^2)^{\frac{3}{2}}\Big]_0^{18} = -\tfrac{2}{3}(0 - 5832) = 3888.$$

A third solution could be given by thinking of the volume as generated by the segment of a circle starting as a semi-circle at the bottom of the notch and moving upward.

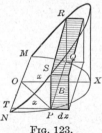

Fig. 123.

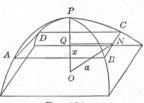

Fig. 124.

Example 3. Two right circular cylinders that each have a radius equal to a, cut each other so that their axes intersect at right angles. Find the volume that is common to the two cylinders.

Solution. One-half of the volume that is common to the two cylinders is shown in Fig. 124. This volume can be thought of as generated by a square starting at the center O where the two axes intersect, moving toward P, and keeping perpendicular to the common radius OP.

When this square has reached any position Q at a distance x from O, its side is $2QN$.

But $\quad QN = \sqrt{\overline{ON}^2 - \overline{OQ}^2} = \sqrt{a^2 - x^2}.$

Then area of square $ABCD = (2\sqrt{a^2 - x^2})^2$
$$= 4(a^2 - x^2).$$
$$\therefore dV = 4(a^2 - x^2)dx.$$

In generating the volume shown in the figure x changes from 0 to a. Using these limits,

$$V = \int_0^a 4(a^2 - x^2)dx = 4a^2 \int_0^a dx - 4\int_0^a x^2 dx$$
$$= (4a^2x - \tfrac{4}{3}x^3) \Big]_0^a = \tfrac{8}{3}a^3.$$

The total volume is therefore $\tfrac{16}{3}\ a^3$.

EXERCISES

1. A tree 24 in. in diameter has a notch cut to the center. Find the volume of the wood removed if the lower face of the notch is horizontal and the upper face makes an angle of 45° with the lower face.

2. Solve for the same as in exercise 1 except that the upper face of the notch makes an angle of 60° with the lower.

3. A gasoline tank in the form of a right circular cylinder lies on an incline so that when the surface of the gasoline reaches the center of one end it is tangent at the lower edge of the other end. If the tank is 8 ft. long and 4 ft. in diameter, find the number of gallons of gasoline in the tank.

4. A piece of wood in the form of a right circular cylinder 24 in. long and 4 in. in diameter is made into a wedge by cutting away the wood so that the two faces of the wedge are planes intersecting along a diameter at one end and are tangent to the circle forming the other end. Find the volume of the wedge.

5. Find the volume of the solid generated by an isosceles triangle of altitude 10 in., moving so that the center of its base moves along the diameter of a circle whose radius is 6 in., and the ends of the base are in the circle the triangle always keeping perpendicular to this diameter.

Suggestion.   The solid generated is shown in Fig. 125.

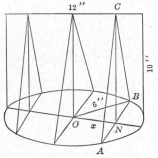

Fig. 125.

The area of the generating triangle at any position ABC, at a distance x from the center is $10\ NB$.

But $NB = \sqrt{\overline{OB}^2 - \overline{ON}^2} = \sqrt{6^2 - x^2}$.

Then $dV = 10\sqrt{6^2 - x^2}\ dx$.

6. Find the volume included between two right circular cylinders each of radius 12 in., whose axes intersect at right angles.

CHAPTER XVIII

FUNCTIONS OF SEVERAL VARIABLES. PARTIAL DIFFERENTIATION

158. More than one independent variable.—Thus far in our study we have considered only functions that depended upon a single independent variable. Always to confine the discussion to such functions is to disregard a large class of functions where more than one independent variable is involved. In fact, quantities that are considered in affairs that are of common occurrence are usually dependent upon several influences which may or may not be independent of each other. The reader who wishes to put himself into a receptive attitude toward the subject we are to deal with, will do well to think over several cases where a quantity depends upon several variables. One can readily think of many such examples.

Thus, the range of a projectile fired from a gun depends upon the weight of the projectile, the angle of elevation of the gun, the resistance of the air, the direction of the wind, the muzzle velocity, and many other conditions. As a second illustration, consider the rate of motion of a man walking on a moving train upon the earth that is revolving and moving around the sun which in turn has a motion through space. As another illustration, think of the very large number of conditions that influence the rate at which a workman in a shop will turn out a certain piece of work. It will depend upon the individual worker, his temperament, skill, health, strength, habits, fatigue, etc. It will depend

upon the surrounding conditions, such as light, heat, venti-
lation, and safety.   It will depend upon tools and equipment and the condition in which these are kept.   Other
influences can be mentioned almost at pleasure, as production
methods and quality of materials used.

Problems dealing with many variables become very
complicated, and the tendency is always to reduce the
number of variables as much as possible and still obtain
results sufficiently accurate.   In doing this the variables
that have minor influence are disregarded.   This is done
by a person when he uses such an expression as, "This will
happen thus, other things being equal."   For simplicity,
the questions considered in this chapter will be confined,
usually, to functions of but two independent variables.

It now remains to decide upon a notation for differentials
and derivatives where there are several independent variables, and to find out how to determine these differentials
and derivatives.

159. Partial differentials and derivatives.   How denoted.
If x and y are independent variables and z a variable
dependent upon them, then, in

$$z = f(x, y),$$

x may be supposed to vary while y remains constant, y
may be supposed to vary while x remains constant, or both
x and y may vary simultaneously.   For these cases we shall
agree upon the following notation:

(1) When y remains constant and x varies.

$\Delta_x z$ is the increment of z due to an increment Δx of x.

$\lim\limits_{\Delta x \to 0} \left[\dfrac{\Delta_x z}{\Delta x} \right] = \dfrac{\partial z}{\partial x}$ is the partial derivative of z with respect

to x. $\dfrac{\partial z}{\partial x}$ is also represented by $\dfrac{\partial}{\partial x} f(x, y)$ or by $\dfrac{\partial f}{\partial x}$.

$d_x z$ is the partial differential of z corresponding to dx.
It follows from **Art. 51** that $d_x z = \dfrac{\partial z}{\partial x} dx$.

(2) When x remains constant and y varies.

$\Delta_y z$ is the increment of z due to an increment Δy of y.

$\displaystyle \lim_{\Delta y \to 0} \left[\dfrac{\Delta_y z}{\Delta y} \right] = \dfrac{\partial z}{\partial y}$ is the partial derivative of z with respect to y. $\dfrac{\partial z}{\partial y}$ is also represented by $\dfrac{\partial}{\partial y} f(x, y)$ or by $\dfrac{\partial f}{\partial y}$.

$d_y z$ is the partial differential of z corresponding to dy.
It follows from **Art. 51** that $d_y z = \dfrac{\partial z}{\partial y} dy$.

(3) When x and y vary simultaneously, dz represents the differential of z due to a variation in both x and y, and is called the **total differential** of z. It is equal to the sum of $d_x z$ and $d_y z$.

It is evident that both x and y may be considered as varying or there may be successive derivatives with respect to either. The following are some of the further notations used.

$\dfrac{\partial^2 z}{\partial x^2} = \dfrac{\partial}{\partial x} \left(\dfrac{\partial z}{\partial x} \right)$ is the second partial derivative of z with respect to x.

$\dfrac{\partial^2 z}{\partial y^2} = \dfrac{\partial}{\partial y} \left(\dfrac{\partial z}{\partial y} \right)$ is the second partial derivative of z with respect to y.

$\dfrac{\partial^2 z}{\partial y\, \partial x} = \dfrac{\partial}{\partial y} \left(\dfrac{\partial z}{\partial x} \right)$ is the second partial derivative of z first with respect to x and second with respect to y.

$\dfrac{\partial^2 z}{\partial x\, \partial y} = \dfrac{\partial}{\partial x} \left(\dfrac{\partial z}{\partial y} \right)$ is the second partial derivative of z first with respect to y and second with respect to x.

The round d written ∂ was introduced by Jacobi who lived from 1804 to 1851, and is used when the meaning would not otherwise be clear.

It is evident that this notation applies to other letters, and could be readily extended to more than two independent variables.

160. Partial differentiation.—No new rules are necessary for finding partial derivatives or partial differentials. All that is necessary when finding the partial derivative or partial differential with respect to one of the independent variables is to consider the other as constant.

Example 1.   Given $z = x^2 + xy + y^2$, find $\dfrac{\partial z}{\partial x}$, $\dfrac{\partial z}{\partial y}$, $d_x z$, $d_y z$, and dz.

Solution. $\dfrac{\partial z}{\partial x} = 2x + y$, considering y constant.

$$\frac{\partial z}{\partial y} = x + 2y, \text{ considering } x \text{ constant.}$$

$$d_x z = \frac{\partial z}{\partial x} dx = (2x + y)dx.$$

$$d_y z = \frac{\partial z}{\partial y} dy = (x + 2y)dy.$$

$$dz = d_x z + d_y z = (2x + y)dx + (x + 2y)dy.$$

Example 2.   Given $z = \cos(ax + by)$, find $\dfrac{\partial z}{\partial x}$ and $\dfrac{\partial z}{\partial y}$.

Solution. $\dfrac{\partial z}{\partial x} = -a \sin(ax + by)$, considering y constant.

$$\frac{\partial z}{\partial y} = -b \sin(ax + by), \text{ considering } x \text{ constant.}$$

Example 3.   Given $pv = k\theta$, where v is the dependent variable, p and θ the independent variables, and k a constant. Find $\dfrac{\partial v}{\partial p}$ and $\dfrac{\partial v}{\partial \theta}$.

Solution.   Given $pv = k\theta$.

Solving for v, $v = \dfrac{k\theta}{p}$.

Differentiating, $\dfrac{\partial v}{\partial p} = -\dfrac{k\theta}{p^2}$, considering θ constant.

Differentiating, $\dfrac{\partial v}{\partial \theta} = \dfrac{k}{p}$, considering p constant.

The partial derivatives can also be found from the implicit function

$$pv = k\theta.$$

Differentiating, $p\dfrac{\partial v}{\partial p} + v = 0$, considering θ constant.

$$\therefore \frac{\partial v}{\partial p} = -\frac{v}{p} = -\frac{k\theta}{p^2}.$$

Differentiating, $\qquad p\dfrac{\partial v}{\partial \theta} = k$, considering p constant.

$$\therefore \frac{\partial v}{\partial \theta} = \frac{k}{p}.$$

Example 4. Given $z = e^{xy}$, find $\dfrac{\partial^2 z}{\partial x^2}, \dfrac{\partial^2 z}{\partial y^2}, \dfrac{\partial^2 z}{\partial y\,\partial x}$, and $\dfrac{\partial^2 z}{\partial x\,\partial y}$.

Solution. $\qquad \dfrac{\partial z}{\partial x} = ye^{xy}$, and $\dfrac{\partial^2 z}{\partial x^2} = \dfrac{\partial}{\partial x}\left(\dfrac{\partial z}{\partial x}\right) = y^2 e^{xy}.$

$$\frac{\partial z}{\partial y} = xe^{xy}, \text{ and } \frac{\partial^2 z}{\partial y^2} = \frac{\partial}{\partial y}\left(\frac{\partial z}{\partial y}\right) = x^2 e^{xy}.$$

$$\frac{\partial^2 z}{\partial y\,\partial x} = \frac{\partial}{\partial y}\left(\frac{\partial z}{\partial x}\right) = \frac{\partial}{\partial y}\left(ye^{xy}\right)$$

$$= y\frac{\partial}{\partial y}\left(e^{xy}\right) + e^{xy}\frac{\partial y}{\partial y}$$

$$= xye^{xy} + e^{xy} = (xy+1)e^{xy}.$$

$$\frac{\partial^2 z}{\partial x\,\partial y} = \frac{\partial}{\partial x}\left(\frac{\partial z}{\partial y}\right) = \frac{\partial}{\partial x}\left(xe^{xy}\right)$$

$$= x\frac{\partial}{\partial x}\left(e^{xy}\right) + e^{xy}\frac{\partial x}{\partial x}$$

$$= xye^{xy} + e^{xy} = (xy+1)e^{xy}.$$

EXERCISES

Find $\dfrac{\partial z}{\partial x}, \dfrac{\partial z}{\partial y}, d_x z, d_y z$, and dz of exercises 1 and 2, and the partial derivatives in the exercises 3 – 8.

1. $z = xy.$

2. $z = \sin (ax + by).$

3. $z = 3x^2 + 4xy + 2y^2.$

4. $z = x^3y^2 - 2xy^4 + 3x^2y^3.$

5. $u = e^x \sin y.$

6. $u = e^y \cos x.$

7. $z = x^{\log y}.$

8. $z = \log (e^x + e^y).$

9. If $z = x^2 - y^2$, show that $\dfrac{\partial^2 z}{\partial x^2} + \dfrac{\partial^2 z}{\partial y^2} = 0.$

10. If $z = \sqrt{x^2 + y^2}$, show that $\dfrac{\partial^2 z}{\partial y\, \partial x} = \dfrac{\partial^2 z}{\partial x\, \partial y}.$

161. Interpretation of partial differentials and derivatives.—Agreeing with the definition of the differential of a dependent variable, **Art. 49**, the differential of z if x is the only independent variable considered as varying, $d_x z$, is what would be its increment, if at the corresponding values considered its change became and remained uniform with respect to x.

A similar interpretation is given for $d_y z$.

Likewise, agreeing with the definition and discussion of a derivative, the partial derivative of z with respect to x, $\dfrac{\partial z}{\partial x}$, expresses the rate of change of z with respect to x if x is the only independent variable considered as varying.

A similar interpretation is given for $\dfrac{\partial z}{\partial y}$.

As an illustration, consider the changes in the area of a rectangle due to a variation in the length of each side separately and when varying together.

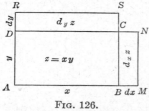
FIG. 126.

In Fig. 126, let $ABCD$ be a variable rectangle of variable base x and variable altitude y, and area $z = xy$.

If y is considered constant while x increases by $BM = dx$, the corresponding change in z is $BMNC = d_x z$.

If x is considered constant while y increases by $DR = dy$, the corresponding change in z is $DCSR = d_y z$.

The total differential of z is

$$BMNC + DCSR = d_x z + d_y z = dz.$$

Further, starting with the equation $z = xy$,

$$\frac{\partial z}{\partial x} = y.$$

$\therefore d_x z = \dfrac{\partial z}{\partial x} dx = y\, dx$, which is the area of $BMNC$.

Likewise, $\dfrac{\partial z}{\partial y} = x.$

$\therefore d_y z = \dfrac{\partial z}{\partial y} dy = x\, dy$, which is the area of $DCSR$.

Example 1.   The total area T of a right circular cone is given by the formula $T = \pi r s + \pi r^2$, where $s =$ slant height and $r =$ radius of base.   Find the rate of change of T with respect to r when s remains constant.

Solution.   Given $T = \pi r s + \pi r^2$.

Differentiating, $\dfrac{\partial T}{\partial r} = \pi s + 2\pi r$, considering s constant.

162. The total derivative.—Since the total differential of $z = f(x, y)$ is

$$dz = \frac{\partial z}{\partial x} dx + \frac{\partial z}{\partial y} dy.$$

if x and y and therefore z are functions of another variable t, by dividing by dt

$$\frac{dz}{dt} = \frac{\partial z}{\partial x}\frac{dx}{dt} + \frac{\partial z}{\partial y}\frac{dy}{dt}.$$

This is the **total derivative** of z with respect to t.   Evidently $\dfrac{dx}{dt}$ and $\dfrac{dy}{dt}$ can be considered as derivatives and represent the rates of change of x and y, respectively, with respect to t.

Example 1.   The variable right triangle, Fig. 127, has a base x, altitude y, and hypotenuse z.   If x is increasing at the rate of 2 in. a minute, and y at the rate of 3 in. a minute, find the rate at which z is changing when $x = 8$ in. and $y = 6$ in.

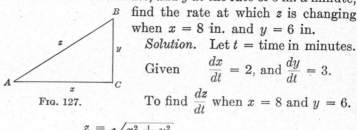

FIG. 127.

Solution.   Let t = time in minutes.

Given $\dfrac{dx}{dt} = 2$, and $\dfrac{dy}{dt} = 3$.

To find $\dfrac{dz}{dt}$ when $x = 8$ and $y = 6$.

$$z = \sqrt{x^2 + y^2}.$$
$$\frac{\partial z}{\partial x} = \frac{x}{\sqrt{x^2 + y^2}}, \quad \frac{\partial z}{\partial y} = \frac{y}{\sqrt{x^2 + y^2}}.$$
$$\frac{dz}{dt} = \frac{\partial z}{\partial x}\frac{dx}{dt} + \frac{\partial z}{\partial y}\frac{dy}{dt}$$
$$= \frac{8}{\sqrt{8^2 + 6^2}} \times 2 + \frac{6}{\sqrt{8^2 + 6^2}} \times 3 = 3.4.$$

Hence at the instant when $x = 8$ and $y = 6$, the hypotenuse is increasing at the rate of 3.4 in. a minute.

Example 2.   Given the formula for a gas $pv = k\theta$, where p is pressure in pounds per square unit, v is volume in corresponding cubic units, θ is absolute temperature, and k is a constant.   If $k = 40$, and at a certain instant $v = 10$ cu. ft. and $\theta = 300$ degrees, find p.   If at this instant the volume is increasing at 0.4 cu. ft. a minute, and the temperature is increasing at 0.5 deg. a minute, find the rate at which the pressure is changing.

Solution.   Substituting $k = 40$, $v = 10$, and $\theta = 300$ in $pv = k\theta$,

$$10p = 40 \times 300. \quad \therefore \ p = 1200.$$

At the instant considered it is given that

$$\frac{dv}{dt} = 0.4, \text{ and } \frac{d\theta}{dt} = 0.5.$$

To find $\dfrac{dp}{dt}$ at the instant considered.

From the equation $p = \dfrac{40\theta}{v}$.

$$\frac{\partial p}{\partial \theta} = \frac{40}{v}, \quad \frac{\partial p}{\partial v} = -\frac{40\theta}{v^2}.$$

$$\frac{dp}{dt} = \frac{\partial p}{\partial \theta}\frac{d\theta}{dt} + \frac{\partial p}{\partial v}\frac{dv}{dt}$$

$$= \frac{40}{10} \times 0.5 + \left(-\frac{40 \times 300}{10^2} \times 0.4\right) = -46.$$

Hence the pressure is decreasing at the rate of 46 pounds per square foot each minute.

EXERCISES

1. A right circular cone has a variable altitude h and a variable radius of base r. Given volume $V = \frac{1}{3}\pi r^2 h$, find $\dfrac{\partial V}{\partial r}$ and $\dfrac{\partial V}{\partial h}$.

2. In an electric circuit where $I = $ current, $E = $ voltage, and $R = $ resistance, $I = \dfrac{E}{R}$. Find $\dfrac{\partial I}{\partial E}$ and $\dfrac{\partial I}{\partial R}$, and explain their meanings.

3. In a right triangle of variable base x, variable hypotenuse z, and variable angle θ between x and z, find $\dfrac{\partial z}{\partial x}$ and $\dfrac{\partial z}{\partial \theta}$, if $z = x \sec \theta$.

4. As in example 2, suppose $k = 50$, and at a given instant $v = 5$ cu. ft., $\theta = 275$ degrees, volume is increasing at a rate of 0.3 cu. ft. a minute, and temperature is increasing at a rate of 0.2 deg. a minute, find the rate of change of the pressure in pounds per square foot a minute.

5. In a variable right circular cone at a certain instant the altitude is 50 in. and is decreasing at the rate of 2 in. a second, the radius of the base is 10 in. and is increasing at the rate of 5 in. a second. Find the rate at which the volume is changing.

Suggestion. Let V, h, and r be the volume, altitude, and radius, respectively, in inches; and t the time in seconds.

$$\frac{dh}{dt} = -2, \quad \frac{dr}{dt} = 5.$$

To find $\dfrac{dV}{dt}$ when $h = 50$ and $r = 10$.

$$V = \tfrac{1}{3}\pi r^2 h.$$
$$\frac{\partial V}{\partial r} = \tfrac{2}{3}\pi r h, \quad \frac{\partial V}{\partial h} = \tfrac{1}{3}\pi r^2.$$

163. Graph of equation of three variables.—In order to understand the geometrical significance of certain partial derivatives it is necessary to know how to graph an equation

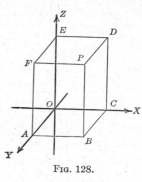

Fig. 128.

of three variables. Just as an equation in two variables gives a curve when plotted with reference to rectangular axes, so an equation of three variables gives a surface. But in order to plot three variables we must have three coördinate axes. These are drawn as shown in Fig. 128, and are named x-axis, y-axis, and z-axis, respectively. Each is perpendicular to the plane determined by the other two.

The three planes determined by the three axes taken two at a time are named from the axes that determine them. They are the **xy-plane,** the **xz-plane,** and the **yz-plane,** together they are called the **coördinate planes.** The coördinate planes divide the space about the origin into eight parts called **octants.** The first octant is the one to the right of the yz-plane, in front of the xz-plane, and above the xy-plane.

If the equation to be plotted is $z = f(x, y)$, for any values given to x and y, as x_1 and y_1, a value of z_1 of z is found, and this value of z measured from the xy-plane determines a point P_1 in the surface, Fig. 129. By giving different pairs of values to x and y, as many points can be located in the surface as desired.

If the same value x_1 is given to x while y is given a series of different values, the points thus determined in the surface will lie on a curve RP_1Q, Fig. 129, that is parallel to the *yz*-plane. If the same value y_1 is given to y while x is given a series of different values, the points thus determined in the surface will lie in a curve TP_1S that is parallel to the *xz*-plane.

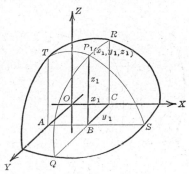

FIG. 129.

Example. Determine the surface represented in the first octant by the equation $x^2 + y^2 + z^2 = 25$.

A fairly clear idea of the surface can be obtained by determining the intersection of the surface with each of the coördinate planes. This is done by putting successively x, y, and z equal to zero and noting the form of each of the resulting equations.

If $x = 0$, the equation becomes

$$y^2 + z^2 = 25,$$

which is a circle of radius 5. Hence the intersection of the surface with the *yz*-plane is a circle of radius 5.

In a similar manner, if $y = 0$, we obtain the equation

$$x^2 + z^2 = 25,$$

a circle of radius 5 in the *xz*-plane; and if $z = 0$, we obtain the equation

$$x^2 + y^2 = 25,$$

a circle of radius 5 in the *xy*-plane.

From this information one may feel fairly certain that the surface is a sphere, but further evidence can be obtained by giving x, y, and z in turn certain values and finding the curves traced as the other two vary. Thus, if $x = 3$,

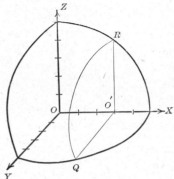

$$y^2 + z^2 = 16,$$

which is a circle of radius 4. This means that the curve traced on the surface when $x = 3$ is a circle. Likewise a circle will be traced on the surface for any other value of x between 0 and 5.

Similar conclusions are drawn if y or z is given any value between 0 and 5.

The portion of the surface lying in the first octant is shown in Fig. 130. This is one-eighth of a sphere of radius 5 with its center at the origin.

Fig. 130.

164. Geometrical interpretation of first partial derivatives.— Given $z = f(x, y)$ a continuous function of which the portion of the surface in the first octant is shown in Fig. 131. If x varies while y remains fixed, say equal to b, the curve APB is traced on the surface. If y varies while x remains fixed, say equal to a, the curve CPD is traced on the surface.

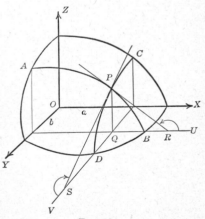

Fig. 131.

It is perhaps evident, and can be shown by a discussion similar to that of **Art. 14,** if we mean by slope the tangent of the angle which the tangent line makes with the xy-plane, that

$$\frac{\partial z}{\partial x} = \text{slope of } PR,$$

and

$$\frac{\partial z}{\partial y} = \text{slope of } PS.$$

Similar interpretations hold for $\frac{\partial y}{\partial x}, \frac{\partial y}{\partial z}$ and for $\frac{\partial x}{\partial y}, \frac{\partial x}{\partial z}$.

Example. Find the slopes of the tangents respectively parallel to the xz-plane and the yz-plane, to the sphere

$$x^2 + y^2 + z^2 = 25.$$

at the point where $x = 3$ and $y = 2$ in the first octant.

Solution. Given $x^2 + y^2 + z^2 = 25$.

Solving for z, $\quad z = \sqrt{25 - x^2 - y^2}$.

Finding the partial derivative with respect to x,

$$\frac{\partial z}{\partial x} = \frac{-x}{\sqrt{25 - x^2 - y^2}}.$$

Finding the partial derivative with respect to y,

$$\frac{\partial z}{\partial y} = \frac{-y}{\sqrt{25 - x^2 - y^2}}.$$

When $x = 3$ and $y = 2$,

$$\frac{\partial z}{\partial x} = \frac{-3}{\sqrt{25 - 3^2 - 2^2}} = -\frac{3}{\sqrt{12}} = -\tfrac{1}{2}\sqrt{3} = -0.866$$

$$\frac{\partial z}{\partial y} = \frac{-2}{\sqrt{25 - 3^2 - 2^2}} = -\frac{2}{\sqrt{12}} = -\tfrac{1}{3}\sqrt{3} = -0.577.$$

The meaning of these is seen in Fig. 131, where the slope of PR is -0.866, and the slope of PS is -0.577.

The slopes of these lines are put to use in finding the angle which the tangent plane determined by these lines makes with the xy-plane. Before taking up this question we will consider a problem in trigonometry, which is simple and useful but not ordinarily given in the texts.

165. A problem in trigonometry.—*Example.* Two vertical planes at right angles to each other intersect a third

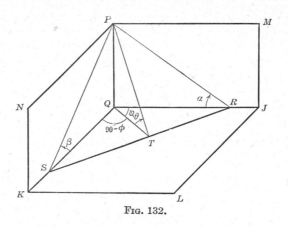

Fig. 132.

plane that is inclined at an unknown angle θ to a horizontal plane. If the intersections of the vertical planes with the third plane make angles of α and β respectively with the horizontal plane, find the secant of θ.

Solution. In Fig. 132, QM and QN are the vertical planes at right angles to each other, and SRP is the inclined plane intersecting QL, the horizontal plane, in the line SR. The angle QTP is the plane angle of the dihedral angle that the plane SRP makes with the plane QL and is the angle θ to be found.

Let angle $RQT = \varphi$, then angle $SQT = 90° - \varphi$.

By geometry we know that both QT and PT are perpendicular to SR.

Then $\qquad \cos \varphi = \dfrac{QT}{QR}.$

But $\qquad QT = \dfrac{QP}{\tan \theta}$, and $QR = \dfrac{QP}{\tan \alpha}.$

Hence $\qquad \cos \varphi = \dfrac{\tan \alpha}{\tan \theta}.$ $\qquad\qquad$ (1)

Also $\cos (90° - \varphi) = \sin \varphi = \dfrac{QT}{QS}.$

But $\qquad QT = \dfrac{QP}{\tan \theta}$, and $QS = \dfrac{QP}{\tan \beta}.$

Hence $\qquad \sin \varphi = \dfrac{\tan \beta}{\tan \theta}.$ $\qquad\qquad$ (2)

Squaring and adding (1) and (2),

$$\cos^2 \varphi + \sin^2 \varphi = \frac{\tan^2 \alpha + \tan^2 \beta}{\tan^2 \theta}.$$

Or $\qquad\qquad 1 = \dfrac{\tan^2 \alpha + \tan^2 \beta}{\tan^2 \theta}.$

$$\therefore \tan^2 \theta = \tan^2 \alpha + \tan^2 \beta.$$

Since $\sec^2 \theta = 1 + \tan^2 \theta$ by trigonometry,

$$\sec^2 \theta = 1 + \tan^2 \alpha + \tan^2 \beta.$$
$$\therefore \sec \theta = \sqrt{1 + \tan^2 \alpha + \tan^2 \beta}.$$

Note. The formula $\tan^2 \theta = \tan^2 \alpha + \tan^2 \beta$ is used by geologists and others in determining the dip, that is, the angle of inclination, of a stratum of rock.

166. Inclination of the tangent plane to a coördinate plane.—Fig. 133 is the same as Fig. 131 with the tangent at the point P represented. Now the tangent plane, the horizontal plane, and the two planes in which the tangents lie fulfill the conditions of the example of the previous article.   It follows at once then that

$$\sec \theta = \sqrt{1 + \tan^2 \alpha + \tan^2 \beta}.$$

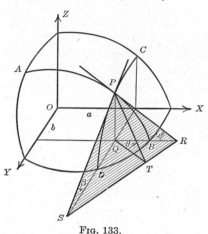

Fig. 133.

But $\tan^2 \alpha = \left(\dfrac{\partial z}{\partial x}\right)^2$ and $\tan^2 \beta = \left(\dfrac{\partial z}{\partial y}\right)^2$.   **Art. 164.**

$$\therefore \sec \theta = \sqrt{1 + \left(\frac{\partial z}{\partial x}\right)^2 + \left(\frac{\partial z}{\partial y}\right)^2},$$

where θ is the angle the tangent plane makes with the xy-plane.

It should be noted that the partial derivatives for the illustration given here are both negative as they are the tangents of the supplements of α and β, but whether they are positive or negative their squares are the same.

Similarly, when θ is the angle the tangent plane makes with the xz-plane,

$$\sec \theta = \sqrt{1 + \left(\frac{\partial y}{\partial x}\right)^2 + \left(\frac{\partial y}{\partial z}\right)^2};$$

and when θ is the angle the tangent plane makes with the yz-plane,

$$\sec \theta = \sqrt{1 + \left(\frac{\partial x}{\partial y}\right)^2 + \left(\frac{\partial x}{\partial z}\right)^2}.$$

Example 1. Use the numerical values of the example of **Art. 164,** and find $\sec \theta$.

Substituting in the formula,

$$\sec \theta = \sqrt{1 + (-\tfrac{1}{2}\sqrt{3})^2 + (-\tfrac{1}{3}\sqrt{3})^2}$$
$$= \sqrt{1 + \tfrac{3}{4} + \tfrac{1}{3}} = \tfrac{5}{6}\sqrt{3} = 1.443.$$

Example 2. Find $\sec \theta$ for the paraboloid $y^2 + z^2 = 4x$ if the plane is tangent at the point in the first octant where $x = 4$ and $y = 2$.

Solution. Given $y^2 + z^2 = 4x$.

Solving for z, $z = \sqrt{4x - y^2}$.

Differentiating, $\dfrac{\partial z}{\partial x} = \dfrac{2}{\sqrt{4x - y^2}}, \dfrac{\partial z}{\partial y} = \dfrac{-y}{\sqrt{4x - y^2}}.$

At the point where $x = 4$ and $y = 2$,

$$\sec \theta = \sqrt{1 + \frac{4}{16 - 4} + \frac{4}{16 - 4}} = \tfrac{1}{3}\sqrt{15}.$$

EXERCISES

1. Given the equation of the sphere $x^2 + y^2 + z^2 = 36$, put $y = 2$ and thus find the equation of the circle formed by the intersection of a plane 2 units in front of the xz-plane with the sphere. Find the circle formed by the intersection of the plane $x = 3$ with the sphere. By the plane $z = 4$. By the xy-plane.

2. Discuss the equation $\dfrac{x^2}{25} + \dfrac{y^2}{16} + \dfrac{z^2}{16} = 1$, and draw the surface that lies in the first octant. Such a surface is an ellipsoid of revolution.

3. Given the sphere whose equation is $x^2 + y^2 + z^2 = 36$, find the slope of the tangent lines parallel respectively to the xz-plane and the yz-plane and at the point in the surface in the first octant where $x = 4$

and $y = 3$.   Compute the secant of the angle the tangent plane at this point makes with the xy-plane.

Discuss each of the following equations and draw the portion of the surface of each lying in the first octant.

   4. $y^2 + z^2 = 4x$.

   5. $x^2 + y^2 = 4z$.

   6. $x^2 + z^2 = 4y$.

   7. Find the secant of the angle the tangent plane to the surface $x^2 + z^2 = 4y$ at the point where $z = 2$ and $x = 2$ in the first octant, makes with the xz-plane.

CHAPTER XIX

DOUBLE AND TRIPLE INTEGRATION. SURFACES, VOLUMES

167. Successive integration.—In **Art. 39** the second derivative of a function was found. In a similar manner third and higher derivatives can be found successively. The inverse process is called **successive integration.** An illustration of this occurred in the solution of exercise 35, page 114.

Example 1. Given $\dfrac{d^2y}{dx^2} = 2$, find y.

Solution. Since $\dfrac{d^2y}{dx^2}$ is the derivative of $\dfrac{dy}{dx}$ with respect to x,

$$\frac{d^2y}{dx^2} = \frac{d}{dx}\left(\frac{dy}{dx}\right) = 2.$$

Multiplying by dx, $d\left(\dfrac{dy}{dx}\right) = 2dx$.

Integrating, $\qquad\qquad \dfrac{dy}{dx} = 2x + C_1.$

Multiplying by dx, $\qquad dy = 2x\ dx + C_1 dx.$
Integrating, $\qquad\qquad y = x^2 + C_1 x + C_2.$

For any particular values of C_1 and C_2, this is the equation of a parabola with its axis parallel to the y-axis and extending upward. If all possible values are given to C_1 and C_2, all such parabolas are found.

From previous experience in determining the constants of integration we should expect that two other facts about the curve would be necessary in order to find definite values for C_1 and C_2. Suppose that these facts are that the curve shall pass through the points $(2, 1)$ and $(-2, -3)$.

Substituting $(2, 1)$ in $y = x^2 + C_1 x + C_2$, gives

$$1 = 4 + 2C_1 + C_2.$$

Substituting $(-2, -3)$, gives

$$-3 = 4 - 2C_1 + C_2.$$

Solving these equations for C_1 and C_2,

$$C_1 = 1, \text{ and } C_2 = -5.$$

Substituting these values in $y = x^2 + C_1 x + C_2$ gives the equation of a definite parabola,

$$y = x^2 + x - 5.$$

In this example it is seen that

$$\frac{dy}{dx} = \int 2 \, dx,$$

and

$$y = \int (\int 2 \, dx) dx.$$

This is also written

$$y = \int \int 2 \, dx \, dx.$$

Similarly any number of successive integrations may be indicated.

Example 2.   Find y if $y = \int \int \int x^2 dx \, dx \, dx$.

Solution.   Integrating successively and noting that there is an arbitrary constant for each integration,

$$
\begin{aligned}
y &= \int \int \int x^2 dx \, dx \, dx \\
&= \int \int (\tfrac{1}{3} x^3 + C_1) dx \, dx \\
&= \int (\tfrac{1}{12} x^4 + C_1 x + C_2) dx \\
&= \tfrac{1}{60} x^5 + \tfrac{1}{2} C_1 x^2 + C_2 x + C_3.
\end{aligned}
$$

If the successive integrations are performed between limits, the constants of integration do not appear.

Example 3.   Evaluate $\int_0^2 \int_1^3 \int_1^2 2x \, dx \, dx \, dx$.

Solution. $\int_0^2 \int_1^3 \int_1^2 2x \; dx \; dx \; dx = \int_0^2 \int_1^3 x^2 \Big]_1^2 \; dx \; dx$

$$= \int_0^2 \int_1^3 3 \; dx \; dx = \int_0^2 3x \Big]_1^3 \; dx$$

$$= \int_0^2 6 \; dx = 6x \Big]_0^2 = 12.$$

Successive integration is employed in finding the equations of the elastic curves of beams under loads. The meanings of the constants used in such equations will not be explained here, but they may be found in any text on mechanics. In such equations, E is the modulus of elasticity, I is the moment of inertia (**Art. 178**) of a cross section of the beam about a gravity axis in the section perpendicular to the applied force, and l is the length of the beam.

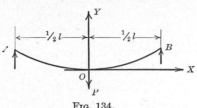

Fig. 134.

Example 4. Find the equation of the elastic curve of a beam supposed weightless, supported at its ends, and having a weight P at its middle point. For such a beam the differential equation is

$$EI\frac{d^2y}{dx^2} = \tfrac{1}{2}P(\tfrac{1}{2}l - x),$$

when the coördinate axes are as shown in Fig. 134.

Solution. Given $EI\frac{d^2y}{dx^2} = \tfrac{1}{2}P(\tfrac{1}{2}l - x)$.

Note that E, I, P, and l are constants, and divide by EI. This gives

$$\frac{d^2y}{dx^2} = \frac{Pl}{4EI} - \frac{P}{2EI}x.$$

Or $\qquad \frac{d}{dx}\Big(\frac{dy}{dx}\Big) = \frac{Pl}{4EI} - \frac{P}{2EI}x.$

Multiplying by dx, $d\left(\dfrac{dy}{dx}\right) = \dfrac{Pl}{4EI}dx - \dfrac{P}{2EI}x\,dx.$

Integrating, $\dfrac{dy}{dx} = \dfrac{Pl}{4EI}x - \dfrac{P}{4EI}x^2 + C_1.$

Multiplying by dx, $dy = \dfrac{Pl}{4EI}x\,dx - \dfrac{P}{4EI}x^2dx + C_1\,dx.$

Integrating, $y = \dfrac{Pl}{8EI}x^2 - \dfrac{P}{12EI}x^3 + C_1x + C_2.$

To find the constants of integration C_1 and C_2, notice that the slope, $\dfrac{dy}{dx}$, of the curve is zero at the point $(0, 0)$, and that the curve passes through the point $(0, 0)$.

Substituting $\dfrac{dy}{dx} = 0$ and $x = 0$ in

$$\frac{dy}{dx} = \frac{Pl}{4EI}x - \frac{P}{4EI}x^2 + C_1,$$

$$0 = 0 - 0 + C_1. \quad \therefore\ C_1 = 0.$$

Substituting $x = 0$ and $y = 0$ in

$$y = \frac{Pl}{8EI}x^2 - \frac{P}{12EI}x^3 + C_1x + C_2,$$

$$0 = 0 - 0 + 0 + C_2. \quad \therefore\ C_2 = 0.$$

Substituting these values of C_1 and C_2 in the final equation gives the equation of the elastic curve in the form

$$y = \frac{Pl}{8EI}x^2 - \frac{P}{12EI}x^3.$$

The deflection of the beam can be found by finding the ordinate of the point B in the figure. This is done by substituting $x = \frac{1}{2}l$ in the equation of the elastic curve.

Then $y = \dfrac{Pl}{8EI}(\tfrac{1}{2}l)^2 - \dfrac{P}{12EI}(\tfrac{1}{2}l)^3 = \dfrac{Pl^3}{48EI},$

which is the deflection of the beam.

EXERCISES

1. Given $\dfrac{d^2y}{dx^2} = 2x$, find y.

2. Given $\dfrac{d^3y}{dx^3} = 0$, find y.

3. $y = \int \int \int e^x\, dx\, dx\, dx$, find y.

4. $y = \int \int (x^3 + x) dx\, dx$, find y.

5. Evaluate $\int_1^2 \int_3^4 \int_0^2 x^3\, dx\, dx\, dx$.

6. Find the equation of the curve at each point of which the rate of change of the slope is three times the abscissa of the point, and which passes through the points $(1, 2)$ and $(-2, -1)$.

Suggestion. The rate at which the slope is changing is expressed by $\dfrac{d^2y}{dx^2}$. $\therefore \dfrac{d^2y}{dx^2} = 3x$.

7. A beam of uniform cross section, Fig. 135, supported at its ends, and weighted uniformly with a weight w per unit of length, has for the differential equation of its elastic curve

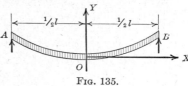

FIG. 135.

$$EI\frac{d^2y}{dx^2} = \tfrac{1}{2}w(\tfrac{1}{4}l^2 - x^2),$$

where E, I, and l have the meanings given for example 4. Find the equation for the elastic curve, noting that the slope, $\dfrac{dy}{dx}$, is zero when $x = 0$, and that the curve passes through the origin.

168. Successive partial integration.—The inverse of partial differentiation gives rise to **partial integration.** As might be expected from its connection with partial differentiation, partial integration involves two or more independent variables, and the integration is performed by considering a single variable as varying at each step of the work. It is also evident that a constant of integration may be a function of the other independent variables. Here only definite integrals will be considered, and in this manner the constants will be avoided and the discussion will be simplified.

The double and triple integrals will now be illustrated by examples, which should be studied carefully, fixing in mind the order the differentials are written. In some textbooks the order is not as given here, for this reason one should always note the order in which a particular writer places the differentials.

Example 1.   Evaluate $\int_1^2 \int_2^4 (x + y) dy\, dx$.

Solution.   It is agreed that

$$\int_1^2 \int_2^4 (x + y) dy\, dx = \int_1^2 \Big[\int_2^4 (x + y) dy \Big] dx,$$

which evidently means that the integral $\int_2^4 (x + y) dy$ is to be evaluated first. It is integrated considering y as the variable and x as a constant.

Then $\int_1^2 \Big[\int_2^4 (x + y) dy \Big] dx = \int_1^2 (xy + \tfrac{1}{2} y^2) \Big]_2^4 dx$
$$= \int_1^2 (2x + 6) dx = (x^2 + 6x)]_1^2 = 9.$$

Example 2.   Evaluate $\int_0^\pi \int_0^{a\cos\theta} \rho \sin\theta\, d\rho\, d\theta$.

Solution. $\int_0^\pi \int_0^{a\cos\theta} \rho \sin\theta\, d\rho\, d\theta = \int_0^\pi \tfrac{1}{2} \rho^2 \sin\theta]_0^{a\cos\theta}\, d\theta$
$= \tfrac{1}{2} a^2 \int_0^\pi \cos^2\theta \sin\theta\, d\theta = -\tfrac{1}{2} a^2 \int_0^\pi \cos^2\theta (-\sin\theta\, d\theta)$
$= -\tfrac{1}{6} a^2 \cos^3\theta]_0^\pi = -\tfrac{1}{6} a^2 [(-1)^3 - 1^3] = \tfrac{1}{3} a^2.$

Example 3.   Evaluate $\int_0^5 \int_0^3 \int_2^4 x^2 y^2 z^2 dz\, dy\, dx$.

Solution.   It is agreed that

$$\int_0^5 \int_0^3 \int_2^4 x^2 y^2 z^2\ dz\ dy\ dx = \int_0^5 \Big\{ \int_0^3 \Big(\int_2^4 x^2 y^2 z^2\ dz \Big) dy \Big\} dx.$$

This means that the innermost integral is to be evaluated first.   Then

$\int_0^5 \Big\{ \int_0^3 \Big(\int_2^4 x^2 y^2 z^2\ dz \Big) dy \Big\} dx = \int_0^5 \Big\{ \int_0^3 \tfrac{1}{3} x^2 y^2 z^3 \Big]_2^4 dy \Big\} dx$
$= \int_0^5 \Big\{ \int^3 \tfrac{56}{3} x^2 y^2 dy \Big\} dx = \int_0^5 \tfrac{56}{9} x^2 y^3 \Big]_0^3\ dx$
$= \int_0^5 168 x^2 dx = 56 x^3 \Big]_0^5\ = 7000.$

EXERCISES

Evaluate the following integrals.

1. $\int_0^2 \int_2^6 xy \, dy \, dx.$

4. $\int_0^a \int_0^{\sqrt{a^2-y^2}} dx \, dy.$

2. $\int_0^1 \int_x^{2\sqrt{x}} x \, dy \, dx.$

5. $\int_{-a}^a \int_{-x}^{2x} \int_0^y (x + y + z) dz \, dy \, dx.$

3. $\int_0^\pi \int_0^{a(1+\cos\theta)} \rho \, d\rho \, d\theta.$

6. $\int_0^2 \int_0^x \int_0^{x+y} e^{x+y+z} \, dz \, dy \, dx.$

169. Plane areas by double integration. Rectangular coördinates.—The methods for finding areas by double integration given here are not given because they are easier than methods already used in finding similar areas, but the

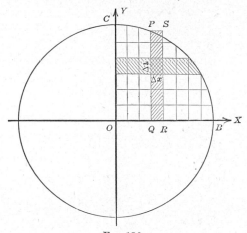

Fig. 136.

insight gained by following through these discussions will assist in understanding the work where double or triple integration is necessary, or advisable, in solving problems. The discussions can be carried forward either from the standpoint of summation or by differentials.

Example 1. Using double integration find the area of the circle $x^2 + y^2 = 25$.

Solution by summation. Plot the circle, noting that it is symmetrical with respect to both coördinate axes. The area can then be found by taking four times the portion lying in the first quadrant.

In Fig. 136, lines are drawn parallel to the y-axis dividing OB into n parts each equal to Δx, and lines are drawn parallel to the x-axis dividing OC into m parts each equal to Δy. A number of small rectangles are thus formed the area of each being $\Delta x \, \Delta y$.

Evidently the area of any one of the vertical strips, as $QRSP$, can be found by taking the sum of the rectangles in it. This will still be true as $\Delta y \to 0$.

Then $\qquad QRSP = \lim_{\Delta y \to 0} \sum_{y=0}^{y=QP} \Delta x \, \Delta y$

The area of the quadrant may be found by taking the limit of the sum of these strips from $x = 0$ to $x = OB$, and is represented by

$$\lim_{\Delta x \to 0} \sum_{x=0}^{x=OB} \left[\lim_{\Delta y \to 0} \sum_{y=0}^{y=QP} \Delta x \, \Delta y \right].$$

Since $QRSP$ is any such strip, the ordinate QP varies for different strips and is determined from the equation of the circle by solving for y. The upper limit of the summation is then $y = \sqrt{25 - x^2}$. Using the definite integral in place of the summation,

$$QRSP = \lim_{\Delta y \to 0} \sum_{y=0}^{y=QP} \Delta x \, \Delta y = \int_0^{\sqrt{25-x^2}} \Delta x \, dy.$$

In finding the summation of the strips the limits are 0 and $OB = 5$. The area of the quadrant is then given by

$$\int_0^5 \int_0^{\sqrt{25-x^2}} dy \, dx.$$

Hence the total area A is

$$A = 4\int_0^5 \int_0^{\sqrt{25-x^2}} dy\ dx$$

$$= 4\int_0^5 y\Big]_0^{\sqrt{25-x^2}} dx = 4\int_0^5 \sqrt{25 - x^2}\ dx$$

$$= 4\cdot\tfrac{1}{2}\Big(x\sqrt{25 - x^2} + 25\ \sin^{-1}\frac{x}{5}\Big)\Big]_0^5 \qquad \text{By formula 55.}$$

$$= 2(5\sqrt{25 - 25} + 25\ \sin^{-1} 1) = 50\cdot\tfrac{1}{2}\pi = 25\pi.$$

It should be noted that the first summation could have been made as well along a horizontal strip. The limits on x would then have been 0 and $\sqrt{25 - y^2}$, and the total area would be

$$A = \int_0^5 \int_0^{\sqrt{25-y^2}} dx\ dy.$$

Solution by differentials. Any such problem can be thought through in terms of differentials if desired. We will not stop here to give but an outline of the method. The strip $QRSP$ can be thought of as generated by a line starting at QR and moving upward. Then, letting A_1 be the area of $QRSP$,

$$dA_1 = \Delta x\ dy.$$

$$\therefore \quad A_1 = \Delta x\int_0^{\sqrt{25-x^2}} dy.$$

But $QRSP$ is exactly the differential of the quadrant if thought of as generated by an ordinate starting at OC and moving toward B.

Then, letting A = area, and using dx for Δx,

$$dA = A_1 = \int_0^{\sqrt{25-x^2}} dy\cdot dx.$$

$$A = 4\int_0^5 \int_0^{\sqrt{25-x^2}} dy\ dx.$$

In general, a plane area in rectangular coördinates is given by the double integrals

[59]   A = $\int\int$ dy dx, or A = $\int\int$ dx dy,

the limits being properly selected. How the limits are selected can best be shown by examples.

Example 2.   Find the area in the first quadrant at the right of the parabola $y^2 = 16x$, and included between the parabola and the circle

$$x^2 + y^2 = 80.$$

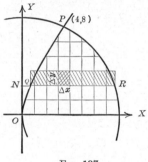

FIG. 137.

Solution. The area is shown divided into rectangles in Fig. 137. Here it is best to make the first summation in a horizontal strip, as then each strip begins at the parabola and ends at the circle. If the summation was first made in a vertical strip, it would be necessary to break the solution into two parts as some of the vertical strips end on the parabola and some on the circle.

The limits on the horizontal are

$$NQ = \tfrac{1}{16}y^2 \text{ and } NR = \sqrt{80 - y^2}.$$

In summing the strips, the limits on y are from 0 to the value of y at the intersection point P, which is found by solving the two equations as simultaneous. This is readily done thus:

Substituting $y^2 = 16x$ in the equation of the circle,

$$x^2 + 16x - 80 = 0.$$

Solving for x, $x = 4$ for the first and fourth quadrants.
Substituting $x = 4$ in $y^2 = 16x$, gives $y = \pm 8$.
The upper limit for y is then $+8$ in first quadrant.

The area required is given by the double integral

$$A = \int_0^8 \int_{\frac{1}{16} y^2}^{\sqrt{80 - y^2}} dx \, dy$$

$$= \int_0^8 x \Big]_{\frac{1}{16} y^2}^{\sqrt{80 - y^2}} dy = \int_0^8 \left(\sqrt{80 - y^2} - \tfrac{1}{16} y^2 \right) dy$$

$$= \left[\tfrac{1}{2} \left(y \sqrt{80 - y^2} + 80 \sin^{-1} \frac{y}{4\sqrt{5}} \right) - \tfrac{1}{48} y^3 \right]_0^8$$

$$= \tfrac{1}{2} \left(8\sqrt{80 - 64} + 80 \sin^{-1} \frac{8}{4\sqrt{5}} \right) - 0 - \tfrac{1}{48} (512 - 0)$$

$$= 16 + 40 \sin^{-1} \frac{2}{\sqrt{5}} - 10\tfrac{2}{3} = 49.62. \quad Ans.$$

$\sin^{-1} \dfrac{2}{\sqrt{5}}$ is computed as follows:

$$\sin^{-1} \frac{2}{\sqrt{5}} = \sin^{-1} 0.8944 = 63° \, 26.2' = 1.1072 \text{ radians.}$$

Example 3. Find the area in the first quadrant bounded by the parabolas $x^2 = 16y$ and $y^2 = 16x$ and the circle $x^2 + y^2 = 80$.

Solution. Plot the three curves as shown in Fig. 138, and find the points of intersection of the parabolas with the circle. This is necessary to determine the proper limits.

Solving $x^2 = 16y$ and $x^2 + y^2 = 80$ gives the coördinates of B as $(8, 4)$. Solving $y^2 = 16x$ and $x^2 + y^2 = 80$ gives the coördinates of C as $(4, 8)$.

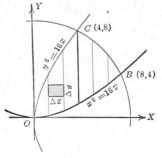

Fig. 138.

It is to be noticed that the vertical strips extend from the parabola OB to the parabola OC while x varies from 0 to 4; and from the parabola OB to the arc of the circle BC while

x varies from 4 to 8. It is then necessary to express the area in two double integrals. Thus,

$$A = \int_0^4 \int_{\frac{1}{16}x^2}^{4\sqrt{x}} dy\ dx + \int_4^8 \int_{\frac{1}{16}x^2}^{\sqrt{80-x^2}} dy\ dx.$$

170. Plane areas by double integration. Polar coördinates.

—The method by double integration can as readily be applied to polar coördinates as to rectangular coördi-

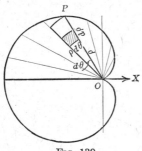

nates, and can be thought through by summation or differentials. Here we will suggest the differential method and state the final formulas.

Example 1. Find by double integration the area of the upper half of the cardioid

$$\rho = 2a(1 - \cos\theta).$$

Solution. The curve is plotted in Fig. 139. Divide the area into

FIG. 139.

sectors and think of one of them as generated by an arc of a circle with center at O. The generating arc starts at O and moves toward P. The differential[1] of this area A_1 is

$$dA_1 = \rho\ d\theta\ d\rho.$$

Then $$A_1 = \int_0^{OP} \rho\ d\rho\ d\theta.$$

And the total area A is $A = \int_0^\pi \int_0^{OP} \rho\ d\rho\ d\theta.$

But $OP = \rho = 2a(1 - \cos\theta).$

$$\therefore A = \int_0^\pi \int_0^{2a(1-\cos\theta)} \rho\ d\rho\ d\theta$$

$$= \int_0^\pi \tfrac{1}{2}\rho^2 \Big]_0^{2a(1-\cos\theta)} d\theta$$

$$= 2a^2 \int_0^\pi (1 - \cos\theta)^2\ d\theta$$

---

[1] If the differential of A_1 was represented exactly it would be a rectangle of dimensions $\rho\,d\theta$ and $d\rho$.

$$= 2a^2 \int_0^\pi (1 - 2\cos\theta + \cos^2\theta)d\theta$$

$$= 2a^2(\theta - 2\sin\theta + \tfrac{1}{2}\theta + \tfrac{1}{4}\sin 2\theta)\Big]_0^\pi$$

$$= 2a^2(\pi - 0 + \tfrac{1}{2}\pi + 0) = 3\pi a^2.$$

In general, the area in polar coördinates by double integration is given by the formula

[60] $$\mathbf{A} = \int\int\rho \, d\rho \, d\theta,$$

where the proper limits must be given as determined from the particular problem.

EXERCISES

Find the following areas by double integration.

1. The circle $x^2 + y^2 = 16$.

2. The segment of the parabola $y^2 = 8x$ cut off by the line $x = 4$.

3. The segment of the circle $x^2 + y^2 = 25$ cut off by the line $x + y = 5$.

4. The area bounded by the two coördinate axes and the line $y = 2x + 8$.

5. The area bounded by the parabolas $x^2 = 16y$ and $y^2 = 16x$.

6. The area of the circle $\rho = 5\cos\theta$.

7. The area bounded by the circles $\rho = 4\sin\theta$ and $\rho = 8\sin\theta$.

8. The area of the ellipse $\dfrac{x^2}{25} + \dfrac{y^2}{16} = 1$.

9. The area bounded by the circle $x^2 + y^2 = 25$, the parabola $3y^2 = 16x$, and the parabola $3x^2 = 16y$.

171. Area of any surface by double integration.—The simple methods of the previous articles evidently cannot be used when the area is not in a plane. In general, a curved surface presents a more difficult problem, which will now be discussed. We will find the surface of a sphere as a first illustration because the method is typical of such problems and can be applied to surfaces that could not be handled in a simpler manner. In using the method of this article the integrations are apt to be tedious if not difficult, and for this reason the method is not used when other methods will apply.

Example. Find by double integration the area of the surface of the sphere $x^2 + y^2 + z^2 = a^2$.

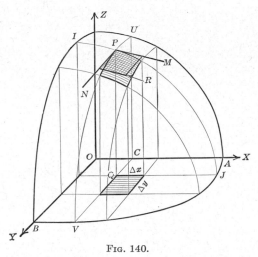

Fɪɢ. 140.

Solution. The equation is that of a sphere with center at the origin and of radius a. The eighth of this sphere that lies in the first octant is shown in Fig. 140. Consider the surface cut into a large number of parts by planes, so that the projection of each of these parts on the xy-plane is a rectangle with dimensions Δx and Δy. One of these parts is shown at P and its projection at Q. At each of the points as P, draw a tangent plane to the surface, and consider the portion of this plane that projects into the rectangle at Q. The portion at P is a parallelogram PR in a plane determined by the two tangent lines PM and PN, and has an area equal to the rectangle at Q, times the secant of the angle γ, the tangent plane makes with the xy-plane.

Then parallelogram $PR = \sec \gamma \; \Delta x \; \Delta y$.

But $\qquad \sec \gamma = \sqrt{1 + \left(\dfrac{\partial z}{\partial x}\right)^2 + \left(\dfrac{\partial z}{\partial y}\right)^2}.$ $\qquad$ By **Art. 166.**

Hence parallelogram $PR = \sqrt{1 + \left(\dfrac{\partial z}{\partial x}\right)^2 + \left(\dfrac{\partial z}{\partial y}\right)^2} \Delta x \; \Delta y.$

This is the element of the area to be found, and the total area is given by taking the limit of the sum of such areas, first, from where $y = 0$ at C to $y = CV$, and, second, from where $x = 0$ to $x = OA$. This can be represented by the double integral

$$\int_0^{OA} \int_0^{CV} \sqrt{1 + \left(\frac{\partial z}{\partial x}\right)^2 + \left(\frac{\partial z}{\partial y}\right)^2} \, dy \; dx.$$

Using S for total surface, and noting that in the sphere $OA = a$ and $CV = \sqrt{a^2 - x^2}$, for the arc AVB is a quadrant of a circle of radius a,

$$S = \int_0^a \int_0^{\sqrt{a^2 - x^2}} \sqrt{1 + \left(\frac{\partial z}{\partial x}\right)^2 + \left(\frac{\partial z}{\partial y}\right)^2} \, dy \; dx$$

From the equation $x^2 + y^2 + z^2 = a^2$,

$$z^2 = a^2 - x^2 - y^2.$$

Finding the partial derivative of this with respect to x,

$$2z \frac{\partial z}{\partial x} = -2x. \quad \therefore \; \frac{\partial z}{\partial x} = -\frac{x}{z}.$$

Finding the partial derivative with respect to y,

$$2z \frac{\partial z}{\partial y} = -2y. \quad \therefore \; \frac{\partial z}{\partial y} = -\frac{y}{z}.$$

Then $\sec \gamma = \sqrt{1 + \dfrac{x^2}{z^2} + \dfrac{y^2}{z^2}} = \sqrt{\dfrac{x^2 + y^2 + z^2}{z^2}}.$

But $x^2 + y^2 + z^2 = a^2$, and $z^2 = a^2 - x^2 - y^2$.

Hence sec $\gamma = \sqrt{\dfrac{a^2}{a^2 - x^2 - y^2}} = \dfrac{a}{\sqrt{a^2 - x^2 - y^2}}$.

Or $S = 8a \displaystyle\int_0^a \int_0^{\sqrt{a^2-x^2}} \dfrac{dy\,dx}{\sqrt{a^2 - x^2 - y^2}}$

$\quad = 8a \displaystyle\int_0^a \left(\int_0^{\sqrt{a^2-x^2}} \dfrac{dy}{\sqrt{(a^2 - \hat{x}^2) - y^2}} \right) dx$

$\quad = 8a \displaystyle\int_0^a \sin^{-1} \dfrac{y}{\sqrt{a^2 - x^2}} \Big]_0^{\sqrt{a^2-x^2}} dx$ By formula 60.

$\quad = 8a \displaystyle\int_0^a \tfrac{1}{2}\pi \, dx = 4\pi a x \Big]_0^a = 4\pi a^2$.

The projection could have been made on either of the other coördinate planes. The corresponding other values of the secant of the angle as given in **Art. 166** would then be used.

If the projection is on the xz-plane,

$$S = \iint \sqrt{1 + \left(\frac{\partial y}{\partial x}\right)^2 + \left(\frac{\partial y}{\partial z}\right)^2} dz \, dx.$$

If the projection is on the yz-plane,

$$S = \iint \sqrt{1 + \left(\frac{\partial x}{\partial y}\right)^2 + \left(\frac{\partial x}{\partial z}\right)^2} dz \, dy.$$

In any one of the three cases the order of integration may be changed; and, in any case, the proper limits must be used. The limits, of course, are determined from the data of the particular problem being solved. It is to be noted that the partial derivatives are always taken from the equation of the surface on which the area lies, and the limits are always determined from the projection on the plane in which the integration is performed.

EXERCISES

1. Find by double integration the area of the surface of the sphere $x^2 + y^2 + z^2 = 36$, that lies between the planes $x = 2$ and $x = 5$.

Suggestion. This is the same as the example of the preceding article except that the limits on x are 2 and 5.

2. Find the surface of the cylinder $x^2 + y^2 = 100$, lying above the xy-plane and between the xy-plane and the plane $z = x$.

Suggestion. Here the projection of the required surface on the xy-plane is an arc of a semicircle, so it is necessary to project either on the xz-plane or on the yz-plane. If the projection is taken on the xz-plane, the surface is

$$S = 2 \int_0^{\cdot 0} \int_0^x \sqrt{1 + \left(\frac{\partial y}{\partial x}\right)^2 + \left(\frac{\partial y}{\partial z}\right)^2} \, dz \, dx,$$

where the partial derivatives are found from $x^2 + y^2 = 100$.

This gives $\dfrac{\partial y}{\partial x} = -\dfrac{x}{y}$, and $\dfrac{\partial y}{\partial z} = 0$.

3. The center of a sphere of radius a is on the surface of a cylinder of diameter a. Find that portion of the surface of the sphere that is cut out by the cylinder.

Suggestion. This was a noted problem of the seventeenth century.

The equation of the sphere is $x^2 + y^2 + z^2 = a^2$. Take the cylinder perpendicular to the xy-plane and its equation $x^2 + y^2 = ax$. One-fourth of the area to be found is the

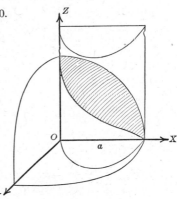

FIG. 141.

shaded portion in Fig. 141. The projection can be made on the xy-plane, and the surface is then given by

$$S = 4 \int_0^a \int_0^{\sqrt{ax - x^2}} \sqrt{1 + \left(\frac{\partial z}{\partial x}\right)^2 + \left(\frac{\partial z}{\partial y}\right)^2} \, dy \, dx,$$

where the partial derivatives must be taken from the equation of the sphere, this gives

$$S = 4a \int_0^a \int_0^{\sqrt{ax - x^2}} \frac{dy \, dx}{\sqrt{a^2 - x^2 - y^2}}.$$

172. Volumes by triple integration.—In many cases the volume of a solid bounded by surfaces whose equations are given may be found by a triple integration more readily than otherwise. The process can be readily followed as an extension of that given for plane areas by double integration, and can be thought through either as a summation or from the standpoint of differentials. Here only the former will be given.

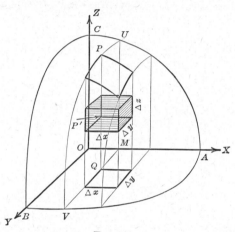

Fig. 142.

Divide the solid considered into small parallelepipeds by planes drawn parallel to the three coördinate planes. One of these parallelepipeds has dimensions Δz, Δy, Δx, and its volume $\Delta z \Delta y \Delta x$ is taken as the element of volume. One of these parallelepipeds is shown at P' in Fig. 142.

The first summation is made to find the volume of a column of parallelepipeds as QP, and the limits on z are from the lower end of the column at Q to the upper end at P which may be any point on the surface and so is determined by the *equation of the surface*.

The second summation is made to find the volume of a slice as VMU, and the limits on y are from 0 at M to MV at V which may be any point where the surface intersects the xy-plane, and so is determined by the equation of this intersection.

The third summation is made to find the sum of the slices, and the limits on x are from O to A, and are constant values.

The limits of these successive summations are represented by

$$\lim_{\Delta x \to 0} \sum \left\{ \lim_{\Delta y \to 0} \sum \left[\lim_{\Delta z \to 0} \sum \Delta z \; \Delta y \; \Delta x \right] \right\}.$$

If we assume that this represents the volume sought, it may be written as the triple definite integral in which the limits must be taken as necessary in the particular problem being considered. This gives the formula

[61] $V = \int \int \int dz \; dy \; dx.$

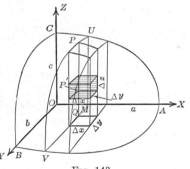

Of course the summation could be taken in any other order if more convenient, that is, the column of parallelepipeds might stand on the xz-plane or on the yz-plane.

Example. Find the volume of the ellipsoid whose equation is

$$\frac{x^2}{a^2} + \frac{y^2}{b^2} + \frac{z^2}{c^2} = 1.$$

Fig. 143.

Solution. One-eighth of this ellipsoid, the part in the first octant, is shown in Fig. 143.

The limits on z are from 0 at Q, to QP at P where QP is the value of z found from the equation of the ellipsoid.

This gives $\qquad QP = c\sqrt{1 - \dfrac{x^2}{a^2} - \dfrac{y^2}{b^2}}$

The limits on y are from 0 at M to $MV = b\sqrt{1 - \dfrac{x^2}{a^2}}$.

The limits on x are from 0 at O to $OA = a$.

Hence $V = 8\displaystyle\int_0^a \int_0^{b\sqrt{1-\frac{x^2}{a^2}}} \int_0^{c\sqrt{1-\frac{x^2}{a^2}-\frac{y^2}{b^2}}} dz\,dy\,dx$

$\qquad = 8c \displaystyle\int_0^a \int_0^{b\sqrt{1-\frac{x^2}{a^2}}} \sqrt{1 - \frac{x^2}{a^2} - \frac{y^2}{b^2}}\,dy\,dx.$

The integral $\displaystyle\int \sqrt{1 - \frac{x^2}{a^2} - \frac{y^2}{b^2}}\,dy$ is readily integrated by formula 55, if we note that $1 - \dfrac{x^2}{a^2}$ is the constant a^2 of the formula and $\dfrac{y^2}{b^2}$ is x^2 of the formula. Applying this formula and substituting the limits,

$$V = \tfrac{4}{3}\pi abc,$$

which is the general formula for finding the volume of any ellipsoid. It becomes the formula $V = \tfrac{4}{3}\pi r^3$ for the volume of a sphere if $a = b = c = r$.

EXERCISES

1. Find the volume that is above the xy-plane and bounded by it, the plane $z = 3x$, and the cylinder $x^2 + y^2 = 100$.

Suggestion. $V = 2\displaystyle\int_0^{10} \int_0^{\sqrt{100-x^2}} \int_0^{3x} dz\,dy\,dx.$

2. Find the volume bounded by the coördinate planes and the plane $\dfrac{x}{a} + \dfrac{y}{b} + \dfrac{z}{c} = 1$.

3. Find the volume of the smaller segment of the sphere
$$x^2 + y^2 + z^2 = 36$$
cut off by the plane $x = 2$.

4. Find the volume bounded by the surface $x^{\frac{2}{3}} + y^{\frac{2}{3}} + z^{\frac{2}{3}} = a^{\frac{2}{3}}$.

CHAPTER XX

CENTER OF GRAVITY. MOMENT OF INERTIA

173. Moment of a force.—Figure 144 represents a lever balanced on a fulcrum at F by the two forces P and W. In studying the lever we learn that, in order to keep the lever in balance, the product of the magnitude of P times the length of its lever arm m must equal to the product of the magnitude of W times its lever arm n, that is,

$$mP = nW.$$

The product mP, or nW, is called the **moment** of that force about the point F.

Similarly the *moment of a force with respect to an axis* perpendicular to its line of direction is the product of the magnitude of the force by the perpendicular distance from its line of direction to the axis. Also the *moment of a force with respect to a plane* parallel to its line of direction is the product of the magnitude of the force by the perpendicular distance from the line of direction to the plane.

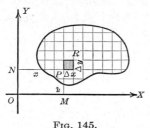

Fig. 145.

Here it is implied that the moment of a force is the measure of the tendency of the force to produce rotation about the axis or point.

174. Moment of area.—Consider any plane area as that shown in Fig. 145. Divide this area into small rectangles

329

of dimensions Δx by Δy. Let PR be one of these, and let the coördinates of P be (x, y). Then we will call the product of the area of PR by x the moment of PR with respect to the y-axis. The summation of all such moments throughout the plane area is called the **moment of the area** with respect to the y-axis. The moment is also called a **moment of the first order** when the first power of the distance is used in the product.

If M_y represents this moment,

$$M_y = \lim_{\Delta x \to 0} \sum \left[\lim_{\Delta y \to 0} \sum x \, \Delta y \, \Delta x \right].$$

Or
$$M_y = \int \int x \, dy \, dx,$$

where the proper limits must be supplied.

Similarly if M_x represents the moment of the area with respect to the x-axis,

$$M_x = \int \int y \, dy \, dx.$$

A similar discussion can be given for moments of lines and moments of volumes. This will be illustrated in particular examples.

175. Center of gravity.—If the moment of an area with respect to an axis is divided by the area, we obtain an average distance at which the total area could be concentrated and give the same moment. If $\bar{x}$ and $\bar{y}$ are these average distances found as follows:

$$\bar{x} = \frac{\int \int x \, dy \, dx}{\int \int dy \, dx}, \text{ and } \bar{y} = \frac{\int \int y \, dy \, dx}{\int \int dy \, dx},$$

then the point $(\bar{x}, \bar{y})$ is called the **center of gravity** of the area. If the area is thought of as a thin material plate, this gives the **center of mass,** or the **centroid** of the plate. It follows from the meaning of moments that, if the body is suspended at the center of gravity, there will be no tendency to rotate. That is, the body will be in perfect balance.

From this we will take for granted that a line or plane of symmetry passes through the center of gravity, and the point of symmetry is at the center of gravity. Hence any figure that has a center of symmetry has its center of gravity at that point. Thus, the center of gravity of a circle or a rectangle is at its center.

Similarly for plane arcs, $\bar{x} = \dfrac{\int x\,ds}{\int ds}$, and $\bar{y} = \dfrac{\int y\,ds}{\int ds}$.

Example 1. Find the center of gravity of the area of a quarter of the circle $x^2 + y^2 = r^2$.

Solution. Consider the quarter of the circle that lies in the first quadrant as shown in Fig. 146.

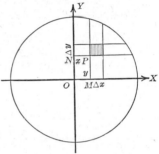

$$\bar{x} = \frac{\int_0^r \int_0^{\sqrt{r^2-x^2}} x\,dy\,dx}{\int_0^r \int_0^{\sqrt{r^2-x^2}} dy\,dx}.$$

$$\bar{y} = \frac{\int_0^r \int_0^{\sqrt{r^2-x^2}} y\,dy\,dx}{\int_0^r \int_0^{\sqrt{r^2-x^2}} dy\,dx}.$$

Here the denominator in each is one-fourth the area of the circle and is therefore $\frac{1}{4}\pi r^2$.

Fig. 146.

It is evident that, because of the symmetry of the figure, the value of $\bar{x}$ is the same as that of $\bar{y}$. Then the numerators must be equal. Here we will evaluate only the first. The student should evaluate the second numerator and verify this statement.

$$\int_0^r \int_0^{\sqrt{r^2-x^2}} x\,dy\,dx = \int_0^r \sqrt{r^2 - x^2}\,x\,dx$$
$$= -\tfrac{1}{2}\int_0^r (r^2 - x^2)^{\frac{1}{2}}(-2x\,dx) = -\tfrac{1}{3}(r^2 - x^2)^{\frac{3}{2}}\Big]_0^r$$
$$= -\tfrac{1}{3}(0 - r^3) = \tfrac{1}{3}r^3.$$
$$\therefore \bar{x} = \frac{\tfrac{1}{3}r^3}{\tfrac{1}{4}\pi r^2} = \frac{4r}{3\pi}.$$

Hence the center of gravity of the quarter of the circle is at the point $\left(\dfrac{4r}{3\pi}, \dfrac{4r}{3\pi}\right)$.

Example 2.   Find the center of gravity of the arc of a semicircle.

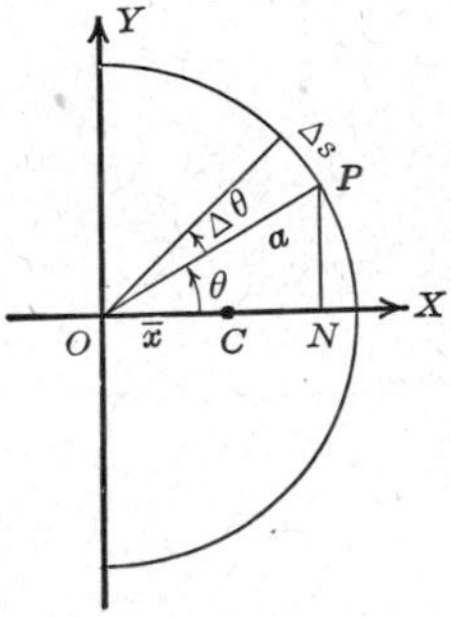

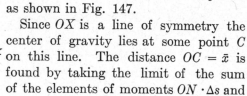

Solution.   Let the semicircle be placed as shown in Fig. 147.

Since OX is a line of symmetry the center of gravity lies at some point C on this line.   The distance $OC = \bar{x}$ is found by taking the limit of the sum of the elements of moments $ON \cdot \Delta s$ and dividing by the length of the semicircle.

Now the length Δs can be expressed in rectangular coördinates, but it is simpler to express it as $\Delta s = a\,\Delta\theta$.

FIG. 147.

Then
$$\bar{x} = \frac{\displaystyle\lim_{\Delta\theta \to 0} \sum_{\theta=-\frac{1}{2}\pi}^{\theta=\frac{1}{2}\pi} ON \cdot a\Delta\theta}{\pi a}$$

$$= \frac{a^2 \displaystyle\int_{-\frac{1}{2}\pi}^{\frac{1}{2}\pi} \cos\theta\, d\theta}{\pi a} = \frac{a^2 \sin\theta \Big]_{-\frac{1}{2}\pi}^{\frac{1}{2}\pi}}{\pi a}$$

$$= \frac{a^2(1+1)}{\pi a} = \frac{2a}{\pi}.$$

Hence the center of gravity of the arc of the semicircle is at the point $\left(\dfrac{2a}{\pi},\, 0\right)$.

Example 3.   Find the center of gravity of the volume of a hemisphere.

First solution.   Let the sphere be $x^2 + y^2 + z^2 = a^2$, and consider the hemisphere shown in Fig. 148.

Because of symmetry the center of gravity is on the x-axis. Hence $\bar{y} = 0$ and $\bar{z} = 0$. It is only necessary then to find $\bar{x}$. This is done by dividing the volume into elements

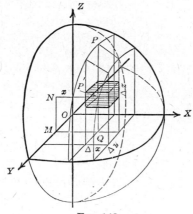

Fig. 148.

$\Delta z\, \Delta y\, \Delta x$, multiplying by $NP' = x$, and summing throughout the volume to find the moment.

Then

$$\bar{x} = \frac{4 \int_0^a \int_0^{\sqrt{a^2-x^2}} \int_0^{\sqrt{a^2-x^2-y^2}} x\, dz\, dy\, dx}{\frac{2}{3}\pi a^3}$$

$$= \frac{4 \int_0^a \int_0^{\sqrt{a^2-x^2}} x\sqrt{a^2 - x^2 - y^2}\, dy\, dx}{\frac{2}{3}\pi a^3}$$

$$= \frac{4 \int_0^a \frac{1}{2}\left\{ y\sqrt{a^2-x^2-y^2} + (a^2-x^2)\sin^{-1}\dfrac{y}{\sqrt{a^2-x^2}} \right\}\Big]_0^{\sqrt{a^2-x^2}} x\, dx}{\frac{2}{3}\pi a^3}$$

$$= \frac{\pi \int_0^a (a^2 - x^2)x\, dx}{\frac{2}{3}\pi a^3} = \frac{-\frac{1}{4}\pi(a^2 - x^2)^2\Big]_0^a}{\frac{2}{3}\pi a^3}$$

$$= \frac{\frac{1}{4}\pi a^4}{\frac{2}{3}\pi a^3} = \frac{3}{8}a$$

Hence the center of gravity of the hemisphere is at the point $(\frac{3}{8}a, 0, 0)$.

Second solution.   Here we will think in terms of differentials though we could as well use summation. Let the hemisphere be thought of as generated by a circle starting at O and moving toward A, Fig. 149. Then the change in the moment with respect to the yz-plane at any instant as the volume increases is the differential of the volume, dV at that instant, times the distance x.

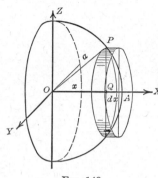

Fig. 149.

At any point $Q, dV = \pi(QP)^2 dx$.

But $$QP = \sqrt{a^2 - x^2}.$$

Hence the differential of the moment is

$$dM = \pi(a^2 - x^2)x \, dx.$$

$$\therefore \bar{x} = \frac{\pi \int_0^a (a^2 - x^2)x \, dx}{\frac{2}{3}\pi a^3} = \frac{3}{8}a.$$

EXERCISES

1. Find the center of gravity of the segment of the parabola $y^2 = 4x$, cut off by the line $x = 4$.

2. Find the center of gravity of the area of a semicircle.

3. Find the center of gravity of the arc of one-third of a circle of radius a.

Suggestion. Place the arc as in example 2 and take the limits from $-\frac{1}{3}\pi$ to $\frac{1}{3}\pi$.

4. Find the center of gravity of the area of a quadrant of the ellipse $\frac{x^2}{a^2} + \frac{y^2}{b^2} = 1$.

5. Find the center of gravity of the area bounded by the cycloid $x = a(\varphi - \sin \varphi)$, $y = a(1 - \cos \varphi)$, and the x-axis.

6. Find the distance from the vertex of a triangle of altitude h and base b to the line parallel to the base and through the center of gravity of the triangle.

Suggestion. Think of the triangle as generated by a line parallel to the base and moving from the vertex O, Fig 150

Then $$dM = xl\,dx.$$

But $$l : b = x : h. \quad \therefore l = \frac{bx}{h}.$$

7. Find the distance from the vertex of a right circular cone of altitude h and radius of base a to its center of gravity.

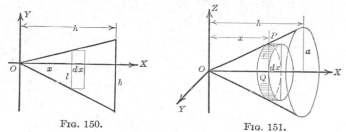

Fig. 150.   Fig. 151.

Suggestion. Think of the cone as generated by a circle starting at O, Fig. 151, and moving toward the base.

Then $$dM = x\pi r^2\,dx.$$

But $$r : a = x : h. \quad \therefore r = \frac{ax}{h}.$$

176. A useful theorem.—*If A_1, A_2, $\cdots$ A_n are n areas lying in the same plane, and if $(\bar{x}_1, \bar{y}_1)$, $(\bar{x}_2, \bar{y}_2)$, $\cdots$ $(\bar{x}_n, \bar{y}_n)$, respectively, are the coördinates of their centers of gravity, then the coördinates $(\bar{x}, \bar{y})$ of the center of gravity of the combined areas are given by the formulas*

$$\bar{x} = \frac{A_1\bar{x}_1 + A_2\bar{x}_2 + \cdots A_n\bar{x}_n}{A_1 + A_2 + \cdots A_n},$$

$$\bar{y} = \frac{A_1\bar{y}_1 + A_2\bar{y}_2 + \cdots A_n\bar{y}_n}{A_1 + A_2 + \cdots A_n}.$$

This follows at once for the numerators are moments of areas and the denominators are the corresponding areas.

It is evident that a similar theorem holds if the areas are replaced by volumes.

Example 1. A square 8 in. on a side is surmounted by an isosceles triangle 8 in. in altitude. Find the center of gravity of the area.

Solution. The area is shown in Fig. 152.

$$\bar{y}_1 = 4, \text{ and } \bar{y}_2 = 10\tfrac{2}{3}.$$

$$\bar{y} = \frac{64 \times 4 + 32 \times 10\tfrac{2}{3}}{64 + 32} = 6\tfrac{2}{9}.$$

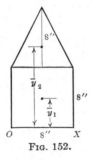

FIG. 152.

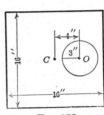

FIG. 153.

Example 2. A square sheet of tin 16 in. on a side has a circular hole of radius 3 in. cut out as shown in Fig. 153. Find the center of gravity.

Solution. Let $\bar{x}$ = the distance the center of gravity is from the center of the square and on the line of centers.

$$\text{Then } \bar{x} = \frac{256 \times 0 - 3.1416 \times 3^2 \times 4}{256 - 3.1416 \times 3^2} = -0.5-.$$

Hence the center of gravity is very nearly $\tfrac{1}{2}$ in. to the left of the center of the square.

EXERCISES

1. Find the coördinates of the center of gravity of the area between a quadrant of a circle and the circumscribing square, if the radius of the circle is 10 in. (See Fig. 154.)

2. Find the center of mass of the solid made up of a right circular cylinder and a right circular cone placed as shown in Fig. 155, and having the dimensions given.

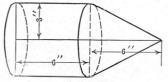

FIG. 154.

FIG. 155.

3. Find the $\bar{x}$ and $\bar{y}$ of the section of an angle iron shown in Fig. 156.

4. Find $\bar{y}$ of the section shown in Fig. 157.

5. Find the center of gravity of the frustum of a right circular cone, the diameters of the bases being 12 in. and 8 in. and the altitude 8 in.

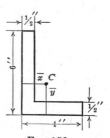

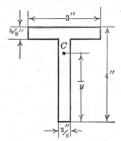

FIG. 156.

FIG. 157.

177. Theorems of Pappus and Guldin.—The two following theorems were known to Pappus, the last great mathematician of the Alexandrian School, who lived about 300 A.D. They were stated and used by Guldin (1577–1643), and were first proved satisfactorily by Cavalieri (1598–1647).

THEOREM I. *The area of a surface of revolution formed by a plane curve revolving about an axis in that plane is equal to the length of the generating curve times the distance its center of gravity moves.*

THEOREM II. *The volume of a solid of revolution formed by a plane area revolving about an axis in that plane is equal to the area of the generating area times the distance its center of gravity moves.*

Proof of Theorem I. Let the x-axis be the axis of revolution, and let S denote the surface, s the length of the curve, and $\bar{y}$ the distance of the center of gravity of the generating curve from the axis of revolution.

Then $\qquad\qquad S = 2\pi \int y \, ds.$ $\qquad$ By **Art. 151.**

Also $\qquad\qquad \bar{y} = \dfrac{\int y \, ds}{s}.$ $\qquad$ By **Art. 175.**

$\qquad\qquad \therefore S = s \cdot 2\pi \bar{y}.$

Proof of Theorem II. Let the x-axis be the axis of revolution, and let V denote the volume, A the generating area, and $\bar{y}$ the distance of the center of gravity of the generating area from the axis of revolution.

Then $V = 2\pi \int \int y \, dy \, dx = \pi \int y^2 \, dx.$ $\qquad$ By [**58**].

Also $\quad \bar{y} = \dfrac{\int \int y \, dy \, dx}{A}.$ $\qquad$ By **Art. 175.**

$\quad \therefore V = A \cdot 2\pi \bar{y}.$

Example. Find the area of the surface and the volume of the torus formed by revolving the circle $x^2 + (y - b)^2 = a^2$, where $b > a$, about the x-axis.

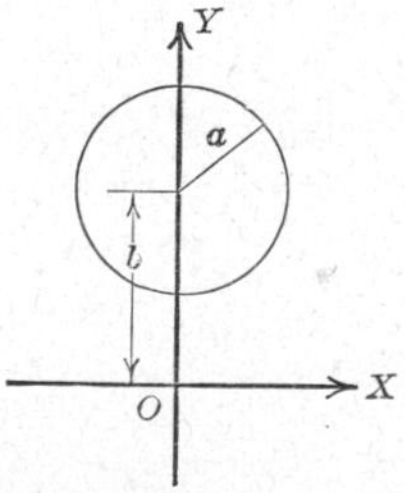

FIG. 158.

Solution. The circle is as shown in Fig. 158.

$s = 2\pi a,\ \bar{y} = b,$ and $A = \pi a^2.$

$S = s \cdot 2\pi \bar{y} = 2\pi a \cdot 2\pi b = 4\pi^2 ab.$

By Theorem I.

$V = A \cdot 2\pi \bar{y} = \pi a^2 \cdot 2\pi b = 2\pi^2 a^2 b.$

By Theorem II.

See exercise 8, page 283, also **P. M. III, Art. 90; H. S., Art. 200.**

EXERCISES

1. An equilateral triangle 6 in. on a side is revolved about an axis in the plane of the triangle, parallel to its base, and 8 in. below its base. Find the area of the surface of the solid formed and its volume.

2. The cross section of the rim of a flywheel is 4 in. by 8 in., and its outer diameter is 10 ft. Find the volume of the rim if the shorter dimension of the rim is in the diameter of the wheel.

3. Use the results of exercise 5, page 334 and find the volume of the solid formed by revolving the area under one arch of the cycloid about its base.

4. An ellipse whose major axis is 8 in. and minor axis 6 in. is revolved about an axis in the plane of the ellipse, parallel to its major axis, and lying 12 in. from the center of the ellipse. Find the volume of the solid generated.

178. Moment of inertia.—In dealing with problems of center of gravity we used moments of the *first order* where the distance of the element from the point, line, or plane was taken to the first power. In an exactly similar manner we have moments of the *second order* where the second power of the distance is taken. Such moments occur frequently in engineering problems when dealing with rotating bodies, the flexure of beams, etc. The formulas are exactly as those for moments of the first order with the exception that the distance is squared. In dealing with material bodies it is usual to consider the mass, and this is done by introducing the factor μ which is the mass per unit of length, area, or volume, when the mass is uniformly distributed throughout the body considered. These moments of the second order are **moments of inertia.**

If the body considered is a plane area having the mass uniformly distributed over it, we have for the moment of inertia, I, the following formulas in rectangular coördinates.

With respect to the x-axis, $I_x = \int\int \mu y^2 \, dy \, dx$.

With respect to the y-axis, $I_y = \int\int \mu x^2 \, dy \, dx$.

With respect to the origin, $I_o = \int\int \mu(x^2 + y^2) dy \, dx$.

Example 1.   Find the moment of inertia of a material line (a thin wire) of length l with respect to an axis through one end.

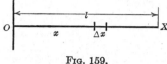

FIG. 159.

Solution. Consider the wire of mass μ per unit length, Fig. 159, divided into elements Δx.

Then
$$I = \lim_{\Delta x \to 0} \sum_{x=0}^{x=l} \mu x^2 \, \Delta x$$
$$= \mu \int_0^l x^2 \, dx = \tfrac{1}{3}\mu x^3 \Big]_0^l = \tfrac{1}{3}\mu l^3.$$

If M is the total mass of the rod, $M = \mu l$ and we may write
$$I = \tfrac{1}{3}Ml^2.$$

Example 2.   Find the moment of inertia of a rectangular plate of base b and altitude h with respect to its base as an axis.   Suppose that it has a mass μ per unit area.

Solution. Place the rectangle as shown in Fig. 160.

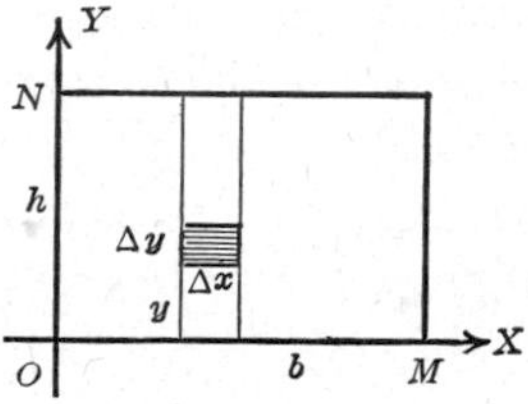

$$I_b = \int_0^b \int_0^h \mu y^2 dy \, dx$$
$$= \mu \int_0^b \tfrac{1}{3} y^3 \Big]_0^h dx = \tfrac{1}{3} h^3 \mu \int_0^b dx$$
$$= \tfrac{1}{3} \mu h^3 x \Big]_0^b = \tfrac{1}{3} \mu b h^3.$$

Since $\mu b h = M$, we may write
$$I_b = \tfrac{1}{3} M h^2.$$

FIG. 160

Example 3.   Find the moment of inertia of a circular plate of radius r with respect to a diameter as axis.   Suppose that it has a mass μ per unit area.

Solution. Place the circle with its center at the origin and take the x-axis as the axis of reference.   The equation of the circle is then $x^2 + y^2 = r^2$.

Evidently the moment of inertia is four times that for one quadrant.

Then $I_x = 4 \int_0^r \int_0^{\sqrt{r^2 - x^2}} \mu y^2 dy \; dx$

$\qquad = 4\mu \int_0^r \frac{1}{3} y^3 \Big]_0^{\sqrt{r^2 - x^2}} \; dx = \frac{4}{3}\mu \int_0^r (r^2 - x^2)^{\frac{3}{2}} dx$

$\qquad = \frac{4}{3}\mu \left\{ \frac{1}{8} x(5r^2 - 2x^2)\sqrt{r^2 - x^2} + \frac{3}{8} r^4 \sin^{-1}\frac{x}{r} \right\} \Big]_0^r$

By formula 56.

$\qquad = \frac{4}{3}\mu(\frac{3}{8}r^4 \cdot \frac{1}{2}\pi) = \frac{1}{4}\mu\pi r^4.$

Since $\mu\pi r^2 = M$, we may write

$$I_x = \frac{1}{4} M r^2.$$

179. Moment of inertia. Parallel axes.—In finding the moment of inertia of solids the integration is often tedious if not difficult. Much of the labor can often be avoided by means of the following:

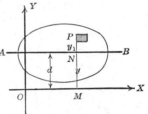

THEOREM. *The moment of inertia of a body with respect to any axis is equal to its moment of inertia with respect to a parallel axis through its center of gravity, increased by the product of the mass by the square of the distance between the axes.*

Fig. 161.

That is, if I stands for moment of inertia with respect to any axis, I_g with respect to the parallel gravity axis, d the distance between the two axes, and M the total mass, then

$$\mathbf{I = I_g + Md^2.}$$

Proof for areas. In Fig. 161, let OX be any axis parallel to the gravity axis AB, and let I be the moment of inertia about OX.

$I = \int\int \mu y^2 dy \; dx = \int\int \mu(y_1 + d)^2 dy \; dx$

$\quad = \int\int \mu y_1{}^2 dy \; dx + 2\mu d \int\int y_1 dy \; dx + d^2 \int\int \mu dy \; dx.$

Now the first integral equals I_g, the second equals zero by **Art. 175**, and the third equals Md^2.

$$\therefore \mathbf{I} = \mathbf{I_g} + \mathbf{Md^2}.$$

A similar proof can be given for a solid, but will be taken for granted here.

It follows from this theorem that

$$\mathbf{I_g} = \mathbf{I} - \mathbf{Md^2}.$$

Example 1.   Find the moment of inertia of a circular plate with respect to a tangent to the circle.

Solution.   From example 3 of the preceding article,

$$I_g = \tfrac{1}{4}\mu\pi r^4.$$

Also $M = \mu\pi r^2$ and $d = r$.

Hence, if I is the moment of inertia with respect to the tangent,

$$I = \tfrac{1}{4}\mu\pi r^4 + \mu\pi r^4 = \tfrac{5}{4}\mu\pi r^4.$$

Example 2.   Find the moment of inertia of a right circular cone, radius of base r and altitude h, with respect

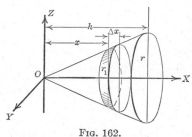

to an axis through the vertex and perpendicular to the axis of the cone. Suppose that μ is the mass per unit volume.

Solution.   Let the cone be placed with its vertex at the origin and axis on the x-axis as shown in Fig.

Fig. 162.

162.   Consider it as cut into plates of thickness Δx.   Then, if Δx is comparatively small, the moment of inertia of a plate about its diameter is approximately, from example 3 of the preceding article,

$$\tfrac{1}{4}\mu\pi r_1^4 \Delta x.$$

From the theorem of this article, the moment of inertia of this plate about OY is

$$\tfrac{1}{4}\mu\pi r_1^4 \Delta x + x^2 \cdot \mu\pi r_1^2 \Delta x.$$

Taking the limit of the sum of such expressions and writing as an integral,

$$I_y = \int_0^h \mu(\tfrac{1}{4}\pi r_1^4 + \pi x^2 r_1^2)dx.$$

But $r_1 : r = x : h.$ $\therefore r_1 = \dfrac{rx}{h}.$

Substituting in the above integral,

$$
\begin{aligned}
I_y &= \mu\pi\int_0^h \Big(\frac{1}{4}\frac{r^4 x^4}{h^4} + \frac{r^2 x^4}{h^2}\Big)dx \\
&= \frac{\mu\pi r^2}{h^2}\Big(\frac{r^2}{4h^2} + 1\Big)\int_0^h x^4\,dx \\
&= \frac{\mu\pi r^2}{h^2}\Big(\frac{r^2}{4h^2} + 1\Big)\frac{x^5}{5}\Big]_0^h \\
&= \frac{\mu\pi r^2}{h^2}\Big(\frac{r^2}{4h^2} + 1\Big)\frac{h^5}{5} = \frac{\mu\pi r^2 h}{20}\Big(r^2 + 4h^2\Big).
\end{aligned}
$$

But $\tfrac{1}{3}\mu\pi r^2 h = M$, the mass of the cone.

$$\therefore\ I_y = \tfrac{3}{20}M(r^2 + 4h^2).$$

180. Polar moment of inertia.—The moment of inertia of an area with respect to an axis perpendicular to its plane is called the **polar moment of inertia** of the area. The moments of inertia with respect to each of two axes at right angles and lying in the plane of the area are sometimes called **rectangular moments of inertia** to distinguish them from the polar moment of inertia.

THEOREM. *The polar moment of inertia of an area is equal to the sum of the rectangular moments of inertia with respect to any two axes at right angles, lying in the plane and passing through the same point as the axis for the polar moment.*

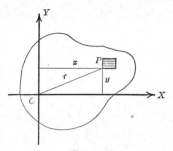

FIG. 163.

Proof. In Fig. 163, consider the element of area at the point $P(x, y)$. Let I_o represent the polar moment of inertia with respect to an axis perpendicular to the plane of the area and through O. Let the two axes at right angles and lying in the plane be taken as the coördinate axes, and let r be the distance from O to P.

Then $\qquad I_o = \int\int \mu r^2 dy\ dx$.

But $\qquad r^2 = x^2 + y^2$.

$\therefore \qquad I_o = \int\int \mu(x^2 + y^2) dy\ dx$

$\qquad\qquad = \int\int \mu x^2 dy\ dx + \int\int \mu y^2 dy\ dx$.

Now these two integrals are respectively I_x and I_y.

$$\therefore I_o = I_x + I_y.$$

Example. Find the polar moment of inertia of a circular area with respect to its center.

Solution. From example 3, **Art. 178**,

$$I_x = \tfrac{1}{4}\mu\pi r^4, \text{ and } I_y = \tfrac{1}{4}\mu\pi r^4.$$

$\therefore \qquad\qquad I_o = I_x + I_y = \tfrac{1}{2}\mu\pi r^4$.

Since the mass M of the circular area is $\mu\pi r^2$,

$$I_o = \tfrac{1}{2}Mr^2.$$

EXERCISES

1. Use the result of example 2, **Art. 178** and find, (*a*) the moment of inertia of a rectangle with respect to the gravity axis parallel to the base, (*b*) the polar moment of inertia with respect to a vertex, (*c*) the polar moment of inertia with respect to the center of gravity.

2. Find the moment of inertia of a triangle of base b and altitude h with respect to its base.

Suggestion. In Fig. 164, take as element of area a strip parallel to the base, of which the area is approximately $b'\Delta y$.

But $b':b = h - y:h.$ $\therefore b' = \dfrac{b(h - y)}{h} = b - \dfrac{b}{h}y.$

Then $I_x = \displaystyle\int_0^h y^2\left(b - \dfrac{b}{h}y\right)dy = \tfrac{1}{12}bh^3.$

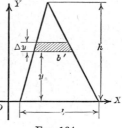

Here the mass is not considered but can be supplied if desired.

3. Given that the center of gravity of a triangle is at a point which is $\tfrac{1}{3}h$ from the base, use the result of exercise 2 and find the moment of inertia of a triangle with respect to an axis parallel to the base and through the center of gravity.

Fig. 164.

4. Find I_x, I_y, and I_o of the area of the ellipse $\dfrac{x^2}{a^2} + \dfrac{y^2}{b^2} = 1.$

Suggestion. In finding I_x take as element a strip parallel to the x-axis, and take $\mu = 1$.

Then $I_x = 4\dfrac{a}{b}\displaystyle\int_0^b y^2\sqrt{b^2 - y^2}dy.$

Similarly, $I_y = 4\dfrac{b}{a}\displaystyle\int_0^a x^2\sqrt{a^2 - x^2}dx.$

5. Prove that the moment of inertia of a system of areas or solids with reference to any axis is equal to the sum of the moments of inertia of the separate areas or solids with reference to that axis.

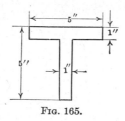

Fig. 165.

6. Find the moment of inertia of the T-section shown in Fig. 165, with respect to a horizontal axis through the center of gravity if $\mu = 1$.

Suggestion. Use results already found, as formulas, first finding the center of gravity, and use the theorem of exercise 5. First cut the area into rectangles.

7. Find the polar moment of inertia with respect to the center, of a plate in the form of a circular ring of inner radius 6 in. and outer radius 8 in. if $\mu = 1$.

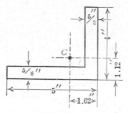

Fig. 166.

8. Find the moment of inertia of the angle iron shown in Fig. 166 with respect to a vertical axis through the center of gravity. It is given that the center of gravity is at C.

9. A right circular cylinder has a radius r and altitude h. Find the moment of inertia of the cylinder with respect, (*a*) to its axis, (*b*) to a diameter at one end.

CHAPTER XXI

FURTHER APPLICATIONS OF INTEGRATION

181. In applying the machinery of mathematics to the solution of practical problems it is advisable to have an intimate knowledge of the subject in which the problem arises, at least, it is necessary to know the exact relations of the quantities involved in the particular problem. In a text on mathematics written for students in general, there are many problems in physics, chemistry, electricity, and other subjects that cannot be treated to advantage because they would require too much in the way of preliminary explanation of the ideas involved. Such questions should be attacked by the student in these particular studies after he has mastered the technique of mathematics.

There are, however, problems arising in mechanics, physics, chemistry, and other sciences where the relations between the quantities may be considered as common knowledge or may be easily explained. Such problems may be attacked with more or less success, and are properly chosen for treatment in a text on applied mathematics. In studying these problems in this text the student has already been advised to omit those that he cannot understand because of a lack of knowledge of the basic subject.

182. Fluid pressure.—A principle known as Pascal's Law states that pressure exerted on a liquid in a closed vessel is transmitted equally and undiminished in all directions.

The pressure at any point of the walls of a reservoir of liquid open at the top is due to the head, that is, to the height of the liquid above that point.

347

From this it follows that the pressure on any horizontal surface equals to the weight of a column of liquid standing on that surface as a base and of height equal to the distance this surface is below the surface of the liquid. The computing of the pressure on any such surface is simply a matter of arithmetic as it does not involve variables.

In determining the pressure on a surface that is not horizontal, the pressure varies with the distance below the surface and variables are involved. It is here that we find an application of calculus.

For a horizontal plane surface of area A at a distance h below the surface, the total pressure P when the liquid weighs w pounds per unit volume, is given by the formula

$$P = whA.$$

If the liquid is water and the measurements are in feet,

$$P = 62.5hA.$$

For a vertical plane the pressure increases with the depth, and the differential of the pressure is evidently the differential of the area times wh. This gives

$$dP = wh\,dA.$$

Hence
$$P = \int_{h_1}^{h_2} wh\,dA,$$

where h_1 and h_2 are the least and greatest heads on the surface and dA must be expressed as a function of h in order to integrate.

Since
$$\int x\,dA = \bar{x}A$$
by **Art. 175,**
$$P = w\bar{h}A,$$

where $\bar{h}$ is the distance of the center of gravity of the area below the surface of the liquid. This formula will save a great deal of time when the center of gravity of the area is known.

Example 1.   A vertical wall of a dam is in the form of a triangle with vertex downward. If the top is 40 ft. and the altitude is 15 ft., find the total pressure on the wall when the water stands at the top.

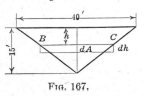

FIG. 167.

Solution. A sketch of the wall is shown in Fig. 167. dA is the differential of the area at depth h.

$$dA = BC \cdot dh.$$

But $\qquad BC:40 = 15 - h : 15. \quad \therefore BC = \dfrac{40(15 - h)}{15}.$

Then $\qquad dA = \dfrac{40(15 - h)}{15} dh.$

Hence $\qquad dP = \dfrac{62.5 \times 40h(15 - h)}{15} dh.$

$$P = \tfrac{500}{3} \int_0^{15}(15h - h^2)dh$$

$$= \tfrac{500}{3}(\tfrac{15}{2}h^2 - \tfrac{1}{3}h^3) \Big]_0^{15} = 93,750.$$

$\therefore$ total pressure $= 93,750$ lb.

The solution can as readily be carried out by summation.

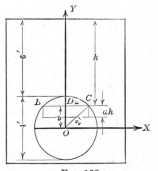

FIG. 168.

By using the result of exercise 6, page 335, from which the center of gravity of the triangle is 5 ft. below the surface, and using the formula $P = w\bar{h}A$

$$P = 62.5 \times 5 \times \tfrac{1}{2} \times 40 \times 15$$

$$= 93,750.$$

Example 2.   A circular opening 4 ft. in diameter has its top 6 ft. below the surface of the water in a reservoir. Find the total pressure necessary to close the opening.

Solution.   The relations are shown in Fig. 168.

$$dA = 2x\,dh, \text{ and } dP = 125hx\,dh.$$

Now we may express x in terms of y and h in terms of y, and use as limits the greatest and least values of y; or all may be expressed in terms of h. The first of these is used here.

$$h = 8 - y, \, dh = -dy, \text{ and } x = \sqrt{4 - y^2}.$$

Substituting these values,

$$dP = -125(8 - y)\sqrt{4 - y^2}dy.$$

The limits for y are 2 when $h = 6$ and -2 when $h = 10$.

$$\therefore P = 125\int_2^{-2}(y - 8)\sqrt{4 - y^2}\,dy$$

$$= 125\int_2^{-2}\sqrt{4 - y^2}\,y\,dy - 1000\int_2^{-2}\sqrt{4 - y^2}\,dy$$

$$= -\tfrac{125}{3}(4 - y^2)^{\frac{3}{2}}\Big]_2^{-2} - 500\Big(y\sqrt{4-y^2}+4\sin^{-1}\tfrac{y}{2}\Big)\Big]_{-2}^{-2}$$

$$= -500(-2\pi - 2\pi) = 2000\pi. \qquad \text{By 58 and 55.}$$

$\therefore$ total pressure is 6283 lb.

Here the integration can be avoided by using

$$P = w\bar{h}A$$
$$= 62.5 \times 8 \times 3.1416 \times 2^2 = 6283.$$

EXERCISES

1. A rectangular opening 4 ft. by 6 ft. is in the wall of a reservoir. Find the total pressure to close the opening if the longer sides are horizontal and the top is 20 ft. below the surface of the water.

2. A water main whose cross section is a circle 6 ft. in diameter is half full of water. Find the pressure on a gate closing the main.

3. The face of a dam is in the form of a parabola with its vertex downward. If the top is 32 ft. and the depth 16 ft., find the total pressure on the dam when the water stands at the top.

Suggestion. The equation of the parabola is $x^2 = 16y$.

4. Find the pressure on the face of a temporary bulkhead 6 ft. in diameter to close a water main whose top is 50 ft. below the surface of the water in a connected reservoir.

183. Emptying tank through orifice at bottom.—From the study of falling bodies we have

$$s = \tfrac{1}{2}gt^2,$$

where s is the distance in feet the body will fall in t seconds.

The velocity v can be found by finding the derivative of s with respect to t.

Then $$v = \frac{ds}{dt} = gt.$$

But from $$s = \tfrac{1}{2}gt^2, \; t = \sqrt{\frac{2s}{g}}.$$

Hence $$v = g\sqrt{\frac{2s}{g}} = \sqrt{2gs}.$$

Which states that a body that has fallen from a height s has a velocity of $\sqrt{2gs}$.

This formula is used to find the velocity of flow of water from an orifice and is stated thus

$$v = \sqrt{2gh},$$

where h is the head in feet.

Example. A right cylindrical tank 4 ft. in diameter and 20 ft. high standing on end, has a circular orifice at the bottom from which a stream $1\frac{1}{2}$ in. in diameter will flow. Find the time to empty the tank when full.

Solution. Using feet and seconds as units we will write two expressions for the quantity Q of water flowing from the tank.

At any instant after the flow starts, if dt, dh, and dQ are corresponding differentials, t being the independent variable,

$$dQ = -4\pi \, dh,$$

which represents the volume of the small cylinder of water that would flow out due to the drop in the tank in time dt

if the flow became and remained as at the instant considered. The negative sign is used because dh is negative.

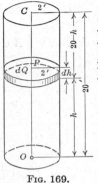

If at the orifice the rate of flow became and remained constant as at that instant, the quantity that would flow out would be the volume of a cylinder $1\frac{1}{2}$ in. $= \frac{1}{8}$ ft. in diameter and of length $\sqrt{2gh}\ dt$. From this

$$dQ = \tfrac{1}{4}\pi(\tfrac{1}{8})^2\sqrt{2gh}\ dt.$$

Equating these values of dQ,

$$\tfrac{1}{256}\pi\sqrt{2gh}\ dt = -4\pi\ dh.$$

Solving for dt, $\qquad dt = -\dfrac{1024}{\sqrt{2g}}h^{-\frac{1}{2}}dh.$

FIG. 169.

The limits on h are from 20 to 0.

Then $t = -\dfrac{1024}{\sqrt{2g}}\displaystyle\int_{20}^{0}h^{-\frac{1}{2}}dh = -\dfrac{1024}{\sqrt{2g}}\times 2h^{\frac{1}{2}}\Big]_{20}^{0} = 512\sqrt{5}.$

$\therefore$ time required is $512\sqrt{5}$ sec. $= 19.1-$ min.

EXERCISES

1. A right circular cylindrical tank standing on end, of height H and diameter D, empties through an orifice at the bottom giving a flow of area a in cross section. Find the time in seconds to empty the tank if dimensions are in feet.

2. A tank in the form of an inverted right circular cone has an altitude of 10 ft. and a diameter of base 8 ft. How long will it take to empty through an orifice in the vertex giving a stream 1 in. in diameter?

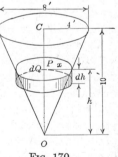

FIG. 170.

Suggestion. The differential of the flow Q in the cone is

$$dQ = -\pi x^2\ dh,$$

and for flow from orifice is

$$dQ = \tfrac{1}{4}\pi(\tfrac{1}{12})^2\sqrt{2gh}\ dt.$$

But $x:4 = h:10$. $\quad\therefore x = \tfrac{2}{5}h.$

PROBLEMS IN WORK

184. Force and work.—When a force acts through a distance the force is said to do work. Thus, if a body weighing 200 lb. is lifted 5 ft., we have a force of 200 lb. acting through a distance of 5 ft.

The unit of measure for work is usually taken as the work necessary to lift 1 lb. 1 ft. This unit is called a **foot-pound.** Other units are also used as, inch-pounds, gram-centimeters, foot-tons, etc.

A force of 1 lb. acting through 10 ft. does 10 ft.-lb. of work, or a force of 10 lb. acting through 1 ft. does 10 ft.-lb. of work. In general, *the number of units of work done is equal to the number of units of force acting times the number of units of distance through which it acts.* If W, F, and s stand for work, force, and distance respectively,

$$W = Fs.$$

If both force and distance are constants, a simple multiplication gives the work; but, if either or both vary, a problem in calculus arises. Here we will study in particular certain problems that actually arise.

The most usual cases for the variation of the force are:

(1) The force varying directly as the distance.

(2) The force varying inversely as some power of the distance.

If the distance is changing during the application of a force, the change in the work due to a change in the distance at any instant, provided that the rate of change at that instant becomes and remains constant, gives the differential of the work. This is expressed by

$$dW = F \, ds,$$

where s is the independent variable. The total work is found by integrating and choosing the proper limits. Of course before integrating, if F is a function of s, it must be so expressed.

185. Work when the force varies directly as the distance. This form of variation, as is well known, is stated in the equation

$$F = ks,$$

where k is a constant. (**P. M. II, Art. 116; H. S., Art. 316.**)

Examples of this are the force necessary to compress or extend a coiled wire spring, or the force necessary to stretch a bar of iron.

Example. A coiled wire (helical) spring is 8 in. long when no force is applied. It is found that a weight of 10 lb. will stretch it 1 in. Find the work done in stretching it from a length of 10 in. to 14 in.

Solution. Here the force varies as the elongation or stretch s, and hence is expressed by the relation

$$F = ks.$$

To find k we are given that a force of 10 lb. gives an elongation of 1 in. Substituting these values,

$$10 = k \cdot 1. \quad \therefore k = 10.$$
$$dW = F \, ds = 10s \, ds.$$

Integrating between the limits on s of 2 and 6, for when the spring is 10 in. long the elongation or stretch is 2 in.,

$$W = \int_2^6 10s \, ds = 5s^2 \Big]_2^6 = 5(6^2 - 2^2) = 160.$$

Since we have used 1 in. as the unit of length, the work done is 160 in.-lb. or $13\frac{1}{3}$ ft.-lb.

186. Work when the force varies inversely as some power of the distance.—This form of variation is expressed by the equation

$$F = \frac{k}{s^n}, \text{ or } Fs^n = k.$$

Example 1.   Air is in a cylinder one end being closed and the other end having a movable piston. Find the work done by the air in expanding from a volume of 4 cu. ft. to a volume of 8 cu. ft. It expands according to the law $pv^{1.41} = k$, where p is the pressure per square unit and v is volume, and has a pressure of 80 lb. per square inch when the volume is 4 cu. ft.

Solution.   Here it will help to keep the units straight if we first express 80 lb. per square inch as 11,520 lb. per square foot.

If A = area of piston, the force is

$$F = pA.$$

But $pv^{1.41} = k$ and hence $p = \dfrac{k}{v^{1.41}}.$

Then $F = \dfrac{Ak}{v^{1.41}}.$ But $dW = Fds.$

$$\therefore dW = \frac{Ak}{v^{1.41}}ds.$$

Here both v and s are variables and it is necessary to express s in terms of v or v in terms of s. We choose the former because the limits are on the volume.

From the formula for the volume of a cylinder

$$v = As. \quad \therefore s = \frac{v}{A}.$$

Differentiating, $ds = \dfrac{dv}{A}.$

Substituting, $dW = \dfrac{Ak}{v^{1.41}} \cdot \dfrac{dv}{A} = \dfrac{k}{v^{1.41}}dv.$

$$W = k\int_4^8 v^{-1.41}dv = -\frac{k}{0.41}v^{-0.41}\Big]_4^8$$

$$= -\frac{k}{0.41}(8^{-0.41} - 4^{-0.41}).$$

But $11,520 \times 4^{1.41} = k.$

$$\therefore W = -\frac{11,520 \times 4^{1.41}}{0.41} (8^{-0.41} - 4^{-0.41})$$

$$= -\frac{11,520 \times 4^{1.41}}{0.41} (0.4263 - 0.5664)$$

$$= \frac{11,520 \times 4^{1.41} \times 0.1401}{0.41} = 27,810.$$

$\therefore$ the work done is 27,810 ft.-lb.

187. Work to move electric charges.—An electric charge repels another like charge with a definite force which is inversely proportional to the square of the distance between the charges and directly proportional to the product of the charges.

Let m_1 and m_2 be the strength of the respective charges and s their distance apart, then if F is the force of repulsion,

$$F = k\frac{m_1 m_2}{s^2}.$$

Example. Suppose a positive charge of electricity of strength m_1 is concentrated at P_1 and a like charge of strength m_2 at P_2 a distance of s from P_1. Find the work done in moving the charge m_2 from $s = a$ to $s = b$.

Solution.   Here $F = k\dfrac{m_1 m_2}{s^2}.$

$$dW = F \, ds = km_1 m_2 \frac{ds}{s^2}.$$

$$W = km_1 m_2 \int_a^b \frac{ds}{s^2} = km_1 m_2 \left(\frac{1}{a} - \frac{1}{b}\right).$$

Here nothing has been said about the units; but if centimeters and grams are used, s is in centimeters and F in dynes. The unit strength of charge is defined as follows: Two charges are of equal and unit strength if they repel each other with a force of 1 dyne when placed 1 centimeter apart in air.

188. Work done in pumping out reservoirs.—In pumping out a reservoir as the surface is lowered the height to which the liquid is raised varies, and the work done is given by a definite integral.

Example. A cistern in the form of an inverted right circular cone is 20 ft. deep and 12 ft. in diameter at the top. If the water is 16 ft. deep in the cistern, find the work done in pumping out the cistern. The water is raised to a point 10 ft. above the top of the cistern and all friction is neglected.

Fig. 171.

Solution. We will consider this problem from the summation standpoint.

In Fig. 171, suppose the volume is divided into elements by planes Δs distance apart. Then if ΔW is the work of lifting one of these elements to S, we have approximately

$$\Delta W = s \cdot 62.5\pi r^2 \Delta s.$$

The total work is $W = \lim_{\Delta s \to 0} \sum_{s=14}^{s=30} 62.5\pi r^2 s \Delta s$

$$= 62.5\pi \int_{14}^{30} r^2 s \, ds.$$

Before integrating r must be expressed in terms of s. To do this we have $r : 6 = PQ : OQ$,

or $\qquad r : 6 = 30 - s : 20. \quad \therefore r = \dfrac{3(30 - s)}{10}.$

Substituting, $W = 62.5\pi \int_{14}^{30} \dfrac{9(30 - s)^2}{100} s \, ds$

$$= \frac{45\pi}{8} \int_{14}^{30} (900 - 60s + s^2)s \, ds$$

$$= \frac{45\pi}{8} (450s^2 - 20s^3 + \tfrac{1}{4}s^4) \Big]_{14}^{30} = 434,295.$$

$\therefore$ the work $= 434,295$ ft.-lb.

EXERCISES

1. Find the work done in stretching a helical spring whose original length is 12 in. from a length of 14 in. to 16 in., if a force of 50 lb. is required to stretch it to a length of 13 in.

2. Find the work done in compressing a helical spring whose original length is 12 in. from a length of 11 in. to 9 in., if a force of 60 lb. is required to compress it to a length of 11 in.

3. A volume of steam compressed in a cylinder by a piston expands in accordance with the law $pv^{\frac{4}{3}} = k$, from a volume of 4 cu. ft. to one of 8 cu. ft. If when $v = 5$ cu. ft., $p = 15,000$ lb. per square foot, find the work done.

4. Find the work required to compress 10 cu. ft. of air at a pressure of 14.5 lb. per square inch to a pressure of 100 lb. per square inch. Suppose that the relation between p and v is $pv^{1.4} = k$.

5. Find the work done in pumping water from a cylindrical tank 20 ft. in diameter and 60 ft. deep, if the water is raised 20 ft. above the top of the tank, and the water is lowered from a depth of 50 ft. to a depth of 20 ft. in the tank. Neglect friction.

6. A water tank is in the form of a hemisphere 16 ft. in diameter surmounted by a right circular cylinder 24 ft. high. Find the work done in pumping out the tank if the water stands 4 ft. from the top and is to be raised 12 ft. above the top of the tank.

7. Find the work done in stretching a round iron rod $\frac{5}{8}$ in. in diameter and 36 in. long to a length of 36.5 in. It is given that the stretching force F is given by the formula

$$F = \frac{EAs}{L},$$

where $E = 3 \times 10^7$ pounds per square inch for iron, A is the area of the cross section, s is elongation, and L is the original length of the bar.

8. Express as an integral with limits v_1 and v_2 the work done by a gas expanding isothermally according to van der Waal's equation

$$\left(p + \frac{a}{v^2} \right)\left(v - b \right) = C,$$

where a, b, and C are constants, from an initial volume v_1 to a final volume v_2.

CHAPTER XXII

SERIES. TAYLOR'S THEOREM

189. Power series.—In reading more advanced mathematics and articles in engineering and other scientific journals, one frequently finds reference to series. The subject of series and their applications has received much attention from mathematicians, and many volumes have been written on the subject. Here we shall devote a few pages to a particular kind of series.

Any succession of numbers as 1, 7, 9, 4, 16, $\cdots$, may be called a series; but since there seems to be no relation holding between the numbers forming the series we should hardly expect to be able to make any use of such a series.

The series 1, 3, 5, 7, 9, 11, $\cdots$, is a succession of numbers increasing by a common difference and is an **arithmetical progression.** Evidently one could find any number in the succession, for instance, the tenth number, and perhaps could make some use of such a series. This kind of series is studied in algebra.

A series of numbers that increase or decrease by a common ratio is called a **geometrical progression.** An example of such a series is 1, 2, 4, 8, 16, $\cdots$, where any one of the numbers divided by the number preceding it gives the same ratio. This series is also studied in algebra.

A **power series** is a series of the form

(1) $\quad a_0 + a_1x + a_2x^2 + a_3x^3 + \cdots + a_nx^n + \cdots,$

where the coefficients a_0, a_1, a_2, $\cdots$ are constants and x is a variable. Such a series may come to an end, that is, may have a definite number of terms, and is then called a **finite power series;** or it may have an unlimited number of terms, and is then called an **infinite power series.**

If the successive terms in an infinite power series decrease in size in such a manner that the limit of the sum of all the terms as their number increases without limit is a definite number, the series is said to be a **convergent series.** If this is not true the series is a **divergent series.**

Thus, if in the series (1) we let all the coefficients equal 1 and put $x = \frac{1}{2}$, we have the series

$$1 + \tfrac{1}{2} + \tfrac{1}{4} + \tfrac{1}{8} + \cdots + \frac{1}{2^n} + \cdots .$$

This is a series in which the terms decrease in such a way that the sum of the terms as a larger and larger number of them is taken becomes more and more nearly equal to 2. If S_n stands for the sum of the first n terms, then in the language of limits,

$$\lim_{n \to \infty} [S_n] = 2.$$

The important thing about the power series in the study of calculus is that a great variety of other functions can be readily expressed as power series; and, since the power series when convergent can be differentiated or integrated term by term, results can be gained that could not otherwise.

It now remains to study how different functions can be expressed as power series. This can sometimes be done in a very elementary manner.

Thus, $\dfrac{1}{1 - x}$ can be expressed as a power series by simple division. Actually performing the division, we find

$$\frac{1}{1 - x} = 1 + x + x^2 + x^3 + \cdots + x^{n-1} + \frac{x^n}{1 - x}.$$

This series can be used in place of the fraction $\dfrac{1}{1-x}$ for values of x which make the series converge. By trial one will find that values of x less than 1 in absolute value will make the series converge; while for values of x greater than 1 in absolute value, $\dfrac{1}{1-x}$ does not converge and does not equal the series.

By the binomial theorem many functions can be expressed as power series; but the theorem that applies in general is Taylor's Theorem. The rest of this chapter is devoted to the derivation and application of this theorem.

190. Law of the Mean.—In **Art. 133** it is shown that the definite integral $\int_a^b f(x)dx$ can be graphically represented by the area bounded by the curve $y = f(x)$, the x-axis, and the two ordinates corresponding to $x = a$ and $x = b$. If this area is divided by $b - a$, the altitude of a rectangle is found that has the same area as given by $\int_a^b f(x)dx$.

If the curve $y = f(x)$ and the area $\int_a^b f(x)dx$ are as in Fig. 172, then the altitude of the equivalent rectangle is equal to $f(x_1)$, where x_1 is a value of x in the interval a to b. In the figure the rectangle

$$MNSR = \int_a^b f(x)dx.$$

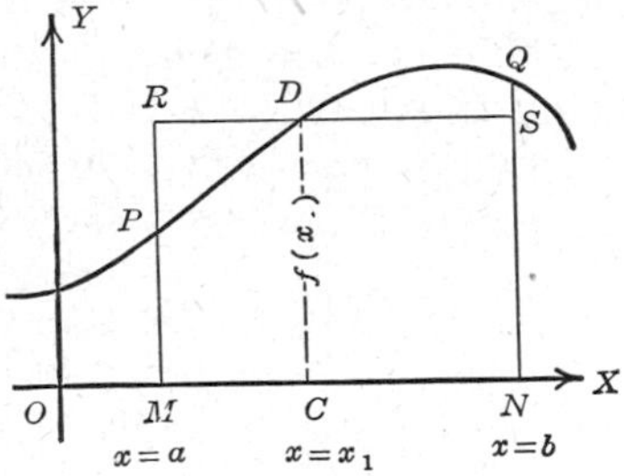

Fig. 172.

The value of $f(x_1)$ is called the **mean value** of $f(x)$ between $x = a$ and $x = b$, and is given by the formula

$$f(x_1) = \frac{\int_a^b f(x)dx}{b - a}.$$

In order to have a suitable notation we will start with $f'(x)$ which is the derivative of $f(x)$, and use as limits a and x, where x may be considered of any value desired.

Then $\qquad f'(x_1) = \dfrac{\int_a^x f'(x)dx}{x - a}.$

But $\int_a^x f'(x)dx = f(x) - f(a).$ $\qquad\qquad$ By **Art. 134.**

$\qquad \therefore f'(x_1) = \dfrac{f(x) - f(a)}{x - a},$

or $\qquad\qquad f(x) = f(a) + f'(x_1)(x - a).$

It is to be noted that x_1 is some constant value that lies in the interval from a to x.

The fact stated in the formula

[62] $\qquad\qquad \mathbf{f(x) = f(a) + f'(x_1)(x - a)}$

is known as the **Law of the Mean** or as the **Mean Value Theorem.**

191. Extended Law of the Mean.—If we start with $f''(x)$, the derivative of $f'(x)$, then as in the previous article,

$$f''(x_2) = \frac{\int_a^x f''(x)dx}{x - a} = \frac{f'(x) - f'(a)}{x - a},$$

or $\qquad\qquad f'(x) = f'(a) + f''(x_2)(x - a).$

Multiplying by dx, $f'(x)dx = f'(a)dx + f''(x_2)\,(x - a)dx.$

Integrating between the limits $x = a$ and $x = x$, noting that $f'(a)$ and $f''(x_2)$ are constants,

$$\int_a^x f'(x)dx = f'(a)\int_a^x dx + f''(x_2)\int_a^x (x - a)dx.$$

$$f(x) - f(a) = f'(a)(x - a) + f''(x_2)\frac{(x - a)^2}{2}.$$

$$\therefore \mathbf{f(x) = f(a) + f'(a)(x - a) + f''(x_2)\frac{(x - a)^2}{2}}.$$

This is the **Law of the Mean once extended.**

In like manner the Law of the Mean can be extended to any number of terms. We will carry it one more step.

Starting with $f'''(x)$, we have from the first extended Law of the Mean

$$f'(x) = f'(a) + f''(a)(x - a) + \frac{f'''(x_3)}{2}(x - a)^2.$$

Multiplying by dx and integrating between the limits $x = a$ and $x = x$,

$$\int_a^x f'(x)dx = f'(a)\int_a^x dx + f''(a)\int_a^x (x - a)dx$$

$$+ \frac{f'''(x_3)}{2}\int_a^x (x - a)^2 dx.$$

$$f(x) - f(a) = f'(a)(x - a) + \frac{f''(a)}{2}(x - a)^2$$

$$+ \frac{f'''(x_3)}{2\cdot 3}(x - a)^3.$$

$$\therefore f(x) = f(a) + f'(a)(x - a) + \frac{f''(a)}{2}(x - a)^2$$

$$+ \frac{(f'''x_3)}{2\cdot 3}(x - a)^3.$$

It should be noted that the right-hand member is a power series in $x - a$, and that, because the area under a curve is dealt with, $f(x)$ and its derivatives must be *single valued* and *continuous*.

192. Taylor's Theorem.—By extending the Law of the Mean to include the n-th derivative we have the proof of the following theorem known as **Taylor's Theorem.**

THEOREM. *If $f(x)$ and its first n derivatives are single valued and continuous throughout the interval from a to x,*

$$[63] \ f(x) = f(a) + f'(a)(x - a) + \frac{f''(a)}{2!}(x - a)^2$$

$$+ \frac{f'''(a)}{3!}(x - a)^3 + \cdots + \frac{f^{(n-1)}(a)}{(n - 1)!}(x - a)^{n-1}$$

$$+ \frac{f^{(n)}(x_n)}{n!}(x - a)^n,$$

where x_n is some value in the interval a to x.

This is generally considered the most far-reaching theorem in the calculus.

If in [63] we put $a = x$ and $x = x + h$, a second form of Taylor's Theorem results as follows:

$$[64] \quad f(x + h) = f(x) + f'(x)h + \frac{f''(x)}{2!} h^2 + \frac{f'''(x)}{3!} h^3 + \cdots$$
$$+ \frac{f^{(n-1)}(x)}{(n-1)!} h^{n-1} + \frac{f^{(n)}(x_n)}{n!} h^n,$$

where x_n is in the interval x to $x + h$.

Taylor's Theorem is named after Dr. Brook Taylor who discovered the theorem and published it in his "Methodus Incrementorum" in 1715.

193. MacLaurin's Theorem.—In 1742 in his "Treatise of Fluxions *Vol. II*," Colin MacLaurin gave a theorem usually called **MacLaurin's Theorem.** He recognized that it was a special case of Taylor's Theorem. MacLaurin's Theorem is readily derived from Taylor's Theorem [63] by putting $a = 0$, that is, by making the interval start at the origin. This gives

$$[65] \quad f(x) = f(0) + xf'(0) + \frac{x^2}{2!} f''(0) + \frac{x^3}{3!} f'''(0) + \cdots$$
$$+ \frac{x^{n-1}}{(n-1)!} f^{(n-1)}(0) + \frac{x^n}{n!} f^{(n)}(x_n),$$

where x_n lies in the interval 0 to x. It is to be noted that this gives a power series in x.

194. The remainder in Taylor's and MacLaurin's Theorems.—The last term given in these theorems is known as the **remainder,** and evidently is equal to the difference between the value of the function and the value of the first n terms of the series. For this reason it is sometimes called the **error term** in the series. *The series is convergent if the limit of the remainder is zero as the number of terms becomes infinite.*

The usefulness of the series depends to a great extent on how rapidly the terms decrease in value as we pass toward the right. This can be brought out more clearly in special examples.

195. Expansion by Taylor's and MacLaurin's Theorems. When a function is expressed as a power series by either Taylor's or MacLaurin's Theorem it is said to be **expanded by that theorem.** It should be noted that:

(1) To expand $f(x)$ into a power series in $x - a$ use Taylor's Theorem **[63]**.

(2) To expand $f(x + h)$ into a power series in h use Taylor's Theorem **[64]**. This can be used to advantage when x has a value such that $f(x)$ and all of its derivatives are readily found.

(3) To expand $f(x)$ into a power series in x use MacLaurin's Theorem **[65]**.

Example 1.   Expand $\cos x$ into a power series in x.

Solution.   Since it is required to expand a function of x into a power series in x, MacLaurin's Theorem is used. In order to substitute in the theorem it is necessary to find $n - 1$ derivatives and their values when $x = 0$.

Differentiating successively and putting $x = 0$,

$$
\begin{aligned}
f(x) &= \cos x, & f(0) &= 1, \\
f'(x) &= -\sin x, & f'(0) &= 0, \\
f''(x) &= -\cos x, & f''(0) &= -1 \\
f'''(x) &= \sin x, & f'''(0) &= 0, \\
f^{IV}(x) &= \cos x, & f^{IV}(0) &= 1, \\
f^{V}(x) &= -\sin x, & f^{V}(0) &= 0, \\
f^{VI}(x) &= -\cos x, & f^{VI}(0) &= -1,
\end{aligned}
$$

$\cdot \quad \cdot \quad \cdot$ $\cdot \quad \cdot \quad \cdot$

Substituting these values in MacLaurin's Theorem,

$$
\cos x = 1 - \frac{x^2}{2!} + \frac{x^4}{4!} - \frac{x^6}{6!} + \cdots
$$

Here the remainder after n terms is $\pm \dfrac{x^n}{n!}(\sin x_n \text{ or } \cos x_n)$,

and in either case is not greater in absolute value than $\dfrac{x^n}{n!}$,

which approaches zero as n becomes infinite.

The meaning of the series

$$\cos x = 1 - \frac{x^2}{2!} + \frac{x^4}{4!} - \frac{x^6}{6!} + \cdots$$

is that for any value of x, expressed in radians, the value of $\cos x$ can actually be computed to any desired degree of accuracy.

Example 2. Using the series of example 1 compute $\cos x$ when $x = \frac{1}{2}$ radian.

Solution. Substituting in the series,

$$\cos \tfrac{1}{2} = 1 - \frac{(\tfrac{1}{2})^2}{2!} + \frac{(\tfrac{1}{2})^4}{4!} - \frac{(\tfrac{1}{2})^6}{6!} + \cdots$$

$$= 1 - 0.125 + 0.002604 - 0.000022 + \cdots$$
$$= 0.877582.$$

Since $\frac{1}{2}$ radian $= 28° \, 38' \, 52.4''$, we should have approximately

$$\cos 28° \, 38' \, 52.4'' = 0.87758.$$

From a table of natural functions the value of the cosine of this angle is found to be 0.87758. In this case then the first four terms of the series gave the result correct to five decimal places. For this value of x we would say that this series is rather rapidly converging. If a smaller value of x is taken, the series will converge still more rapidly; and a largervalue for x will make the series converge less rapidly.

Example 3. Expand into a power series in $x + 2$, the function $f(x) = x^4 - 3x^3 + 2x^2 - x + 2$.

Solution. Here it is necessary to use Taylor's Theorem [63].

Differentiating successively and finding the values when -2 is substituted for x,

$$f(x) = x^4 - 3x^3 + 2x^2 - x + 2,$$
$$f'(x) = 4x^3 - 9x^2 + 4x - 1,$$
$$f''(x) = 12x^2 - 18x + 4,$$
$$f'''(x) = 24x - 18,$$
$$f^{IV}(x) = 24,$$
$$f^{V}(x) = 0,$$

$$f(a) = f(-2) = 52,$$
$$f'(a) = f'(-2) = -77,$$
$$f''(a) = f''(-2) = 88,$$
$$f'''(a) = f'''(-2) = -66,$$
$$f^{IV}(a) = f^{IV}(-2) = 24,$$
$$f^{V}(a) = f^{V}(-2) = 0.$$

Here the fifth and all higher derivatives are zero. Hence the series ends with the fifth term. Substituting the values above in the formula [**63**],

$$f(x) = 52 - 77(x + 2) + \frac{88}{2!}(x + 2)^2 - \frac{66}{3!}(x + 2)^3$$
$$+ \frac{24}{4!}(x + 2)^4$$

$$= 52 - 77(x + 2) + 44(x + 2)^2 - 11(x + 2)^3 + (x + 2)^4.$$

Example 4. Expand e^{2x} into a power series in x and express the remainder.

Solution. This is a function to be expressed as a power series in x, so we use MacLaurin's Theorem.

$$f(x) = e^{2x}, \qquad\qquad f(0) = 1,$$
$$f'(x) = 2e^{2x}, \qquad\qquad f'(0) = 2,$$
$$f''(x) = 2^2 e^{2x}, \qquad\qquad f''(0) = 2^2,$$
$$f'''(x) = 2^3 e^{2x}, \qquad\qquad f'''(0) = 2^3,$$

$$\cdots \qquad\qquad\qquad \cdots$$

$$f^{(n)}(x) = 2^n e^{2x}, \qquad\qquad f^{(n)}(0) = 2^n.$$

Substituting in the formula [**65**],

$$e^{2x} = 1 + 2x + 2x^2 + \frac{2^2}{3}x^3 + \frac{2^3}{3}x^4 + \frac{2^4}{15}x^5 + \cdots + \frac{2^n}{n!}e^{2 \times n}$$

where x_n lies in the interval 0 to x. Show that the remainder term approaches zero as n becomes infinite.

Example 5.   Expand $\log (x + h)$ into a power series in h when x has the value a.

Solution.   Use Taylor's Theorem [**64**].

$$f(x + h) = \log (x + h), \qquad f(a + h) = \log (a + h),$$
$$f(x) = \log x, \qquad f(a) = \log a,$$
$$f'(x) = \frac{1}{x}, \qquad f'(a) = \frac{1}{a},$$
$$f''(x) = -\frac{1}{x^2}, \qquad f''(a) = -\frac{1}{a^2},$$
$$f'''(x) = \frac{2}{x^3}, \qquad f'''(a) = \frac{2}{a^3},$$
$$f^{IV}(x) = -\frac{3!}{x^4}, \qquad f^{IV}(a) = -\frac{3!}{a^4},$$

Substituting in the formula,

$$\log (a + h) = \log a + \frac{h}{a} - \frac{h^2}{2a^2} + \frac{h^3}{3a^3} - \frac{h^4}{4a^4} + \cdots$$

If $a = 1$ this becomes

$$\log (1 + h) = 0 + h - \tfrac{1}{2}h^2 + \tfrac{1}{3}h^3 - \tfrac{1}{4}h^4 + \cdots$$

EXERCISES

1. Expand $\sin x$ into a power series in x.   Use the series to compute the value of $\sin (\tfrac{1}{2}$ radian).   Of $\sin 1$.

2. Expand e^x into a power series in x.   Use the series to evaluate e by putting $x = 1$ in the expansion.

3. Expand $4x^3 - 18x^2 + 12x - 3$ into a power series in $x - 4$.

4. Expand $\sin x$ into a power series in $x - a$.

5. Expand $e^{\sin x}$ into a power series in x.

6. Use the expansion of exercise 1 and integrate $\int \frac{\sin x}{x} dx$. The result should be the integral formula 192.

7. Integrate $\int \frac{\cos x}{x} dx$, and thus derive the formula 193.

8. Evaluate $\int_0^1 e^{-x^2} dx$. This is a very important integral in the theory of probability.

196. Indeterminate forms.—The usual way to find the value of a function corresponding to a particular value of the independent variable is to substitute that value of the independent variable into the expression defining the function. In certain cases when this is done no value is found. Seven such cases arise of which the following are illustrations:

(1) If 2 is substituted for x in $\frac{x^2 - 4}{x - 2}$, it takes the form $\frac{0}{0}$.

(2) If 0 is substituted for x in $\frac{\log x}{\cot x}$, it takes the form $-\frac{\infty}{\infty}$.

(3) If 0 is substituted for x in $x \cot x$, it takes the form $0 \cdot \infty$.

(4) If 1 is substituted for x in $\frac{1}{x - 1} - \frac{1}{\log x}$, it takes the form $\infty - \infty$.

(5) If 0 is substituted for x in $(\sin x)^{\tan x}$, it takes the form 0^0.

(6) If 0 is substituted for x in $(\csc x)^{\tan x}$, it takes the form ∞^0.

(7) If $2a$ is substituted for x in $\left(3 - \frac{x}{a}\right)^{\tan \frac{\pi x}{4a}}$, it takes the form 1^∞.

Definitions. When a function takes one of the forms

$$\frac{0}{0}, \ \frac{\infty}{\infty}, \ 0 \cdot \infty, \ \infty - \infty, \ 0^0, \ \infty^0, \ 1^\infty,$$

for a certain value of the independent variable, it is said

to be **indeterminate** and its value is not found by the substitution.

These seven forms are called **indeterminate forms**.

If when a is substituted for x, $f(x)$ takes an indeterminate form then $\lim_{x \to a} [f(x)]$ is defined to be the **value of the function** for $x = a$.

The limits may often be found by some algebraic. or trigonometric transformation. In this manner

$$\lim_{x \to 0} \left[\frac{\sin x}{x} \right] = 1$$

was found in **Art. 70.** More general methods for finding these limits or, as we say, for evaluating the indeterminate forms, depend upon differentiating, and are proved by Taylor's Theorem. These methods will now be outlined.

RULE. *To evaluate a function which takes the form $\frac{0}{0}$ when the particular value of the variable is substituted, first, find the derivative of the numerator for a new numerator and the derivative of the denominator for a new denominator; second, substitute the value of the variable in the new fraction. If this gives a definite value, it is the value required, if it is still of the form $\frac{0}{0}$, repeat the process until a definite form is found.*

This rule can be established by Taylor's Theorem as follows:

Let $f(x)$ and $\varphi(x)$ be two functions such that $f(x) = 0$ and $\varphi(x) = 0$ when $x = a$.

Then $\frac{f(x)}{\varphi(x)}$ takes the form $\frac{0}{0}$ when a is substituted for x.

Expand both $f(x)$ and $\varphi(x)$ by Taylor's Theorem into a power series in $x - a$.

$$\frac{f(x)}{\varphi(x)} =$$

$$\frac{f(a) + f'(a)(x-a) + \dfrac{f''(a)}{2!}(x-a)^2 + \dfrac{f'''(a)}{3!}(x-a)^3 + \cdots}{\varphi(a) + \varphi'(a)(x-a) + \dfrac{\varphi''(a)}{2!}(x-a)^2 + \dfrac{\varphi'''(a)}{3!}(x-a)^3 + \cdots}.$$

Now it is given that $f(a) = 0$ and $\varphi(a) = 0$. Dropping these and dividing both numerator and denominator by $x - a$, gives

$$\lim_{x \to a} \left[\frac{f(x)}{\varphi(x)}\right]$$

$$= \lim_{x \to a} \left[\frac{f'(a) + \dfrac{f''(a)}{2!}(x-a) + \dfrac{f'''(a)}{3!}(x-a)^2 + \cdots}{\varphi'(a) + \dfrac{\varphi''(a)}{2!}(x-a) + \dfrac{\varphi'''(a)}{3!}(x-a)^2 + \cdots}\right]$$

$$= \frac{f'(a)}{\varphi'(a)}.$$

If this is definite it is the $\lim\limits_{x \to a}\left[\dfrac{f(x)}{\varphi(x)}\right]$. If it is of the form $\dfrac{0}{0}$, both $f'(a)$ and $\varphi'(a)$ are zero and after dividing the numerator and denominator by $x - a$, we have

$$\lim_{x \to a}\left[\frac{f(x)}{\varphi(x)}\right] = \frac{f''(a)}{\varphi''(a)}.$$

If this is definite, it is the limit sought. If it is not definite, the same reasoning is continued.

In applying the rule, the expressions in numerator and denominator should be kept in their simplest forms at each step of the work.

Example 1. Find $\lim\limits_{x \to 0}\left[\dfrac{e^x + e^{-x} - 2}{x \sin x}\right]$ or, as we say, find the value of $\dfrac{e^x + e^{-x} - 2}{x \sin x}$ when $x = 0$.

Solution. Substituting 0 for x, the fraction takes the form $\frac{0}{0}$.

Then by the rule differentiate both numerator and denominator.

$$\lim_{x \to 0}\left[\frac{e^x + e^{-x} - 2}{x \sin x}\right] = \lim_{x \to 0}\left[\frac{e^x - e^{-x}}{x \cos x + \sin x}\right].$$

Now substitute 0 for x in $\frac{e^x - e^{-x}}{x \cos x + \sin x}$. If the value is definite, it is the limit sought. Here it is of the form $\frac{0}{0}$, and the differentiating process is repeated.

$$\lim_{x \to 0}\left[\frac{e^x - e^{-x}}{x \cos x + \sin x}\right] = \lim_{x \to 0}\left[\frac{e^x + e^{-x}}{2 \cos x - x \sin x}\right].$$

Substituting $x = 0$ gives the definite value 1.

$$\therefore \lim_{x \to 0}\left[\frac{e^x + e^{-x} - 2}{x \sin x}\right] = 1.$$

The form $\frac{\infty}{\infty}$. It can be readily shown that the function that gives the form $\frac{\infty}{\infty}$ when a certain value of the variable is substituted can be evaluated in exactly the same manner as that of the form $\frac{0}{0}$.

Example 2. Find the value of $\frac{\log x}{\cot x}$ when $x = 0$.

Solution. Applying the differentiation process as for $\frac{0}{0}$,

$$\lim_{x \to 0}\left[\frac{\log x}{\cot x}\right] = \lim_{x \to 0}\left[\frac{\frac{1}{x}}{-\csc^2 x}\right] = \lim_{x \to 0}\left[\frac{-\sin^2 x}{x}\right]$$

$$= \lim_{x \to 0}\left[\frac{-2 \sin x \cos x}{1}\right] = 0.$$

The form $0 \cdot \infty$. Functions of this form are put into one of the forms $\dfrac{0}{0}$ or $\dfrac{\infty}{\infty}$ by putting the reciprocal of one of the functions as a denominator.

Example 3. Find the value of $(x - \tfrac{1}{2}\pi) \tan x$ when $x = \tfrac{1}{2}\pi$.

Solution. Since $\tan x = \dfrac{1}{\cot x}$,

$$(x - \tfrac{1}{2}\pi) \tan x = \frac{x - \tfrac{1}{2}\pi}{\cot x},$$

which takes the form $\dfrac{0}{0}$ when $x = \tfrac{1}{2}\pi$.

Then $\displaystyle\lim_{x \to \tfrac{1}{2}\pi}\left[\frac{x - \tfrac{1}{2}\pi}{\cot x}\right] = \lim_{x \to \tfrac{1}{2}\pi}\left[\frac{1}{-\csc^2 x}\right] = -1.$

The form $\infty - \infty$. This can be put in the form $\dfrac{0}{0}$ or $\dfrac{\infty}{\infty}$ as illustrated in the following example.

Example 4. Evaluate $\dfrac{1}{x - 1} - \dfrac{1}{\log x}$ when $x = 1$.

Solution. Uniting the fractions,

$$\frac{1}{x - 1} - \frac{1}{\log x} = \frac{\log x - x + 1}{(x - 1) \log x},$$

which takes the form $\dfrac{0}{0}$ when 1 is substituted for x.

Then $\displaystyle\lim_{x \to 1}\left[\frac{\log x - x + 1}{(x - 1) \log x}\right] = \lim_{x \to 1}\left[\frac{\dfrac{1}{x} - 1}{(x - 1)\dfrac{1}{x} + \log x}\right]$

$= \displaystyle\lim_{x \to 1}\left[\frac{1 - x}{x - 1 + x \log x}\right] = \lim_{x \to 1}\left[\frac{-1}{1 + 1 + \log x}\right] = -\tfrac{1}{2}.$

The forms $0^0, \infty^0,$ *and* 1^∞. These are called the **exponential forms** and arise from such a form as $[f(x)]^{\varphi(x)}$. They can be evaluated as follows:

Let $$u = [f(x)]^{\varphi(x)}.$$

Taking logarithms, $\log u = \varphi(x) \log f(x)$.

This can readily be put into the form $\frac{0}{0}$ or $\frac{\infty}{\infty}$ and evaluated.

Example 5.   Evaluate $(\cos 2x)^{\frac{1}{x^2}}$ when $x = 0$.
Solution.   This is of the form 1^{∞}.

Let $$u = (\cos 2x)^{\frac{1}{x^2}}.$$

Then $\log u = \dfrac{\log \cos 2x}{x^2}$, which is of the form $\dfrac{0}{0}$.

Then
$$\lim_{x \to 0}\left[\frac{\log \cos 2x}{x^2}\right] = \lim_{x \to 0}\left[\frac{-\dfrac{2 \sin 2x}{\cos 2x}}{2x}\right]$$

$$= \lim_{x \to 0}\left[\frac{-\tan 2x}{x}\right] = \lim_{x \to 0}\left[\frac{-2 \sec^2 2x}{1}\right] = -2.$$

Hence $\log u = -2$ or $u = \dfrac{1}{e^2}$ when $x \to 0$.

$$\therefore \lim_{x \to 0}\left[(\cos 2x)^{\frac{1}{x^2}}\right] = \frac{1}{e^2}.$$

EXERCISES

Evaluate the following functions for the values of the variables given in each case:

1. $\dfrac{\cos x - 1}{x}$ when $x = 0$.

2. $\dfrac{x \sin x}{x - 2 \sin x}$ when $x = 0$.

3. $\sec x - \tan x$ when $x = \frac{1}{2}\pi$.

4. $\dfrac{\tan x}{\tan 3x}$ when $x = \frac{1}{2}\pi$.

5. x^x when $x = 0$.

6. $x \sin \dfrac{2}{x}$ when $x = \infty$.

7. $\dfrac{x}{e^{ax}}$ when $x = \infty$.

8. $\left(\dfrac{1}{x}\right)^{\tan x}$ when $x = 0$.

9. $(x + e^x)^{\frac{1}{x}}$ when $x = 0$.

10. $x \log \left(1 + \dfrac{a}{x}\right)$ when $x = \infty$

11. $\left(3 - \dfrac{x}{a}\right)^{\tan \frac{\pi x}{4a}}$ when $x = 2a$.

12. $\dfrac{\log \tan 2x}{\log \tan x}$ when $x = \frac{1}{2}\pi$.

13. $(\log x)^x$ when $x = 0$.

14. $\dfrac{e}{e^x - e} - \dfrac{1}{x - 1}$ when $x = 1$

15. $(e^x + x)^{\frac{1}{x}}$ when $x = 0$.

16. $2^x \sin \dfrac{a}{2^x}$ when $x = \infty$.

CHAPTER XXIII

ANALYTIC GEOMETRY

197. In the treatment of the calculus in the previous chapters some knowledge of analytic geometry is assumed. The student who has this minimum acquaintance with the accepted manner of representing curves by equations, and

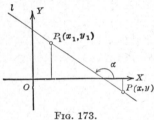

Fig. 173.

conversely, should have no great difficulties in understanding the usual subjects of calculus. However, if one expects to appreciate fully certain subjects in calculus he should gain a more extensive knowledge of analytic geometry. In various places in the previous chapters certain ideas in analytic geometry have been developed and discussed; but it was not always convenient to bridge gaps that occurred. In order to help close up these gaps a few other facts than those already discussed are gathered in this chapter.

198. Straight line and its equation.—The different forms of the equation of a straight line are derived from the different sets of conditions that determine a straight line. Suppose the straight line l, Fig. 173, passes through the point $P_1(x_1, y_1)$, and that its direction is given by its slope $m = \tan \alpha$. If $P(x, y)$ is any point on l, then the slope of PP_1 must be constant and equal to m.

But the slope m of PP_1 is $m = \dfrac{y - y_1}{x - x_1}.$

376

Clearing this equation of fractions,

$$y - y_1 = m(x - x_1),$$

which is the **point slope form** of the **equation of a straight line.**

In Fig. 174, let the intercept of the line on the y-axis equal b and let the slope of the line equal m. Since the y-intercept has the coördinates $(0, b)$ this problem is a special case of the point slope form.

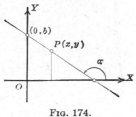

Fig. 174.

Putting $x_1 = 0$ and $y_1 = b$ in $y - y_1 = m(x - x_1)$ gives

$$y - b = mx, \text{ or}$$

$$y = mx + b,$$

which is the **slope intercept form** of the **equation of a straight line.**

Let the two points through which the line passes be $P_1(x_1, y_1)$ and $P_2(x_2, y_2)$. Since P_1 is a point on the line and m is the slope of P_1P_2, then by substituting for m its value $\dfrac{y_1 - y_2}{x_1 - x_2}$ in the equation $y - y_1 = m(x - x_1)$ gives the equation

$$y - y_1 = \frac{y_1 - y_2}{x_1 - x_2}(x - x_1),$$

which is the **two point form** of the **equation of the straight line.**

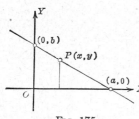

Fig. 175.

If the straight line cuts both axes, let its x-intercept, Fig. 175, equal a and its y-intercept equal b. Its equation can now be derived from the equation ·

$$y - y_1 = \frac{y_1 - y_2}{x_1 - x_2}(x - x_1)$$

by replacing (x_1, y_1) by $(a, 0)$ and (x_2, y_2) by $(0, b)$.   This gives

$$y = \frac{-b}{a}(x - a).$$

Multiplying both sides of this equation by $\frac{1}{b}$, and transposing the x-term to the left-hand side gives

$$\frac{x}{a} + \frac{y}{b} = 1,$$

which is the **intercept form of the equation of a straight line.**

Equation of first degree.   As might be expected from the equations already given of a straight line, we have the following:

THEOREM.   *Every equation of a straight line is of the first degree in one or two variables.*

The converse of this theorem is also true.   Therefore the general equation of the first degree, which is stated in the form

$$Ax + By + C = 0,$$

is the equation of a straight line.

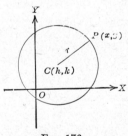

FIG. 176.

199. The circle and its equation.— A circle is defined to be the locus of all points in a plane equidistant from a fixed point in the plane called the center of the circle.

Let the center of the circle be the fixed point $C(h, k)$, Fig. 176, and let the constant distance, or radius, be r.

Then if $P(x, y)$ is any point on the circle, the distance $PC = r$.

But $PC = \sqrt{(x - h)^2 + (y - k)^2}.$

Then $\sqrt{(x - h)^2 + (y - k)^2} = r$

$\therefore (x - h)^2 + (y - k)^2 = r^2,$

which is the equation of a circle with its center at the point (h, k) and with a radius r.

If the center of the circle is at the origin, $h = 0$ and $k = 0$. Then the equation of the circle becomes

$$\mathbf{x}^2 + \mathbf{y}^2 = \mathbf{r}^2.$$

General equation of a circle. The equation

$$(x - h)^2 + (y - k)^2 = r^2$$

when expanded becomes

$$x^2 + y^2 - 2hx - 2ky + h^2 + k^2 - r^2 = 0.$$

This is of the form

$$x^2 + y^2 + Dx + Ey + F = 0,$$

where $D = -2h$, $E = -2k$, and $F = h^2 + k^2 - r^2$.

Solving these three equations for h, k, and r in terms of D, E, and F,

$$h = -\tfrac{1}{2}D, \; k = -\tfrac{1}{2}E, \text{ and } r = \tfrac{1}{2}\sqrt{D^2 + E^2 - 4F}.$$

These formulas can be used to find the coördinates of the center and the radius of any circle whose equation is in the form

$$x^2 + y^2 + Dx + Ey + F = 0.$$

Thus, $x^2 + y^2 - 2x - 4y - 4 = 0$ is the equation of a circle having its center at the point $(1, 2)$, found from

$$h = -\tfrac{1}{2}D = 1, \text{ and } k = -\tfrac{1}{2}E = 2;$$

and having a radius 3, found from

$$r = \tfrac{1}{2}\sqrt{D^2 + E^2 - 4F} = \tfrac{1}{2}\sqrt{4 + 16 + 16} = 3.$$

200. Conic sections.—When a plane intersects a circular cone there may be formed a circle, a parabola, an ellipse, an hyperbola, or, for certain positions of the plane, a point, two intersecting straight lines, or two coincident straight lines.

In Fig 177, plane C is perpendicular to the axis of the cone and forms a circle; plane E is inclined to the axis but intersects only one nappe of the cone and forms an ellipse;

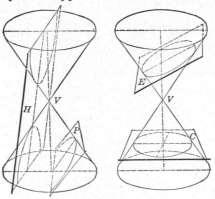

Fig. 177.

plane P is parallel to an element of the cone and forms a parabola; plane H intersects both nappes of the cone and forms an hyperbola. The intersection is a point when a plane passes through the point V only; two intersecting straight lines are formed when the plane passes through V and intersects the nappes; and two coincident lines are formed when the plane passes through V and is tangent to the cone.

The conic sections were first studied by the Greeks, who discovered and discussed their properties by methods of geometry. The modern method of studying these figures is by the help of algebra, which makes the treatment much simpler. For the purpose of this method of treatment, other definitions of the conic sections are given; but it can be readily shown that these definitions agree with the definitions mentioned above.

201. The parabola.—The equations

$$y^2 = 2px \text{ and } x^2 = 2py$$

are equations of parabolas with vertices at the origin. The parabola $y^2 = 2px$ has its axis along the x-axis; and the para-

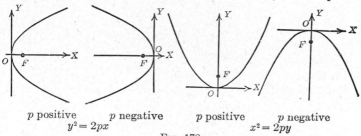

p positive	p negative	p positive	p negative
$y^2 = 2px$		$x^2 = 2py$	

Fig. 178.

bola $x^2 = 2py$ has its axis along the y-axis. In each case $\frac{1}{2}p$ is the distance between the focus V and the vertex F of the parabola. These relations are shown in Fig. 178.

A parabola having its vertex at the point (h, k) has the equation

$$(y - k)^2 = 2p(x - h)$$

when its axis is parallel to the x-axis; and the equation

$$(x - h)^2 = 2p(y - k)$$

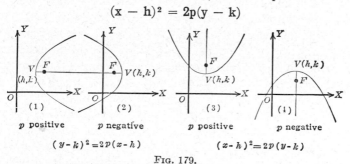

p positive	p negative	p positive	p negative
$(y-k)^2 = 2p(x-h)$		$(x-h)^2 = 2p(y-k)$	

Fig. 179.

when its axis is parallel to the y-axis. These relations are shown in Fig. 179.

Every equation of the form

$$y^2 + Dx + Ey + F = 0,$$

where $D \neq 0$, represents a parabola whose axis is parallel to the x-axis; and every equation of the form

$$x^2 + Dx + Ey + F = 0,$$

where $E \neq 0$, represents a parabola whose axis is parallel to the y-axis.

202. The ellipse.—In the equations of the ellipse a is the semimajor axis and b is the semiminor axis.

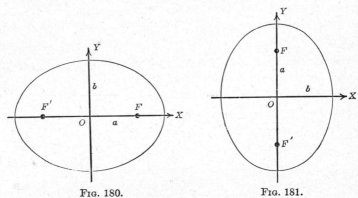

FIG. 180.   FIG. 181.

When the center is at the origin and the major axis on the x-axis, Fig. 180, the equation is

$$\frac{x^2}{a^2} + \frac{y^2}{b^2} = 1.$$

When the center is at the origin and the major axis on the y-axis, Fig. 181, the equation is

$$\frac{y^2}{a^2} + \frac{x^2}{b^2} = 1.$$

When the center is at the point (h, k) and the major axis parallel to the x-axis the equation is

$$\frac{(x - h)^2}{a^2} + \frac{(y - k)^2}{b^2} = 1.$$

When the center is at the point (h, k) and the major axis parallel to the y-axis the equation is

$$\frac{(y - k)^2}{a^2} + \frac{(x - h)^2}{b^2} = 1.$$

Every equation of the form

$$Ax^2 + Cy^2 + Dx + Ey + F = 0,$$

where A and C have like signs but different values, represents an ellipse with axes parallel to the coördinate axes.

203. The hyperbola.—In the equations of the hyperbola $2a$ is the length of the principal axis between the vertices, and $2b$ the length of the conjugate axis.

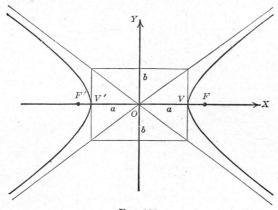

Fig. 182.

When the center is at the origin and the principal axis along the x-axis, Fig. 182, the equation is

$$\frac{x^2}{a^2} - \frac{y^2}{b^2} = 1.$$

When the center is at the origin and the principal axis along the y-axis the equation is

$$\frac{y^2}{a^2} - \frac{x^2}{b^2} = 1.$$

When the center is at the point (h, k) and the principal axis parallel to the x-axis the equation is

$$\frac{(x - h)^2}{a^2} - \frac{(y - k)^2}{b^2} = 1.$$

When the center is at the point (h, k) and the principal axis parallel to the y-axis the equation is

$$\frac{(y - k)^2}{a^2} - \frac{(x - h)^2}{b^2} = 1.$$

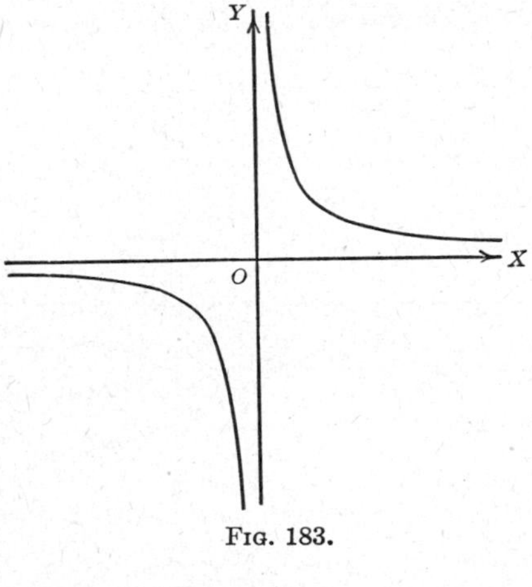

Fig. 183.

Every equation of the form

$$Ax^2 + Cy^2 + Dx + Ey + F = 0,$$

where A and C have unlike signs, represents an hyperbola with axes parallel to the coördinate axes.

Equilateral hyperbola. When $a = b$ the equation

$$\frac{x^2}{a^2} - \frac{y^2}{b^2} = 1 \text{ becomes } x^2 - y^2 = a^2,$$

and the hyperbola is said to be **equilateral.**

The form of the equation of the equilateral hyperbola most frequently used is

$$xy = c,$$

where c is a constant. This hyperbola lies in the first and third quadrants as shown in Fig. 183.

204. The cycloid.—The plane curve traced by a fixed point on a circle as the circle rolls along a fixed straight line is called a **cycloid.** The rolling circle is called the **generator circle** and the fixed straight line the **base.**

The parametric equations of the cycloid can be derived as follows:

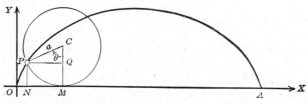

Fig. 184.

In Fig. 184, let OX be the fixed straight line, C the generator circle of radius a, and $P(x, y)$ the tracing point. Also suppose the circle is rolling towards the right.

Choose OX as the x-axis and the origin O where the tracing point is in contact with the fixed line. Also choose as parameter the angle θ, through which the radius to the tracing point turns. Draw the lines shown in the figure.

Then $\quad x = ON = OM - NM = OM - PQ,$

and $\quad y = NP = MC - QC.$

But OM = arc MP = $a\theta$, PQ = $a \sin \theta$, MC = a, and QC = $a \cos \theta$.

Substituting these values gives

$$x = a(\theta - \sin \theta),$$
$$y = a(1 - \cos \theta).$$

These are the forms of the equations most frequently used in dealing with the cycloid. If θ is eliminated, the equation in x and y is

$$x = a \operatorname{vers}^{-1} \frac{y}{a} - \sqrt{2ay - y^2},$$

a form that is seldom used.

205. Polar coördinates.—There are two common methods of locating a place on the surface of the earth. These two methods we carry over into mathematics and find them very convenient and useful.

First, a house in a city is located by giving its street and number, that is, by stating its distance and direction from each of two intersecting streets.

Second, a town or city may be located by giving its distance and direction from another city.

The two corresponding methods in mathematics for locating a point in a plane are, first, the *rectangular coördinate* method, and second, the method by *polar coördinates.* The first method is the one that is usually used; but the second method is sometimes found more convenient and simpler.

In polar coördinates we locate a point in a plane by giving its distance and direction from a given fixed point in the plane. Thus, in Fig. 185, giving the fixed point O in the fixed directed line OX, then any point P in the plane may be located by stating its distance $OP = \rho$ from O, and the angle θ through which OX must turn to coincide with OP

Definitions. The fixed point O is called the **pole,** or **origin;** the fixed line OX the **initial line,** or **polar axis;** the line segment $OP = \rho$ is called the **radius vector** of P; and the angle θ the **vectorial angle,** or **directional angle** of P. Together ρ and θ are the **polar coördinates** of P, and are written (ρ, θ).

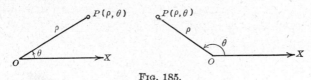

Fɪɢ. 185.

In order to use both positive and negative numbers as coördinates of points, the usual conventions of trigonometry as to positive and negative angles of any size are accepted. It is also agreed that the radius vector is positive if measured from O along the terminal side of the angle θ, and negative if measured in the opposite direction.

Thus, in Fig. 186, the point P_1 has the coördinates $(5, 60°)$, the angle being measured counter-clockwise and the radius vector along the terminal side in the positive direction. The point P_2 has as coördinates $(4, -30°)$ for here the angle is measured in the clockwise direction and is negative. If the line OP_1 were extended in the opposite direction a distance of 5 units, the point $(-5, 60°)$ would be located.

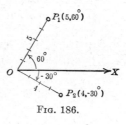

Fɪɢ. 186.

An equation using polar coördinates may define the locus of a point, and may be plotted by adhering to the meaning of polar coördinates.

Thus, the equation $\rho = 5$, evidently, defines a **circle** of radius 5 and center at the origin, for the locus of all points at a distance 5 from the origin and in the plane is such a circle.

The cardioid that is shown in Fig. 104 has the equation $\rho = a(1 - \cos \theta)$ and can readily be plotted by assigning a series of values to θ and computing the corresponding values of ρ.

In a polar coördinate equation using θ but not involving a trigonometric function of θ, we agree that θ shall be expressed in radians.

TABLE I

INTEGRATION FORMULAS

I. General Formulas

(u, v, and w are any functions of x.)

1. $\int c \, du = c \int du.$

2. $\int (du \pm dv \pm dw \pm \ldots) = \int du \pm \int dv \pm \int dw \pm \cdots.$

3. $\int u^n du = \dfrac{u^{n+1}}{n+1}.$ $n \neq -1.$

4. $\int u^{-1} du = \int \dfrac{du}{u} = \log u.$

5. $\int u \, dv = uv - \int v \, du.$ (Integration by parts.)

II. Algebraic Forms

A. *Integrand Containing* $(a + bx)$.

6. $\int (a + bx)^n dx = \dfrac{(a + bx)^{n+1}}{b(n + 1)}.$ $n \neq -1.$

7. $\int \dfrac{dx}{a + bx} = \dfrac{1}{b} \log (a + bx).$

8. $\int \dfrac{x \, dx}{a + bx} = \dfrac{1}{b^2} [a + bx - a \log (a + bx)].$

9. $\int \dfrac{x^2 \, dx}{a + bx} = \dfrac{1}{b^3} [\tfrac{1}{2}(a + bx)^2 - 2a(a + bx) + a^2 \log (a + bx)].$

10. $\int \dfrac{dx}{x(a + bx)} = -\dfrac{1}{a} \log \dfrac{a + bx}{x}.$

11. $\int \dfrac{dx}{x^2(a + bx)} = -\dfrac{1}{ax} + \dfrac{b}{a^2} \log \dfrac{a + bx}{x}.$

12. $\displaystyle\int \frac{dx}{(a+bx)^2} = -\frac{1}{b(a+bx)}.$

13. $\displaystyle\int \frac{dx}{(a+bx)^3} = -\frac{1}{2b(a+bx)^2}.$

14. $\displaystyle\int \frac{x\,dx}{(a+bx)^2} = \frac{1}{b^2}\Big[\log{(a+bx)} + \frac{a}{a+bx}\Big].$

15. $\displaystyle\int \frac{x\,dx}{(a+bx)^3} = \frac{1}{b^2}\Big[-\frac{1}{a+bx} + \frac{a}{2(a+bx)^2}\Big].$

16. $\displaystyle\int \frac{x^2\,dx}{(a+bx)^2} = \frac{1}{b^3}\Big[a+bx-2a\log{(a+bx)} - \frac{a^2}{a+bx}\Big].$

17. $\displaystyle\int \frac{dx}{x(a+bx)^2} = \frac{1}{a(a+bx)} - \frac{1}{a^2}\log\frac{a+bx}{x}.$

B. *Integrand Containing $(a^2 \pm x^2)$ or $(a + bx^2)$.*

18. $\displaystyle\int \frac{dx}{a^2+x^2} = \frac{1}{a}\tan^{-1}\frac{x}{a}.$

19. $\displaystyle\int \frac{dx}{a^2-x^2} = \frac{1}{2a}\log\frac{a+x}{a-x}, \text{ or } \frac{1}{2a}\log\frac{x+a}{x-a}.$

20. $\displaystyle\int \frac{dx}{x^2-a^2} = \frac{1}{2a}\log\frac{x-a}{x+a}, \text{ or } \frac{1}{2a}\log\frac{a-x}{a+x}.$

21. $\displaystyle\int \frac{dx}{a+bx^2} = \frac{1}{\sqrt{ab}}\tan^{-1}x\sqrt{\frac{b}{a}}, \text{ when } a>0 \text{ and } b>0.$

22. $\displaystyle\int \frac{dx}{a+bx^2} = \frac{1}{2\sqrt{-ab}}\,\log\frac{\sqrt{a}+x\sqrt{-b}}{\sqrt{a}-x\sqrt{-b}}, \text{ when } a>0 \text{ and}$
$$b<0.$$

23. $\displaystyle\int \frac{x\,dx}{a+bx^2} = \frac{1}{2b}\log\Big(x^2+\frac{a}{b}\Big).$

24. $\displaystyle\int \frac{x^2\,dx}{a+bx^2} = \frac{x}{b} - \frac{a}{b}\int\frac{dx}{a+bx^2}. \quad \text{Use 21 or 22.}$

25. $\displaystyle\int \frac{dx}{x(a+bx^2)} = \frac{1}{2a}\log\frac{x^2}{a+bx^2}.$

26. $\displaystyle\int \frac{dx}{x^2(a+bx^2)} = -\frac{1}{ax} - \frac{b}{a}\int\frac{dx}{a+bx^2}. \quad \text{Use 21 or 22.}$

27. $\displaystyle\int \frac{dx}{(a+bx^2)^2} = \frac{x}{2a(a+bx^2)} + \frac{1}{2a}\int\frac{dx}{a+bx^2}. \quad \text{Use 21 or 22.}$

C. *Integrand Containing* $x^m(a + bx^n)^p$

(Reduction formulas.   See page 231.)

28. $\displaystyle\int x^m(a + bx^n)^p\,dx$

$\displaystyle= \frac{x^{m-n+1}(a + bx^n)^{p+1}}{(np + m + 1)b} - \frac{(m - n + 1)a}{(np + m + 1)b}\int x^{m-n}(a + bx^n)^p dx.$

29. $\displaystyle\int x^m(a + bx^n)^p\,dx$

$\displaystyle= \frac{x^{m+1}(a + bx^n)^p}{np + m + 1} + \frac{anp}{np + m + 1}\int x^m(a + bx^n)^{p-1}dx.$

30. $\displaystyle\int x^m(a + bx^n)^p\,dx$

$\displaystyle= \frac{x^{m+1}(a + bx^n)^{p+1}}{(m + 1)a} - \frac{(np + m + n + 1)b}{(m + 1)a}\int x^{m+n}(a + bx^n)^p dx.$

31. $\displaystyle\int x^m(a + bx^n)^p\,dx$

$\displaystyle= -\frac{x^{m+1}(a + bx^n)^{p+1}}{n(p + 1)a} + \frac{np + m + n + 1}{n(p + 1)a}\int x^m(a + bx^n)^{p+1}dx.$

D. *Integrand Containing* $\sqrt{a + bx}$.

32. $\displaystyle\int \sqrt{a + bx}\,dx = \frac{2\sqrt{(a + bx)^3}}{3b}.$

33. $\displaystyle\int x\sqrt{a + bx}\,dx = -\frac{2(2a - 3bx)\sqrt{(a + bx)^3}}{15b^2}$

34. $\displaystyle\int \frac{dx}{\sqrt{a + bx}} = \frac{2}{b}\sqrt{a + bx}.$

35. $\displaystyle\int \frac{x\,dx}{\sqrt{a + bx}} = -\frac{2(2a - bx)\sqrt{a + bx}}{3b^2}.$

36. $\displaystyle\int \frac{x^2 dx}{\sqrt{a + bx}} = \frac{2(8a^2 - 4abx + 3b^2x^2)\sqrt{a + bx}}{15b^3}.$

37. $\displaystyle\int \frac{dx}{x\sqrt{a + bx}} = \frac{1}{\sqrt{a}}\log\frac{\sqrt{a + bx} - \sqrt{a}}{\sqrt{a + bx} + \sqrt{a}}, \text{when } a > 0.$

38. $\displaystyle\int \frac{dx}{x\sqrt{a + bx}} = \frac{2}{\sqrt{-a}}\tan^{-1}\frac{\sqrt{a + bx}}{\sqrt{-a}}, \text{when } a < 0.$

39. $\int \dfrac{dx}{x^2\sqrt{a+bx}} = -\dfrac{\sqrt{a+bx}}{ax} - \dfrac{b}{2a}\int \dfrac{dx}{x\sqrt{a+bx}}$. Use 37 or 38.

40. $\int \dfrac{\sqrt{a+bx}\,dx}{x} = 2\sqrt{a+bx} + a\int \dfrac{dx}{x\sqrt{a+bx}}$. Use 37 or 38.

E. *Integrand Containing* $\sqrt{a^2 + x^2}$.

41. $\int \sqrt{a^2+x^2}\,dx = \frac{1}{2}x\sqrt{a^2+x^2} + \frac{1}{2}a^2 \log(x + \sqrt{a^2+x^2})$.

42. $\int \sqrt{(a^2+x^2)^3}\,dx$
$$= \tfrac{1}{8}x(2x^2+5a^2)\sqrt{a^2+x^2} + \tfrac{3}{8}a^4 \log(x + \sqrt{a^2+x^2}).$$

43. $\int \sqrt{(a^2+x^2)^n}\,dx = \dfrac{x\sqrt{(a^2+x^2)^n}}{n+1} + \dfrac{a^2 n}{n+1}\int \sqrt{(a^2+x^2)^{n-2}}\,dx.$

44. $\int x\sqrt{(a^2+x^2)^n}\,dx = \dfrac{\sqrt{(a^2+x^2)^{n+2}}}{n+2}.$

45. $\int x^2\sqrt{a^2+x^2}\,dx$
$$= \tfrac{1}{8}x(2x^2+a^2)\sqrt{a^2+x^2} - \tfrac{1}{8}a^4\log(x + \sqrt{a^2+x^2}).$$

46. $\int \dfrac{dx}{\sqrt{a^2+x^2}} = \log(x + \sqrt{a^2+x^2}).$

47. $\int \dfrac{x\,dx}{\sqrt{a^2+x^2}} = \sqrt{a^2+x^2}.$

48. $\int \dfrac{x^2\,dx}{\sqrt{a^2+x^2}} = \frac{1}{2}x\sqrt{a^2+x^2} - \frac{1}{2}a^2 \log(x + \sqrt{a^2+x^2}).$

49. $\int \dfrac{x^2\,dx}{\sqrt{(a^2+x^2)^3}} = -\dfrac{x}{\sqrt{a^2+x^2}} + \log(x + \sqrt{a^2+x^2}).$

50. $\int \dfrac{dx}{x\sqrt{a^2+x^2}} = \dfrac{1}{a}\log \dfrac{x}{a + \sqrt{a^2+x^2}}.$

51. $\int \dfrac{dx}{x^2\sqrt{a^2+x^2}} = -\dfrac{\sqrt{a^2+x^2}}{a^2 x}.$

52. $\int \dfrac{dx}{x^3\sqrt{a^2+x^2}} = -\dfrac{\sqrt{a^2+x^2}}{2a^2 x^2} + \dfrac{1}{2a^3}\log \dfrac{a + \sqrt{a^2+x^2}}{x}.$

53. $\int \dfrac{\sqrt{a^2+x^2}\,dx}{x} = \sqrt{a^2+x^2} - a\log \dfrac{a + \sqrt{a^2+x^2}}{x}.$

54. $\int \dfrac{\sqrt{a^2 + x^2}\, dx}{x^2} = -\dfrac{\sqrt{a^2 + x^2}}{x} + \log\left(x + \sqrt{a^2 + x^2}\right).$

F. Integrand Containing $\sqrt{a^2 - x^2}$.

55. $\int \sqrt{a^2 - x^2}\, dx = \frac{1}{2}\left(x\sqrt{a^2 - x^2} + a^2 \sin^{-1}\dfrac{x}{a}\right).$

56. $\int \sqrt{(a^2 - x^2)^3}\, dx = \frac{1}{8}x(5a^2 - 2x^2)\sqrt{a^2 - x^2} + \frac{3}{8}a^4 \sin^{-1}\dfrac{x}{a}.$

57. $\int \sqrt{(a^2 - x^2)^n}\, dx$

$$= \dfrac{x\sqrt{(a^2 - x^2)^n}}{n + 1} + \dfrac{a^2 n}{n + 1}\int \sqrt{(a^2 - x^2)^{n-2}}\, dx.$$

68. $\int x\sqrt{(a^2 - x^2)^n}\, dx = -\dfrac{\sqrt{(a^2 - x^2)^{n+2}}}{n + 2}.$

59. $\int x^2\sqrt{a^2 - x^2}\, dx = \frac{1}{8}x(2x^2 - a^2)\sqrt{a^2 - x^2} + \frac{1}{8}a^4 \sin^{-1}\dfrac{x}{a}.$

60. $\int \dfrac{dx}{\sqrt{a^2 - x^2}} = \sin^{-1}\dfrac{x}{a}.$

61. $\int \dfrac{dx}{\sqrt{(a^2 - x^2)^3}} = \dfrac{x}{a^2\sqrt{a^2 - x^2}}.$

62. $\int \dfrac{x\, dx}{\sqrt{a^2 - x^2}} = -\sqrt{a^2 - x^2}.$

63. $\int \dfrac{x^2\, dx}{\sqrt{a^2 - x^2}} = -\frac{1}{2}x\sqrt{a^2 - x^2} + \frac{1}{2}a^2 \sin^{-1}\dfrac{x}{a}.$

64. $\int \dfrac{x^2\, dx}{\sqrt{(a^2 - x^2)^3}} = \dfrac{x}{\sqrt{a^2 - x^2}} - \sin^{-1}\dfrac{x}{a}.$

65. $\int \dfrac{dx}{x\sqrt{a^2 - x^2}} = \dfrac{1}{a}\log\dfrac{x}{a + \sqrt{a^2 - x^2}}.$

66. $\int \dfrac{dx}{x^4\sqrt{a^2 - x^2}} = -\dfrac{\sqrt{a^2 - x^2}}{a^2 x}.$

67. $\int \dfrac{dx}{x^3\sqrt{a^2 - x^2}} = -\dfrac{\sqrt{a^2 - x^2}}{2a^2 x^2} + \dfrac{1}{2a^3}\log\dfrac{x}{a + \sqrt{a^2 - x^2}}.$

68. $\int \dfrac{\sqrt{a^2 - x^2}\, dx}{x} = \sqrt{a^2 - x^2} - a\log\dfrac{a + \sqrt{a^2 - x^2}}{x}.$

69. $\int \dfrac{\sqrt{a^2 - x^2}\, dx}{x^2} = -\dfrac{\sqrt{a^2 - x^2}}{x} - \sin^{-1}\dfrac{x}{a}.$

G. *Integrand Containing* $\sqrt{x^2 - a^2}$.

70. $\int \sqrt{x^2 - a^2}\, dx = \frac{1}{2}[x\sqrt{x^2 - a^2} - a^2 \log(x + \sqrt{x^2 - a^2})].$

71. $\int \sqrt{(x^2 - a^2)^3}\, dx$

$= \frac{1}{8}x(2x^2 - 5a^2)\sqrt{x^2 - a^2} + \frac{3}{8}a^4 \log(x + \sqrt{x^2 - a^2}).$

72. $\int \sqrt{(x^2 - a^2)^n}\, dx = \dfrac{x\sqrt{(x^2 - a^2)^n}}{n + 1} - \dfrac{a^2 n}{n + 1}\int \sqrt{(x^2 - a^2)^{n-2}}\, dx.$

73. $\int x\sqrt{(x^2 - a^2)^n}\, dx = \dfrac{\sqrt{(x^2 - a^2)^{n+2}}}{n + 2}.$

74. $\int x^2\sqrt{x^2 - a^2}\, dx$

$= \frac{1}{8}x(2x^2 - a^2)\sqrt{x^2 - a^2} - \frac{1}{8}a^4 \log(x + \sqrt{x^2 - a^2}).$

75. $\int \dfrac{dx}{\sqrt{x^2 - a^2}} = \log(x + \sqrt{x^2 - a^2}).$

76. $\int \dfrac{dx}{\sqrt{(x^2 - a^2)^3}} = -\dfrac{x}{a^2\sqrt{x^2 - a^2}}.$

77. $\int \dfrac{x\, dx}{\sqrt{x^2 - a^2}} = \sqrt{x^2 - a^2}.$

78. $\int \dfrac{x^2 dx}{\sqrt{x^2 - a^2}} = x\sqrt{x^2 - a^2} + \frac{1}{2}a^2 \log(x + \sqrt{x^2 - a^2}).$

79. $\int \dfrac{x^2\, dx}{\sqrt{(x^2 - a^2)^3}} = -\dfrac{x}{\sqrt{x^2 - a^2}} + \log(x + \sqrt{x^2 - a^2}).$

80. $\int \dfrac{dx}{x\sqrt{x^2 - a^2}} = \frac{1}{a} \cos^{-1}\dfrac{a}{x}.$

81. $\int \dfrac{dx}{x^2\sqrt{x^2 - a^2}} = \dfrac{\sqrt{x^2 - a^2}}{a^2 x}.$

82. $\int \dfrac{dx}{x^3\sqrt{x^2 - a^2}} = \dfrac{\sqrt{x^2 - a^2}}{2a^2 x^2} + \frac{1}{2a^3} \cos^{-1}\dfrac{a}{x}.$

83. $\int \dfrac{\sqrt{x^2 - a^2}\, dx}{x} = \sqrt{x^2 - a^2} - a \cos^{-1}\dfrac{a}{x}.$

84. $\int \dfrac{\sqrt{x^2 - a^2}\, dx}{x^2} = -\dfrac{\sqrt{x^2 - a^2}}{x} + \log(x + \sqrt{x^2 - a^2}).$

H. *Integrand Containing* $\sqrt{2ax - x^2}$ or $\sqrt{2ax + x^2}$.

85. $\int \sqrt{2ax - x^2}\, dx = \frac{1}{2}(x - a)\sqrt{2ax - x^2} + \frac{1}{2}a^2 \sin^{-1}\dfrac{x - a}{a}.$

86. $\int \sqrt{2ax + x^2}\, dx$

$$= \tfrac{1}{2}(x + a)\sqrt{2ax + x^2} - \tfrac{1}{2}a^2 \log\,(x + a + \sqrt{2ax + x^2}).$$

87. $\int x\sqrt{2ax - x^2}\, dx$

$$= -\tfrac{1}{6}(3a^2 + ax - 2x^2)\sqrt{2ax - x^2} + \tfrac{1}{2}a^3 \sin^{-1}\frac{x - a}{a}.$$

88. $\int x\sqrt{2ax + x^2}\, dx = \tfrac{1}{3}\sqrt{(2ax + x^2)^3} - a\int \sqrt{2ax + x^2}\, dx.$

89. $\int x^n\sqrt{2ax - x^2}\, dx$

$$= -\frac{x^{n-1}\sqrt{(2ax - x^2)^3}}{n + 2} + \frac{(2n + 1)a}{n + 2}\int x^{n-1}\sqrt{2ax - x^2}\, dx.$$

90. $\int \dfrac{dx}{\sqrt{2ax - x^2}} = \text{vers}^{-1}\dfrac{x}{a},\ \text{or } \sin^{-1}\dfrac{x - a}{a}.$

91. $\int \dfrac{dx}{\sqrt{2ax + x^2}} = \log\,(x + a + \sqrt{2ax + x^2}).$

92. $\int \dfrac{dx}{\sqrt{(2ax - x^2)^3}} = \dfrac{x - a}{a^2\sqrt{2ax - x^2}}.$

93. $\int \dfrac{dx}{\sqrt{(2ax + x^2)^3}} = -\dfrac{x + a}{a^2\sqrt{2ax + x^2}}.$

94. $\int \dfrac{x\, dx}{\sqrt{2ax - x^2}} = -\sqrt{2ax - x^2} + a \sin^{-1}\dfrac{x - a}{a}.$

95. $\int \dfrac{x\, dx}{\sqrt{2ax + x^2}} = \sqrt{2ax + x^2} - a\log\,(x + a + \sqrt{2ax + x^2}).$

96. $\int \dfrac{x\, dx}{\sqrt{(2ax \pm x^2)^3}} = \dfrac{x}{a\sqrt{2ax \pm x^2}}.$

97. $\int \dfrac{x^2\, dx}{\sqrt{2ax - x^2}} = -\tfrac{1}{2}(x + 3a)\sqrt{2ax - x^2} + \tfrac{3}{2}a^2 \sin^{-1}\dfrac{x - a}{a}.$

98. $\int \dfrac{x^n\, dx}{\sqrt{2ax - x^2}} = -\dfrac{x^{n-1}\sqrt{2ax - x^2}}{n} - \dfrac{a(1 - 2n)}{n}\int \dfrac{x^{n-1}\, dx}{\sqrt{2ax - x^2}}$

99. $\int \dfrac{dx}{x\sqrt{2ax \pm x^2}} = -\dfrac{\sqrt{2ax \pm x^2}}{ax}.$

100. $\int \dfrac{dx}{x^n\sqrt{2ax - x^2}} = \dfrac{\sqrt{2ax - x^2}}{a(1 - 2n)x^n} + \dfrac{n - 1}{(2n - 1)a}\int \dfrac{dx}{x^{n-1}\sqrt{2ax - x^2}}.$

101. $\int \dfrac{\sqrt{2ax - x^2}\, dx}{x} = \sqrt{2ax - x^2} + a \sin^{-1}\dfrac{x - a}{a}.$

102. $\int \dfrac{\sqrt{2ax + x^2}\, dx}{x} = \sqrt{2ax + x^2} + a \log (x+a+\sqrt{2ax + x^2})$.

103. $\int \dfrac{\sqrt{2ax - x^2}\, dx}{x^2} = -\dfrac{2\sqrt{2ax - x^2}}{x} - \sin^{-1} \dfrac{x-a}{a}$.

104. $\int \dfrac{\sqrt{2ax + x^2}\, dx}{x^2} = -\dfrac{2\sqrt{2ax + x^2}}{x} + \log (x+a+\sqrt{2ax+ x^2})$.

105. $\int \dfrac{\sqrt{2ax - x^2}\, dx}{x^n}$

$$= \dfrac{\sqrt{(2ax - x^2)^3}}{(3 - 2n)ax^n} + \dfrac{n - 3}{(2n - 3)a} \int \dfrac{\sqrt{2ax - x^2}\, dx}{x^{n-1}}.$$

I. *Integrand Containing* $ax^2 + bx + c$.

106. $\int \dfrac{dx}{ax^2 + bx + c} = \dfrac{2}{\sqrt{4ac - b^2}} \tan^{-1} \dfrac{2ax + b}{\sqrt{4ac - b^2}}$,

$$\text{when } b^2 - 4ac < 0.$$

107. $\int \dfrac{dx}{ax^2 + bx + c} = \dfrac{1}{\sqrt{b^2 - 4ac}} \log \dfrac{2ax + b - \sqrt{b^2 - 4ac}}{2ax + b + \sqrt{b^2 - 4ac}}$,

$$\text{when } b^2 - 4ac > 0.$$

108. $\int \dfrac{x\, dx}{ax^2 + bx + c} = \dfrac{1}{2a} \log (ax^2+bx+c) - \dfrac{b}{2a} \int \dfrac{dx}{ax^2 + bx + c}$.

109. $\int \dfrac{x^2\, dx}{ax^2 + bx + c}$

$$= \dfrac{x}{a} - \dfrac{b}{2a^2} \log (ax^2 + bx + c) + \dfrac{b^2 - 4ac}{2a^3} \int \dfrac{dx}{ax^2 + bx + c}.$$

110. $\int \dfrac{dx}{x(ax^2 + bx + c)} = \dfrac{1}{2c} \log \dfrac{x^2}{ax^2 + bx + c} - \dfrac{b}{2c} \int \dfrac{dx}{ax^2 + bx+c}$.

111. $\int \dfrac{dx}{x^2(ax^2 + bx + c)}$

$$= \dfrac{b}{2c^2} \log \dfrac{ax^2 + bx + c}{x^2} - \dfrac{1}{cx} + \left(\dfrac{b^2}{2c^2} - \dfrac{a}{c}\right) \int \dfrac{dx}{ax^2 + bx + c}.$$

J. *Integrand Containing* $\sqrt{ax^2 + bx + c}$.

112. $\int \sqrt{ax^2 + bx + c}\, dx$

$$= \dfrac{2ax + b}{4a} \sqrt{ax^2 + bx + c} - \dfrac{b^2 - 4ac}{8a} \int \dfrac{dx}{\sqrt{ax^2 + bx + c}}$$

113. $\displaystyle\int \frac{dx}{\sqrt{ax^2 + bx + c}} = \frac{1}{\sqrt{a}} \log\ (2ax + b + 2\sqrt{a}\sqrt{ax^2 + bx + c})$

$$\text{when } a > 0.$$

114. $\displaystyle\int \frac{dx}{\sqrt{ax^2 + bx + c}} = \frac{1}{\sqrt{-a}} \sin^{-1} \frac{-2ax - b}{\sqrt{b^2 - 4ac}}, \quad \text{when} \quad a < 0.$

115. $\displaystyle\int \frac{x\ dx}{\sqrt{ax^2 + bx + c}} = \frac{1}{a}\sqrt{ax^2 + bx + c} - \frac{b}{2a}\int \frac{dx}{\sqrt{ax^2 + bx + c}}.$

116. $\displaystyle\int \frac{x^2 dx}{\sqrt{ax^2 + bx + c}}$

$$= \left(\frac{x}{2a} - \frac{3b}{4a^2}\right)\sqrt{ax^2 + bx + c} + \frac{3b^2 - 4ac}{8a^2}\int \frac{dx}{\sqrt{ax^2 + bx + c}}.$$

117. $\displaystyle\int \frac{dx}{x\sqrt{ax^2 + bx + c}}$

$$= -\frac{1}{\sqrt{c}} \log\left(\frac{\sqrt{ax^2 + bx + c} + \sqrt{c}}{x} + \frac{b}{2\sqrt{c}}\right), \text{when } c > 0.$$

118. $\displaystyle\int \frac{dx}{x\sqrt{ax^2 + bx + c}} = \frac{1}{\sqrt{-c}} \sin^{-1}\left(\frac{bx + 2c}{x\sqrt{b^2 - 4ac}}\right),$

$$\text{when } c < 0.$$

119. $\displaystyle\int \frac{dx}{x^2\sqrt{ax^2 + bx + c}}$

$$= -\frac{\sqrt{ax^2 + bx + c}}{cx} - \frac{b}{2c}\int \frac{dx}{x\sqrt{ax^2 + bx + c}}.$$

K. *Miscellaneous Algebraic Forms.*

120. $\displaystyle\int \sqrt{\frac{a + x}{b + x}}\ dx$

$$= \sqrt{(a + x)(b + x)} + (a - b) \log\ (\sqrt{a + x} + \sqrt{b + x}).$$

121. $\displaystyle\int \sqrt{\frac{a + x}{b - x}}\ dx = -\sqrt{(a + x)(b - x)} - (a + b)\sin^{-1} \sqrt{\frac{b - x}{a + b}}$

122. $\displaystyle\int \sqrt{\frac{a - x}{b + x}}\ dx = \sqrt{(a - x)(b + x)} + (a + b) \sin^{-1} \sqrt{\frac{b + x}{a + b}}.$

123. $\displaystyle\int \frac{dx}{x\sqrt{x^n - a^2}} = \frac{2}{an} \sec^{-1} \frac{\sqrt{x^n}}{a}.$

III. Exponential and Logarithmic Forms

124. $\int e^x dx = e^x.$
125. $\int a^x dx = \dfrac{a^x}{\log a}.$

126. $\int e^{ax} dx = \dfrac{e^{ax}}{a}.$
127. $\int a^{bx} dx = \dfrac{a^{bx}}{b \log a}.$

128. $\int \log x \, dx = x \log x - x.$

129. $\int \dfrac{dx}{\log x} = \log(\log x) + \log x + \dfrac{(\log x)^2}{2 \cdot 2!} + \dfrac{(\log x)^3}{3 \cdot 3!} + \cdots.$

130. $\int \dfrac{dx}{x \log x} = \log(\log x)$

131. $\int x e^{ax} dx = \dfrac{e^{ax}}{a^2}(ax - 1).$

132. $\int x^n e^{ax} dx = \dfrac{x^n e^{ax}}{a} - \dfrac{n}{a} \int x^{n-1} e^{ax} dx.$

133. $\int \dfrac{e^{ax} dx}{x} = \log x + ax + \dfrac{a^2 x^2}{2 \cdot 2!} + \dfrac{a^3 x^3}{3 \cdot 3!} + \cdots.$

134. $\int \dfrac{e^{ax} dx}{x^n} = \dfrac{1}{n-1}\left(-\dfrac{e^{ax}}{x^{n-1}} + a \int \dfrac{e^{ax} dx}{x^{n-1}}\right).$

135. $\int x a^x dx = \dfrac{a^x x}{\log a} - \dfrac{a^x}{(\log a)^2}.$

136. $\int \dfrac{a^x dx}{x} = \log x + x \log a + \dfrac{(x \log a)^2}{2 \cdot 2!} + \dfrac{(x \log a)^3}{3 \cdot 3!} + \cdots.$

137. $\int x \log x \, dx = \frac{1}{2} x^2 (\log x - \frac{1}{2}).$

138. $\int x^2 \log x \, dx = \frac{1}{3} x^3 (\log x - \frac{1}{3}).$

139. $\int x^n \log x \, dx = \dfrac{x^{n+1}}{n+1}\left(\log x - \dfrac{1}{n+1}\right).$

140. $\int e^{ax} \log x \, dx = \dfrac{e^{ax} \log x}{a} - \dfrac{1}{a} \int \dfrac{e^{ax}}{x} dx.$

141. $\int \dfrac{dx}{1 + e^x} = \log \dfrac{e^x}{1 + e^x}.$

142. $\int \dfrac{dx}{a + be^{nx}} = \dfrac{1}{an}[nx - \log(a + be^{nx})].$

143. $\int \dfrac{dx}{ae^{nx} + be^{-nx}} = \dfrac{1}{n\sqrt{ab}} \tan^{-1}\left(e^{nx}\sqrt{\dfrac{a}{b}}\right).$

144. $\int \log(a^2 + x^2) dx = x \log(a^2 + x^2) - 2x + 2a \tan^{-1}\dfrac{x}{a}.$

IV. Trigonometric Forms

145. $\int \sin x\, dx = -\cos x.$

146. $\int \sin^2 x\, dx = \frac{1}{2}x - \frac{1}{2}\cos x \sin x = \frac{1}{2}x - \frac{1}{4}\sin 2x.$

147. $\int \sin^n x\, dx = -\dfrac{\sin^{n-1} x \cos x}{n} + \dfrac{n-1}{n}\int \sin^{n-2} x\, dx.$

148. $\int \cos x\, dx = \sin x.$

149. $\int \cos^2 x\, dx = \frac{1}{2}x + \frac{1}{2}\sin x \cos x = \frac{1}{2}x + \frac{1}{4}\sin 2x$

150. $\int \cos^n x\, dx = \dfrac{\cos^{n-1} x \sin x}{n} + \dfrac{n-1}{n}\int \cos^{n-2} x\, dx.$

151. $\int \tan x\, dx = -\log \cos x.$

152. $\int \tan^2 x\, dx = \tan x - x.$

153. $\int \tan^n x\, dx = \dfrac{\tan^{n-1} x}{n-1} - \int \tan^{n-2} x\, dx.$

154. $\int \cot x\, dx = \log \sin x.$

155. $\int \cot^2 x\, dx = -\cot x - x.$

156. $\int \cot^n x\, dx = -\dfrac{\cot^{n-1} x}{n-1} - \int \cot^{n-2} x\, dx.$

157. $\int \sec x\, dx = \log \tan (\frac{1}{4}\pi + \frac{1}{2}x) = \frac{1}{2}\log \dfrac{1+\sin x}{1-\sin x}.$

158. $\int \sec^2 x\, dx = \tan x.$

159. $\int \sec^n x\, dx = \dfrac{\sin x \sec^{n-1} x}{n-1} + \dfrac{n-2}{n-1}\int \sec^{n-2} x\, dx.$

160. $\int \csc x\, dx = \log \tan \frac{1}{2}x.$

161. $\int \csc^2 x\, dx = -\cot x.$

162. $\int \csc^n x\, dx = -\dfrac{\cos x \csc^{n-1} x}{n-1} + \dfrac{n-2}{n-1}\int \csc^{n-2} x\, dx.$

163. $\int \sin x \cos x\, dx = \frac{1}{2}\sin^2 x$ or $-\frac{1}{2}\cos^2 x.$

164. $\int \sin^n x \cos x\, dx = \dfrac{\sin^{n+1} x}{n+1}.$

165. $\int \cos^n x \sin x \, dx = -\dfrac{\cos^{n+1} x}{n + 1}.$

166. $\int \sin^2 x \cos^2 x \, dx = \frac{1}{8}(x - \frac{1}{4} \sin 4x).$

167. $\int \sin^n x \cos^m x \, dx$

$$= -\frac{\sin^{n-1} x \cos^{m+1} x}{m + n} + \frac{n - 1}{m + n} \int \sin^{n-2} x \cos^m x \, dx,$$

or $\quad = \dfrac{\sin^{n+1} x \cos^{m-1} x}{m + n} + \dfrac{m - 1}{m + n} \int \sin^n x \cos^{m-2} x \, dx.$

168. $\int \dfrac{\sin^n x \, dx}{\cos^m x} = \dfrac{1}{n - m}\left[-\dfrac{\sin^{n-1} x}{\cos^{m-1} x} + (n - 1) \int \dfrac{\sin^{n-2} x \, dx}{\cos^m x} \right],$

or $\quad = \dfrac{1}{m - 1}\left[\dfrac{\sin^{n+1} x}{\cos^{m-1} x} - (n - m + 2) \int \dfrac{\sin^n x \, dx}{\cos^{m-2} x} \right].$

169. $\int \dfrac{\cos^n x \, dx}{\sin^m x} = -\dfrac{1}{m - 1}\left[\dfrac{\cos^{n+1} x}{\sin^{m-1} x} + (n - m + 2) \int \dfrac{\cos^n x \, dx}{\sin^{m-2} x} \right]$

or $\quad = \dfrac{1}{n - m}\left[\dfrac{\cos^{n-1} x}{\sin^{m-1} x} + (n - 1) \int \dfrac{\cos^{n-2} x \, dx}{\sin^m x} \right].$

170. $\int \dfrac{dx}{1 + \sin x} = -\tan \left(\frac{1}{4}\pi - \frac{1}{2}x\right).$

171. $\int \dfrac{dx}{1 - \sin x} = \cot \left(\frac{1}{4}\pi - \frac{1}{2}x\right) = \tan \left(\frac{1}{4}\pi + \frac{1}{2}x\right).$

172. $\int \dfrac{dx}{1 + \cos x} = \tan \frac{1}{2}x.$

173. $\int \dfrac{dx}{1 - \cos x} = -\cot \frac{1}{2}x.$

174. $\int \dfrac{dx}{a + b \sin x} = \dfrac{2}{\sqrt{a^2 - b^2}} \tan^{-1} \dfrac{a \tan \frac{1}{2}x + b}{\sqrt{a^2 - b^2}},$ when $a > b.$

175. $\int \dfrac{dx}{a + b \sin x} = \dfrac{1}{\sqrt{b^2 - a^2}} \log \dfrac{a \tan \frac{1}{2}x + b - \sqrt{b^2 - a^2}}{a \tan \frac{1}{2}x + b + \sqrt{b^2 - a^2}},$

when $a < b.$

176. $\int \dfrac{dx}{a + b \cos x} = \dfrac{2}{\sqrt{a^2 - b^2}} \tan^{-1} \left(\sqrt{\dfrac{a - b}{a + b}} \tan \frac{1}{2}x \right),$

when $a > b.$

177. $\int \dfrac{dx}{a + b \cos x} = \dfrac{1}{\sqrt{b^2 - a^2}} \log \dfrac{\sqrt{b - a} \tan \frac{1}{2}x + \sqrt{b + a}}{\sqrt{b - a} \tan \frac{1}{2}x - \sqrt{b + a}},$

when $a < b.$

178. $\int \sec x \tan x \, dx = \sec x.$

179. $\int \csc x \cot x \, dx = -\csc x.$

180. $\int \dfrac{dx}{a^2 \cos^2 x + b^2 \sin^2 x} = \dfrac{1}{ab} \tan^{-1}\left(\dfrac{b \tan x}{a}\right).$

181. $\int \sin mx \sin nx \, dx = \dfrac{\sin (m-n)x}{2(m-n)} - \dfrac{\sin (m+n)x}{2(m+n)}.$

182. $\int \cos mx \cos nx \, dx = \dfrac{\sin (m-n)x}{2(m-n)} + \dfrac{\sin (m+n)x}{2(m+n)}.$

183. $\int \sin mx \cos nx \, dx = -\dfrac{\cos (m-n)x}{2(m-n)} - \dfrac{\cos (m+n)x}{2(m+n)}.$

184. $\int \sin^{-1} x \, dx = x \sin^{-1} x + \sqrt{1-x^2}.$

185. $\int \cos^{-1} x \, dx = x \cos^{-1} x - \sqrt{1-x^2}.$

V. Algebraic and Trigonometric Forms

186. $\int x \sin x \, dx = \sin x - x \cos x.$

187. $\int x^2 \sin x \, dx = 2x \sin x - (x^2 - 2) \cos x.$

188. $\int x^n \sin x \, dx = -x^n \cos x + n \int x^{n-1} \cos x \, dx.$

189. $\int x \cos x \, dx = \cos x + x \sin x.$

190. $\int x^2 \cos x \, dx = 2x \cos x + (x^2 - 2) \sin x.$

191. $\int x^n \cos x \, dx = x^n \sin x - n \int x^{n-1} \sin x \, dx.$

192. $\int \dfrac{\sin x}{x} dx = x - \dfrac{x^3}{3 \cdot 3!} + \dfrac{x^5}{5 \cdot 5!} - \dfrac{x^7}{7 \cdot 7!} + \cdots .$

193. $\int \dfrac{\cos x}{x} dx = \log x - \dfrac{x^2}{2 \cdot 2!} + \dfrac{x^4}{4 \cdot 4!} - \dfrac{x^6}{6 \cdot 6!} + \cdots .$

194. $\int \dfrac{x \, dx}{1 + \sin x} = 2 \log \cos \tfrac{1}{2}(\tfrac{1}{2}\pi - x) - x \tan \tfrac{1}{2}(\tfrac{1}{2}\pi - x).$

195. $\int \dfrac{x \, dx}{1 - \sin x} = 2 \log \sin \tfrac{1}{2}(\tfrac{1}{2}\pi - x) + x \cot \tfrac{1}{2}(\tfrac{1}{2}\pi - x).$

196. $\int \dfrac{x \, dx}{1 + \cos x} = 2 \log \cos \tfrac{1}{2}x + x \tan \tfrac{1}{2}x.$

197. $\int \dfrac{x \, dx}{1 - \cos x} = 2 \log \sin \tfrac{1}{2}x - x \cot \tfrac{1}{2}x$

VI. Exponential and Trigonometric Forms

198. $\displaystyle\int e^{ax} \sin x \, dx = \frac{e^{ax}(a \sin x - \cos x)}{1 + a^2}.$

199. $\displaystyle\int e^{ax} \cos x \, dx = \frac{e^{ax}(\sin x + a \cos x)}{1 + a^2}.$

200. $\displaystyle\int e^{ax} \sin nx \, dx = \frac{e^{ax}(a \sin nx - n \cos nx)}{a^2 + n^2}.$

201. $\displaystyle\int e^{ax} \cos nx \, dx = \frac{e^{ax}(n \sin nx + a \cos nx)}{a^2 + n^2}.$

TABLE II

SUMMARY OF FORMULAS IN TEXT

[1] $y - y_1 = m(x - x_1).$

[2] $y - y_1 = \dfrac{dy}{dx}\bigg|_{x = x_1} (x - x_1).$

[3] $y - y_1 = -\dfrac{1}{\dfrac{dy}{dx}\bigg|_{x = x_1}} (x - x_1).$

[4] $\dfrac{dx}{dx} = 1.$

[5] $\dfrac{dc}{dx} = 0.$

[6] $\dfrac{d(u + v + w + \cdots)}{dx} = \dfrac{du}{dx} + \dfrac{dv}{dx} + \dfrac{dw}{dx} + \cdots.$

[7] $\dfrac{d(uv)}{dx} = u\dfrac{dv}{dx} + v\dfrac{du}{dx}.$

[8] $\dfrac{d(cu)}{dx} = c\dfrac{du}{dx}.$

[9] $\dfrac{d\left(\dfrac{u}{v}\right)}{dx} = \dfrac{v\dfrac{du}{dx} - u\dfrac{dv}{dx}}{v^2}.$

[10] $\dfrac{d(u^n)}{dx} = nu^{n-1}\dfrac{du}{dx}.$

[11] $ds^2 = dx^2 + dy^2.$

[12] $dy = f'(x)dx.$

[13] $\displaystyle\int u^n du = \dfrac{u^{n+1}}{n + 1} + C.$

[14] $\int c\,du = c\int du.$

[15] $\int (du + dv + \cdots) = \int du + \int dv + \cdots$

[16] $\dfrac{d(\sin u)}{dx} = \cos u \dfrac{du}{dx}.$

[17] $\dfrac{d(\cos u)}{dx} = -\sin u \dfrac{du}{dx}.$

[18] $\lim\limits_{\theta \to 0}\left[\dfrac{\theta}{\sin \theta}\right] = 1.$

[19] $\lim\limits_{\theta \to 0}\left[\dfrac{\theta}{\tan \theta}\right] = 1.$

[20] $\int \sin u\,du = -\cos u + C.$

[21] $\int \cos u\,du = \sin u + C.$

[22] $\dfrac{d(\tan u)}{dx} = \sec^2 u \dfrac{du}{dx}.$

[23] $\dfrac{d(\cot u)}{dx} = -\csc^2 u \dfrac{du}{dx}.$

[24] $\dfrac{d(\sec u)}{dx} = \sec u \tan u \dfrac{du}{dx}.$

[25] $\dfrac{d(\csc u)}{dx} = -\csc u \cot u \dfrac{du}{dx}.$

[26] $\dfrac{d(\text{vers } u)}{dx} = \sin u \dfrac{du}{dx}.$

[27] $\dfrac{d(\sin^{-1} u)}{dx} = \dfrac{\dfrac{du}{dx}}{\sqrt{1 - u^2}}.$

[28] $\dfrac{d(\cos^{-1} u)}{dx} = -\dfrac{\dfrac{du}{dx}}{\sqrt{1 - u^2}}.$

[29] $\dfrac{d(\tan^{-1} u)}{dx} = \dfrac{\dfrac{du}{dx}}{1 + u^2}.$

[30] $\dfrac{d(\cot^{-1} u)}{dx} = -\dfrac{\dfrac{du}{dx}}{1 + u^2}.$

[31] $\dfrac{d(\sec^{-1} u)}{dx} = \dfrac{\dfrac{du}{dx}}{u\sqrt{u^2 - 1}}.$

[32] $\dfrac{d(\csc^{-1} u)}{dx} = -\dfrac{\dfrac{du}{dx}}{u\sqrt{u^2 - 1}}.$

[33] $\dfrac{d(\text{vers}^{-1} u)}{dx} = \dfrac{\dfrac{du}{dx}}{\sqrt{2u - u^2}}.$

[34] $\dfrac{d(\log_e u)}{dx} = \dfrac{1}{u}\dfrac{du}{dx}.$

[35] $\dfrac{d(\log_a u)}{dx} = \dfrac{1}{u}\dfrac{du}{dx}\log_a e.$

[36] $\dfrac{d(a^u)}{dx} = a^u \dfrac{du}{dx}\log_e a.$

[37] $\dfrac{d(e^u)}{dx} = e^u \dfrac{du}{dx}.$

[38] $\dfrac{d(u^v)}{dx} = vu^{v-1}\dfrac{du}{dx} + u^v \dfrac{dv}{dx}\log_e u.$

[39] $\log_{10} e = 0.434294+ = M.$

[40] $\log_e 10 = 2.302585+ = \dfrac{1}{M}.$

[41] $\log_e N = 2.302585 \log_{10} N.$

[42] $\log_{10} N = 0.434294 \log_e N.$

[43] $\log_b N = \dfrac{1}{\log_a b}\log_a N.$

[44] $\displaystyle\int \dfrac{du}{u} = \log u + C.$

[45] $\int e^u du = e^u + C.$

[46] $\displaystyle\int a^u du = \dfrac{a^u}{\log a} + C.$

[47] $K = \dfrac{\dfrac{d^2 y}{dx^2}}{\left[1 + \left(\dfrac{dy}{dx}\right)^2\right]^{\frac{3}{2}}}.$

[48] $R = \dfrac{\left[1 + \left(\dfrac{dy}{dx}\right)^2\right]^{\frac{3}{2}}}{\dfrac{d^2 y}{dx^2}} = \dfrac{1}{K}.$

[49] $\int u\, dv = uv - \int v\, du.$

[50] $\int_a^b f(x)dx = F(b) - F(a).$

[51] $A = \int_a^b f(x)dx.$

[52] $A = \int_\alpha^\beta \frac{1}{2}[f(\theta)]^2 d\theta.$

[53₁] $A = \lim_{n \to \infty} \sum_{x=a}^{=b} y \Delta x.$

[53₂] $A = \lim_{n \to \infty} \sum_{x=a}^{=b} f(x) \Delta x.$

[54] $\lim_{n \to \infty} \sum_{x=a}^{x=b} = \int_a^b f(x)dx.$

[55₁] $s = \int_a^b \sqrt{1 + \left(\frac{dy}{dx}\right)^2} dx.$

[55₂] $s = \int_c^d \sqrt{1 + \left(\frac{dx}{dy}\right)^2} dy.$

[56] $s = \int_\alpha^\beta \sqrt{\rho^2 + \left(\frac{d\rho}{d\theta}\right)^2} d\theta.$

[57] $S = 2\pi \int_a^b y \sqrt{1 + \left(\frac{dy}{dx}\right)^2} dx.$

[58] $V = \pi \int_a^b y^2 \, dx.$

[59] $A = \int \int dy \, dx$ or $A = \int \int dx \, dy.$

[60] $A = \int \int \rho d\rho d\theta.$

[61] $V = \int \int \int dz \, dy \, dx.$

[62] $f(x) = f(a) + f'(x_1)(x - a). \quad a < x_1 < x.$

[63] $f(x) = f(a) + f'(a)(x - a) + \frac{f''(a)}{2!}(x - a)^2 +$

$\frac{f'''(a)}{3!}(x - a)^3 + \cdots + \frac{f^{(n-1)}(a)}{(n - 1)!}(x - a)^{n-1} + \frac{f^{(n)}(x_n)}{n!}(x - a)^n.$

[64] $f(x + h) = f(x) + f'(x)h + \frac{f''(x)}{2!}h^2 + \frac{f'''(x)}{3!}h^3 + \cdots$

$+ \frac{f^{(n-1)}(x)}{(n - 1)!}h^{n-1} + \frac{f^{(n)}(x_n)}{n!}h^n.$

[65] $f(x) = f(0) + xf'(0) + \frac{x^2}{2!}f''(0) + \frac{x^3}{3!}f'''(0) + \cdots$

$+ \frac{x^{n-1}}{(n - 1)!}f^{(n-1)}(0) + \frac{x^n}{n!}f^n(x_n).$

TABLE III

TRIGONOMETRY FORMULAS

(1) 2π radians $= 360°$, π radians $= 180°$.

(2) 1 radian $= \dfrac{180°}{\pi} = 57.2957795° = 57° \ 17' \ 44.8''$.

(3) $1° = \dfrac{\pi}{180} = 0.0174533$ radians.

(4) $\sin^2 \theta + \cos^2 \theta = 1$.

(5) $1 + \tan^2 \theta = \sec^2 \theta$.

(6) $1 + \cot^2 \theta = \csc^2 \theta$.

(7) $\sin \theta = \dfrac{1}{\csc \theta}$, and $\csc \theta = \dfrac{1}{\sin \theta}$.

(8) $\cos \theta = \dfrac{1}{\sec \theta}$, and $\sec \theta = \dfrac{1}{\cos \theta}$.

(9) $\tan \theta = \dfrac{1}{\cot \theta}$, and $\cot \theta = \dfrac{1}{\tan \theta}$.

(10) $\tan \theta = \dfrac{\sin \theta}{\cos \theta} = \dfrac{\sec \theta}{\csc \theta}$.

(11) $\cot \theta = \dfrac{\cos \theta}{\sin \theta} = \dfrac{\csc \theta}{\sec \theta}$.

(12) $\sin (\alpha + \beta) = \sin \alpha \cos \beta + \cos \alpha \sin \beta$.

(13) $\cos (\alpha + \beta) = \cos \alpha \cos \beta - \sin \alpha \sin \beta$.

(14) $\sin (\alpha - \beta) = \sin \alpha \cos \beta - \cos \alpha \sin \beta$.

(15) $\cos (\alpha - \beta) = \cos \alpha \cos \beta + \sin \alpha \sin \beta$.

(16) $\tan (\alpha + \beta) = \dfrac{\tan \alpha + \tan \beta}{1 - \tan \alpha \tan \beta}$.

(17) $\tan (\alpha - \beta) = \dfrac{\tan \alpha - \tan \beta}{1 + \tan \alpha \tan \beta}$.

(18) $\sin 2\theta = 2 \sin \theta \cos \theta$.

(19) $\cos 2\theta = \cos^2 \theta - \sin^2 \theta = 1 - 2 \sin^2 \theta = 2 \cos^2 \theta - 1$.

(20) $\tan 2\theta = \dfrac{2 \tan \theta}{1 - \tan^2 \theta}$.

(21) $\sin \tfrac{1}{2}\theta = \pm \sqrt{\dfrac{1 - \cos \theta}{2}}$.

(22) $\cos \tfrac{1}{2}\theta = \pm \sqrt{\dfrac{1 + \cos \theta}{2}}$.

(23) $\tan \frac{1}{2}\theta = \pm \sqrt{\dfrac{1 - \cos \theta}{1 + \cos \theta}} = \dfrac{1 - \cos \theta}{\sin \theta} = \dfrac{\sin \theta}{1 + \cos \theta}$.

(24) $\sin \alpha + \sin \beta = 2 \sin \frac{1}{2}(\alpha + \beta) \cos \frac{1}{2}(\alpha - \beta)$.

(25) $\sin \alpha - \sin \beta = 2 \cos \frac{1}{2}(\alpha + \beta) \sin \frac{1}{2}(\alpha - \beta)$.

(26) $\cos \alpha + \cos \beta = 2 \cos \frac{1}{2}(\alpha + \beta) \cos \frac{1}{2}(\alpha - \beta)$.

(27) $\cos \alpha - \cos \beta = -2 \sin \frac{1}{2}(\alpha + \beta) \sin \frac{1}{2}(\alpha - \beta)$.

(28) $\sin \alpha \cos \beta = \frac{1}{2} \sin (\alpha + \beta) + \frac{1}{2} \sin (\alpha - \beta)$.

(29) $\cos \alpha \sin \beta = \frac{1}{2} \sin (\alpha + \beta) - \frac{1}{2} \sin (\alpha - \beta)$.

(30) $\cos \alpha \cos \beta = \frac{1}{2} \cos (\alpha + \beta) + \frac{1}{2} \cos (\alpha - \beta)$.

(31) $\sin \alpha \sin \beta = -\frac{1}{2} \cos (\alpha + \beta) + \frac{1}{2} \cos (\alpha - \beta)$.

(32) $\dfrac{a}{\sin \alpha} = \dfrac{b}{\sin \beta} = \dfrac{c}{\sin \gamma}$.   (Sine Law.)

(33) $a^2 = b^2 + c^2 - 2bc \cos \alpha$.   (Cosine Law.)

(34) $\sin (\frac{1}{2}\pi - \theta) = \cos \theta$.

$\cos (\frac{1}{2}\pi - \theta) = \sin \theta$.

$\tan (\frac{1}{2}\pi - \theta) = \cot \theta$.

$\cot (\frac{1}{2}\pi - \theta) = \tan \theta$.

(35) $\sin (\frac{1}{2}\pi + \theta) = \cos \theta$.

$\cos (\frac{1}{2}\pi + \theta) = -\sin \theta$.

$\tan (\frac{1}{2}\pi + \theta) = -\cot \theta$.

$\cot (\frac{1}{2}\pi + \theta) = -\tan \theta$.

(36) $\sin (\pi - \theta) = \sin \theta$.

$\cos (\pi - \theta) = -\cos \theta$.

$\tan (\pi - \theta) = -\tan \theta$.

$\cot (\pi - \theta) = -\cot \theta$.

(37) $\sin (\pi + \theta) = -\sin \theta$.

$\cos (\pi + \theta) = -\cos \theta$.

$\tan (\pi + \theta) = \tan \theta$.

$\cot (\pi + \theta) = \cot \theta$.

(38) $\sin (\frac{3}{2}\pi - \theta) = -\cos \theta$.

$\cos (\frac{3}{2}\pi - \theta) = -\sin \theta$.

$\tan (\frac{3}{2}\pi - \theta) = \cot \theta$.

$\cot (\frac{3}{2}\pi - \theta) = \tan \theta$.

(39) $\sin (\frac{3}{2}\pi + \theta) = -\cos \theta$.

$\cos (\frac{3}{2}\pi + \theta) = \sin \theta$.

$\tan (\frac{3}{2}\pi + \theta) = -\cot \theta$.

$\cot (\frac{3}{2}\pi + \theta) = -\tan \theta$.

(40) $\sin (2\pi - \theta) = -\sin \theta$.

$\cos (2\pi - \theta) = \cos \theta$.

$\tan (2\pi - \theta) = -\tan \theta$.

$\cot (2\pi - \theta) = -\cot \theta$.

(41) $\sin (-\theta) = -\sin \theta$.

$\cos (-\theta) = \cos \theta$.

$\tan (-\theta) = -\tan \theta$.

$\cot (-\theta) = -\cot \theta$.

TABLE IV
ANY TRIGONOMETRIC FUNCTION IN TERMS OF EACH OF THE OTHERS

	$\sin\theta$	$\cos\theta$	$\tan\theta$	$\cot\theta$	$\sec\theta$	$\csc\theta$
$\sin\theta$	$\sin\theta$	$\sqrt{1-\cos^2\theta}$	$\dfrac{\tan\theta}{\sqrt{1+\tan^2\theta}}$	$\dfrac{1}{\sqrt{1+\cot^2\theta}}$	$\dfrac{\sqrt{\sec^2\theta-1}}{\sec\theta}$	$\dfrac{1}{\csc\theta}$
$\cos\theta$	$\sqrt{1-\sin^2\theta}$	$\cos\theta$	$\dfrac{1}{\sqrt{1+\tan^2\theta}}$	$\dfrac{\cot\theta}{\sqrt{1+\cot^2\theta}}$	$\dfrac{1}{\sec\theta}$	$\dfrac{\sqrt{\csc^2\theta-1}}{\csc\theta}$
$\tan\theta$	$\dfrac{\sin\theta}{\sqrt{1-\sin^2\theta}}$	$\dfrac{\sqrt{1-\cos^2\theta}}{\cos\theta}$	$\tan\theta$	$\dfrac{1}{\cot\theta}$	$\sqrt{\sec^2\theta-1}$	$\dfrac{1}{\sqrt{\csc^2\theta-1}}$
$\cot\theta$	$\dfrac{\sqrt{1-\sin^2\theta}}{\sin\theta}$	$\dfrac{\cos\theta}{\sqrt{1-\cos^2\theta}}$	$\dfrac{1}{\tan\theta}$	$\cot\theta$	$\dfrac{1}{\sqrt{\sec^2\theta-1}}$	$\sqrt{\csc^2\theta-1}$
$\sec\theta$	$\dfrac{1}{\sqrt{1-\sin^2\theta}}$	$\dfrac{1}{\cos\theta}$	$\sqrt{1+\tan^2\theta}$	$\dfrac{\sqrt{1+\cot^2\theta}}{\cot\theta}$	$\sec\theta$	$\dfrac{\sec\theta}{\sqrt{\sec^2\theta-1}}$
$\csc\theta$	$\dfrac{1}{\sin\theta}$	$\dfrac{1}{\sqrt{1-\cos^2\theta}}$	$\dfrac{\sqrt{1+\tan^2\theta}}{\tan\theta}$	$\sqrt{1+\cot^2\theta}$	$\dfrac{\sec\theta}{\sqrt{\sec^2\theta-1}}$	$\csc\theta$

TABLE V

FREQUENTLY USED TRIGONOMETRIC FUNCTIONS

$\theta°$	θ in radians	$\sin \theta$	$\cos \theta$	$\tan \theta$	$\cot \theta$	$\sec \theta$	$\csc \theta$
0°	0	0	1	0	∞	1	∞
30°	$\dfrac{\pi}{6}$	$\dfrac{1}{2}$	$\dfrac{\sqrt{3}}{2}$	$\dfrac{\sqrt{3}}{3}$	$\sqrt{3}$	$\dfrac{2\sqrt{3}}{3}$	2
45°	$\dfrac{\pi}{4}$	$\dfrac{\sqrt{2}}{2}$	$\dfrac{\sqrt{2}}{2}$	1	1	$\sqrt{2}$	$\sqrt{2}$
60°	$\dfrac{\pi}{3}$	$\dfrac{\sqrt{3}}{2}$	$\dfrac{1}{2}$	$\sqrt{3}$	$\dfrac{\sqrt{3}}{3}$	2	$\dfrac{2\sqrt{3}}{3}$
90°	$\dfrac{\pi}{2}$	1	0	∞	0	∞	1
120°	$\dfrac{2\pi}{3}$	$\dfrac{\sqrt{3}}{2}$	$-\dfrac{1}{2}$	$-\sqrt{3}$	$-\dfrac{\sqrt{3}}{3}$	-2	$\dfrac{2\sqrt{3}}{3}$
135°	$\dfrac{3\pi}{4}$	$\dfrac{\sqrt{2}}{2}$	$-\dfrac{\sqrt{2}}{2}$	-1	-1	$-\sqrt{2}$	$\sqrt{2}$
150°	$\dfrac{5\pi}{6}$	$\dfrac{1}{2}$	$-\dfrac{\sqrt{3}}{2}$	$-\dfrac{\sqrt{3}}{3}$	$-\sqrt{3}$	$-\dfrac{2\sqrt{3}}{3}$	2
180°	π	0	-1	0	∞	-1	∞
210°	$\dfrac{7\pi}{6}$	$-\dfrac{1}{2}$	$-\dfrac{\sqrt{3}}{2}$	$\dfrac{\sqrt{3}}{3}$	$\sqrt{3}$	$-\dfrac{2\sqrt{3}}{3}$	-2
225°	$\dfrac{5\pi}{4}$	$-\dfrac{\sqrt{2}}{2}$	$-\dfrac{\sqrt{2}}{2}$	1	1	$-\sqrt{2}$	$-\sqrt{2}$
240°	$\dfrac{4\pi}{3}$	$-\dfrac{\sqrt{3}}{2}$	$-\dfrac{1}{2}$	$\sqrt{3}$	$\dfrac{\sqrt{3}}{3}$	-2	$-\dfrac{2\sqrt{3}}{3}$
270°	$\dfrac{3\pi}{2}$	-1	0	∞	0	∞	-1
300°	$\dfrac{5\pi}{3}$	$-\dfrac{\sqrt{3}}{2}$	$\dfrac{1}{2}$	$-\sqrt{3}$	$-\dfrac{\sqrt{3}}{3}$	2	$-\dfrac{2\sqrt{3}}{3}$
315°	$\dfrac{7\pi}{4}$	$-\dfrac{\sqrt{2}}{2}$	$\dfrac{\sqrt{2}}{2}$	-1	-1	$\sqrt{2}$	$-\sqrt{2}$
330°	$\dfrac{11\pi}{6}$	$-\dfrac{1}{2}$	$\dfrac{\sqrt{3}}{2}$	$-\dfrac{\sqrt{3}}{3}$	$-\sqrt{3}$	$\dfrac{2\sqrt{3}}{3}$	-2
360°	2π	0	1	0	∞	1	∞

TABLE VI

VALUES OF e^x FROM x = 0 TO x = 4.9

x	0.0	0.1	0.2	0.3	0.4	0.5	0 6	0.7	0.8	0.9
0	1.00	1.11	1 22	1.35	1.49	1.65	1.82	2.01	2.23	2.46
1	2.72	3.00	3.32	3.67	4.06	4.48	4.95	5.47	6.05	6 69
2	7.39	8.17	9.03	9.97	11.0	12.2	13.5	14.9	16.4	18 2
3	20.1	22.2	24.5	27.1	30.0	33.1	36.6	40.4	44.7	49.4
4	54.6	60.3	66.7	73.7	81.5	90.0	99 5	109.9	121.5	134.3

VALUES OF e^{-x} FROM x = 0 TO x = 4.9

x	0 0	0.1	0.2	0.3	0.4	0.5	0.6	0.7	0.8	0.9
0	1 00	0.90	0.82	0.74	0.67	0.61	0 55	0.50	0.45	0.41
1	0.37	0 33	0.30	0.27	0.25	0.22	0 20	0.18	0.17	0.15
2	0.14	0.12	0.11	0.10	0 09	0.08	0.07	0.07	0 06	0.06
3	0.05	0.05	0.04	0.04	0 03	0.03	0 03	0.02	0.02	0.02
4	0.02	0.02	0.01	0.01	0.01	0.01	0.01	0.01	0.01	0.01

TABLE VII.—COMMON LOGARITHMS

N.	0	1	2	3	4	5	6	7	8	9
10	0000	0043	0086	0128	0170	0212	0253	0294	0334	0374
11	0414	0453	0492	0531	0569	0607	0645	0682	0719	0755
12	0792	0828	0864	0899	0934	0969	1004	1038	1072	1106
13	1139	1173	1206	1239	1271	1303	1335	1367	1399	1430
14	1461	1492	1523	1553	1584	1614	1644	1673	1703	1732
15	1761	1790	1818	1847	1875	1903	1931	1959	1987	2014
16	2041	2068	2095	2122	2148	2175	2201	2227	2253	2279
17	2304	2330	2355	2380	2405	2430	2455	2480	2504	2529
18	2553	2577	2601	2625	2648	2672	2695	2718	2742	2765
19	2788	2810	2833	2856	2878	2900	2923	2945	2967	2989
20	3010	3032	3054	3075	3096	3118	3139	3160	3181	3201
21	3222	3243	3263	3284	3304	3324	3345	3365	3385	3404
22	3424	3444	3464	3483	3502	3522	3541	3560	3579	3598
23	3617	3636	3655	3674	3692	3711	3729	3747	3766	3784
24	3802	3820	3838	3856	3874	3892	3909	3927	3945	3962
25	3979	3997	4014	4031	4048	4065	4082	4099	4116	4133
26	4150	4166	4183	4200	4216	4232	4249	4265	4281	4298
27	4314	4330	4346	4362	4378	4393	4409	4425	4440	4456
28	4472	4487	4502	4518	4533	4548	4564	4579	4594	4609
29	4624	4639	4654	4669	4683	4698	4713	4728	4742	4757
30	4771	4786	4800	4814	4829	4843	4857	4871	4886	4900
31	4914	4928	4942	4955	4969	4983	4997	5011	5024	5038
32	5051	5065	5079	5092	5105	5119	5132	5145	5159	5172
33	5185	5198	5211	5224	5237	5250	5263	5276	5289	5302
34	5315	5328	5340	5353	5366	5378	5391	5403	5416	5428
35	5441	5453	5465	5478	5490	5502	5514	5527	5539	5551
36	5563	5575	5587	5599	5611	5623	5635	5647	5658	5670
37	5682	5694	5705	5717	5729	5740	5752	5763	5775	5786
38	5798	5809	5821	5832	5843	5855	5866	5877	5888	5899
39	5911	5922	5933	5944	5955	5966	5977	5988	5999	6010
40	6021	6031	6042	6053	6064	6075	6085	6096	6107	6117
41	6128	6138	6149	6160	6170	6180	6191	6201	6212	6222
42	6232	6243	6253	6263	6274	6284	6294	6304	6314	6325
43	6335	6345	6355	6365	6375	6385	6395	6405	6415	6425
44	6435	6444	6454	6464	6474	6484	6493	6503	6513	6522
45	6532	6542	6551	6561	6571	6580	6590	6599	6609	6618
46	6628	6637	6646	6656	6665	6675	6684	6693	6702	6712
47	6721	6730	6739	6749	6758	6767	6776	6785	6794	6803
48	6812	6821	6830	6839	6848	6857	6866	6875	6884	6893
49	6902	6911	6920	6928	6937	6946	6955	6964	6972	6981
50	6990	6998	7007	7016	7024	7033	7042	7050	7059	7067
51	7076	7084	7093	7101	7110	7118	7126	7135	7143	7152
52	7160	7168	7177	7185	7193	7202	7210	7218	7226	7235
53	7243	7251	7259	7267	7275	7284	7292	7300	7308	7316
54	7324	7332	7340	7348	7356	7364	7372	7380	7388	7396
N.	0	1	2	3	4	5	6	7	8	9

TABLE VII.—COMMON LOGARITHMS—*Continued*

N.	0	1	2	3	4	5	6	7	8	9
55	7404	7412	7419	7427	7435	7443	7451	7459	7466	7474
56	7482	7490	7497	7505	7513	7520	7528	7536	7543	7551
57	7559	7566	7574	7582	7589	7597	7604	7612	7619	7627
58	7634	7642	7649	7657	7664	7672	7679	7686	7694	7701
59	7709	7716	7723	7731	7738	7745	7752	7760	7767	7774
60	7782	7789	7796	7803	7810	7818	7825	7832	7839	7846
61	7853	7860	7868	7875	7882	7889	7896	7903	7910	7917
62	7924	7931	7938	7945	7952	7959	7966	7973	7980	7987
63	7993	8000	8007	8014	8021	8028	8035	8041	8048	8055
64	8062	8069	8075	8082	8089	8096	8102	8109	8116	8122
65	8129	8136	8142	8149	8156	8162	8169	8176	8182	8189
66	8195	8202	8209	8215	8222	8228	8235	8241	8248	8254
67	8261	8267	8274	8280	8287	8293	8299	8306	8312	8319
68	8325	8331	8338	8344	8351	8357	8363	8370	8376	8382
69	8388	8395	8401	8407	8414	8420	8426	8432	8439	8445
70	8451	8457	8463	8470	8476	8482	8488	8494	8500	8506
71	8513	8519	8525	8531	8537	8543	8549	8555	8561	8567
72	8573	8579	8585	8591	8597	8603	8609	8615	8621	8627
73	8633	8639	8645	8651	8657	8663	8669	8675	8681	8686
74	8692	8608	8704	8710	8716	8722	8727	8733	8739	8745
75	8751	8756	8762	8768	8774	8779	8785	8791	8797	8802
76	8808	8814	8820	8825	8831	8837	8842	8848	8854	8859
77	8865	8871	8876	8882	8887	8893	8899	8904	8910	8915
78	8921	8927	8932	8938	8943	8949	8954	8960	8965	8971
79	8976	8982	8987	8993	8998	9004	9009	9015	9020	9025
80	9031	9036	9042	9047	9053	9058	9063	9069	9074	9079
81	9085	9090	9096	9101	9106	9112	9117	9122	9128	9133
82	9138	9143	9149	9154	9159	9165	9170	9175	9180	9186
83	9191	9196	9201	9206	9212	9217	9222	9227	9232	9238
84	9243	9248	9253	9258	9263	9269	9274	9279	9284	9289
85	9294	9299	9304	9309	9315	9320	9325	9330	9335	9340
86	9345	9350	9355	9360	9365	9370	9375	9380	9385	9390
87	9395	9400	9405	9410	9415	9420	9425	9430	9435	9440
88	9445	9450	9455	9460	9465	9469	9474	9479	9484	9489
89	9494	9499	9504	9509	9513	9518	9523	9528	9533	9538
90	9542	9547	9552	9557	9562	9566	9571	9576	9581	9586
91	9590	9595	9600	9605	9609	9614	9619	9624	9628	9633
92	9638	9643	9647	9652	9657	9661	9666	9671	9675	9680
93	9685	9689	9694	9699	9703	9708	9713	9717	9722	9727
94	9731	9736	9741	9745	9750	9754	9759	9763	9768	9773
95	9777	9782	9786	9791	9795	9800	9805	9809	9814	9818
96	9823	9827	9832	9836	9841	9845	9850	9854	9859	9863
97	9868	9872	9877	9881	9886	9890	9894	9899	9903	9908
98	9912	9917	9921	9926	9930	9934	9939	9943	9948	9952
99	9956	9961	9965	9969	9974	9978	9983	9987	9991	9996
N.	0	1	2	3	4	5	6	7	8	9

412   *PRACTICAL CALCULUS FOR HOME STUDY*

TABLE VIII.—TRIGONOMETRIC FUNCTIONS

Angles	Sines		Cosines		Tangents		Cotangents		Angles
	Nat.	Log.	Nat.	Log.	Nat.	Log.	Nat.	Log.	
0° 00′	.0000	∞	1.0000	0.0000	.0000	∞	∞	∞	90° 00′
10	.0029	7.4637	1.0000	0000	.0029	7.4637	343.77	2.5363	50
20	.0058	7648	1.0000	0000	.0058	7648	171.89	2352	40
30	.0087	9408	1.0000	0000	.0087	9409	114.59	0591	30
40	.0116	8.0658	.9999	0000	.0116	8.0658	85.940	1.9342	20
50	.0145	1627	.9999	0000	.0145	1627	68.750	8373	10
1° 00′	.0175	8.2419	.9998	9.9999	.0175	8.2419	57.290	1.7581	89° 00′
10	.0204	3088	.9998	9999	.0204	3089	49.104	6911	50
20	.0233	3668	.9997	9999	.0233	3669	42.964	6331	40
30	.0262	4179	.9997	9999	.0262	4181	38.188	5819	30
40	.0291	4637	.9996	9998	.0291	4638	34.368	5362	20
50	.0320	5050	.9995	9998	.0320	5053	31.242	4947	10
2° 00′	.0349	8.5428	.9994	9.9997	.0349	8.5431	28.636	1.4569	88° 00′
10	.0378	5776	.9993	9997	.0378	5779	26.432	4221	50
20	.0407	6097	.9992	9996	.0407	6101	24.542	3899	40
30	.0436	6397	.9990	9996	.0437	6101	22.904	3599	30
40	.0165	6677	.9989	9995	.0466	6682	21.470	3318	20
50	.0494	6940	.9988	9995	.0495	6945	20.206	3055	10
3° 00′	.0523	8.7188	.9986	9.9994	.0524	8.7194	19.081	1.2806	87° 00′
10	.0552	7423	.9985	9993	.0553	7429	18.075	2571	50
20	.0581	7645	.9983	9993	.0582	7652	17.169	2348	40
30	.0610	7857	.9981	9992	.0612	7865	16.350	2135	30
40	.0640	8059	.9980	9991	.0641	8067	15.605	1933	20
50	.0669	8251	.9978	9990	.0670	8261	14.924	1739	10
4° 00′	.0698	8.8436	.9976	9.9989	.0699	8.8446	14.301	1.1554	86° 00′
10	.0727	8613	.9974	9989	.0729	8624	13.727	1376	50
20	.0756	8783	.9971	9988	.0758	8795	13.197	1205	40
30	.0785	8946	.9969	9987	.0787	8960	12.706	1040	30
40	.0814	9104	.9967	9986	.0816	9118	12.251	0882	20
50	.0843	9256	.9964	9985	.0846	9272	11.826	0728	10
5° 00′	.0872	8.9403	.9962	9.9983	.0875	8.9420	11.430	1.0580	85° 00′
10	.0901	9545	.9959	9982	.0904	9563	11.059	0437	50
20	.0929	9682	.9957	9981	.0934	9701	10.712	0299	40
30	.0958	9816	.9954	9980	.0963	9836	10.385	0164	30
40	.0987	9945	.9951	9979	.0992	9966	10.078	0034	20
50	.1016	9.0070	.9948	9977	.1022	9.0093	9.7882	0.9907	10
6° 00′	.1045	9.0192	.9945	9.9976	.1051	9.0216	9.5144	0.9784	84° 00′
10	.1074	0311	.9942	9975	.1080	0336	9.2553	9664	50
20	.1103	0426	.9939	9973	.1110	0453	9.0098	9547	40
30	.1132	0539	.9936	9972	.1139	0567	8.7769	9433	30
40	.1161	0648	.9932	9971	.1169	0678	8.5555	9322	20
50	.1190	0755	.9929	9969	.1198	0786	8.3450	9214	10
7° 00′	.1219	9.0859	.9925	9.9968	.1228	9.0891	8.1443	0.9109	83° 00′
10	.1248	0961	.9922	9966	.1257	0995	7.9530	9005	50
20	.1276	1060	.9918	9964	.1287	1096	7.7704	8904	40
30	.1305	1157	.9914	9963	.1317	1194	7.5958	8806	30
40	.1334	1252	.9911	9961	.1346	1291	7.4287	8709	20
50	.1363	1345	.9907	9959	.1376	1385	7.2687	8615	10
8° 00′	.1392	9.1436	.9903	9.9958	.1405	9.1478	7.1154	0.8522	82° 00′
10	.1421	1525	.9899	9956	.1435	1569	6.9682	8431	50
20	.1449	1612	.9894	9954	.1465	1658	6.8269	8342	40
30	.1478	1697	.9890	9952	.1495	1745	6.6912	8255	30
40	.1507	1781	.9886	9950	.1524	1831	6.5606	8169	20
50	.1536	1863	.9881	9948	.1554	1915	6.4348	8085	10
9° 00′	.1564	9.1943	.9877	9.9946	.1584	9.1997	6.3138	0.8003	81° 00′
	Nat.	Log.	Nat.	Log.	Nat.	Log.	Nat.	Log.	
Angles	Cosines		Sines		Cotangents		Tangents		Angles

TABLE VIII.—TRIGONOMETRIC FUNCTIONS—*Continued*

Angles	Sines		Cosines		Tangents		Cotangents		Angles
	Nat.	Log.	Nat.	Log.	Nat.	Log.	Nat.	Log.	
9° 00′	.1564	9.1943	.9877	9.9946	.1584	9.1997	6.3138	0.8003	81° 00′
10	.1593	2022	.9872	9944	.1614	2078	6.1970	7922	50
20	.1622	2100	.9868	9942	.1644	2158	6 0844	7842	40
30	.1650	2176	.9863	9940	.1673	2256	5.9758	7764	30
40	.1679	2251	.9858	9938	.1703	2313	5.8708	7687	20
50	.1708	2324	.9853	9936	.1733	2389	5.7694	7611	10
10° 00′	.1736	9.2397	.9848	9.9934	.1763	9.2463	5.6713	0.7537	80° 00′
10	.1765	2468	.9843	9031	.1793	2536	5.5764	7464	50
20	.1794	2538	.9838	9929	.1823	2609	5.4845	7391	40
30	.1822	2606	.9833	9927	.1853	2680	5.3955	7320	30
40	.1851	2674	.9827	9924	.1883	2750	5.3093	7250	20
50	.1880	2740	.9822	9922	.1914	2819	5.2257	7181	10
11° 00′	.1908	9.2806	.9816	9.9919	.1944	9.2887	5.1446	0.7113	79° 00′
10	.1937	2870	.9811	9917	.1974	2953	5.0658	7047	50
20	.1965	2934	.9805	9914	.2004	3020	4.9894	6980	40
30	.1994	2997	.9799	9912	.2035	3085	4.9152	6915	30
40	.2022	3058	.9793	9909	.2065	3149	4.8430	6851	20
50	.2051	3119	.9787	9907	.2095	3212	4.7729	6788	10
12° 00′	.2079	9.3179	.9781	9.9904	.2126	9.3275	4.7046	0.6725	78° 00′
10	.2108	3238	.9775	9901	.2156	3336	4.6382	6664	50
20	.2136	3296	.9769	9899	.2186	3397	4.5736	6603	40
30	.2164	3353	.9763	9896	.2217	3458	4.5107	6542	30
40	.2193	3410	.9757	9893	.2247	3517	4.4494	6483	20
50	.2221	3466	.9750	9890	.2278	3576	4.3897	6424	10
13° 00′	.2250	9.3521	.9744	9.9887	.2309	9.3634	4.3315	0.6366	77° 00′
10	.2278	3575	.9737	9884	.2339	3691	4.2747	6309	50
20	.2306	3629	.9730	9881	.2370	3748	4.2193	6252	40
30	.2334	3682	.9724	9878	.2401	3804	4.1653	6196	30
40	.2363	3734	.9717	9875	.2432	3859	4.1126	6141	20
50	.2391	3786	.9710	9872	.2462	3914	4.0611	6086	10
14° 00′	.2419	9.3837	.9703	9.9869	.2493	9.3968	4.0108	0.6032	76° 00′
10	.2447	3887	.9696	9866	.2524	4021	3.9617	5979	50
20	.2476	3937	.9689	9863	.2555	4074	3.9136	5926	40
30	.2504	3986	.9681	9859	.2586	4127	3.8667	5873	30
40	.2532	4035	.9674	9856	.2617	4178	3.8208	5822	20
50	.2560	4083	.9667	9853	.2648	4230	3.7760	5770	10
15° 00′	.2588	9.4130	.9659	9.9849	.2679	9.4281	3.7321	0.5719	75° 00′
10	.2616	4177	.9652	9846	.2711	4331	3.6891	5669	50
20	.2644	4223	.9644	9843	.2742	4381	3.6470	5619	40
30	.2672	4269	.9636	9839	.2773	4430	3.6059	5570	30
40	.2700	4314	.9628	9836	.2805	4479	3.5656	5521	20
50	.2728	4359	.9621	9832	.2836	4527	3.5261	5473	10
16° 00′	.2756	9.4403	.9613	9.9828	.2867	9.4575	3.4874	0.5425	74° 00′
10	.2784	4447	.9605	9825	.2899	4622	3.4495	5378	50
20	.2812	4491	.9596	9821	.2931	4669	3.4124	5331	40
30	.2840	4533	.9588	9817	.2962	4716	3.3759	5284	30
40	.2868	4576	.9580	9814	.2994	4762	3.3402	5238	20
50	.2896	4618	.9572	9810	.3026	4808	3.3052	5192	10
17° 00′	.2924	9.4659	.9563	9.9806	.3057	9.4853	3.2709	0.5147	73° 00′
10	.2952	4700	.9555	9802	.3089	4898	3.2371	5102	50
20	.2979	4741	.9546	9798	.3121	4943	3.2041	5057	40
30	.3007	4781	.9537	9794	.3153	4987	3.1716	5013	30
40	.3035	4821	.9528	9790	.3185	5031	3 1397	4969	20
50	.3062	4861	.9520	9786	.3217	5075	3.1084	4925	10
18° 00′	.3090	9.4900	.9511	9.9782	.3249	9.5118	3.0777	0.4882	72° 00′
	Nat.	Log.	Nat.	Log.	Nat.	Log.	Nat.	Log.	
Angles	Cosines		Sines		Cotangents		Tangents		Angles

TABLE VIII.—TRIGONOMETRIC FUNCTIONS—*Continued*

Angles	Sines		Cosines		Tangents		Cotangents		Angles
	Nat.	Log.	Nat.	Log.	Nat.	Log.	Nat.	Log.	
18° 00′	.3090	9.4900	.9511	9.9782	.3249	9.5118	3.0777	0.4882	72° 00′
10	.3118	4939	.9502	9778	.3281	5161	3.0475	4839	50
20	.3145	4977	.9492	9774	.3314	5203	3.0178	4797	40
30	.3173	5015	.9483	9770	.3346	5245	2.9887	4755	30
40	.3201	5052	.9474	9765	.3378	5287	2.9600	4713	20
50	.3228	5090	.9465	9761	.3411	5329	2.9319	4671	10
19° 00′	.3256	9.5126	.9455	9.9757	.3443	9.5370	2.9042	0.4630	71° 00′
10	.3283	5163	.9446	9752	.3476	5411	2.8770	4589	50
20	.3311	5199	.9436	9748	.3508	5451	2.8502	4549	40
30	.3338	5235	.9426	9743	.3541	5491	2.8239	4509	30
40	.3365	5270	.9417	9739	.3574	5531	2.7980	4469	20
50	.3393	5306	.9407	9734	.3607	5571	2.7725	4429	10
20° 00′	.3420	9.5341	.9397	9.9730	.3640	9.5611	2.7475	0.4389	70° 00′
10	.3448	5375	.9387	9725	.3673	5650	2.7228	4350	50
20	.3475	5409	.9377	9721	.3706	5689	2.6985	4311	40
30	.3502	5443	.9367	9716	.3739	5727	2.6746	4273	30
40	.3529	5477	.9356	9711	.3772	5766	2.6511	4234	20
50	.3557	5510	.9346	9706	.3805	5804	2.6279	4196	10
21° 00′	.3584	9.5543	.9336	9.9702	.3839	9.5842	2.6051	0.4158	69° 00′
10	.3611	5576	.9325	9697	.3872	5879	2.5826	4121	50
20	.3638	5609	.9315	9692	.3906	5917	2.5605	4083	40
30	.3665	5641	.9304	9687	.3939	5954	2.5386	4046	30
40	.3692	5673	.9293	9682	.3973	5991	2.5172	4009	20
50	.3719	5704	.9283	9677	.4006	6028	2.4960	3972	10
22° 00′	.3746	9.5736	.9272	9.9672	.4040	9.6064	2.4751	0.3936	68° 00′
10	.3773	5767	.9261	9667	.4074	6100	2.4545	3900	50
20	.3800	5798	.9250	9661	.4108	6136	2.4342	3864	40
30	.3827	5828	.9239	9656	.4142	6172	2.4142	3828	30
40	.3854	5859	.9228	9651	.4176	6208	2.3945	3792	20
50	.3881	5889	.9216	9646	.4210	6243	2.3750	3757	10
23° 00′	.3907	9.5919	.9205	9.9640	.4245	9.6279	2.3559	0.3721	67° 00′
10	.3934	5948	.9194	9635	.4279	6314	2.3369	3686	50
20	.3961	5978	.9182	9629	.4314	6348	2.3183	3652	40
30	.3987	6007	.9171	9624	.4348	6383	2.2998	3617	30
40	.4014	6036	.9159	9618	.4383	6417	2.2817	3583	20
50	.4041	6065	.9147	9613	.4417	6452	2.2637	3548	10
24° 00′	.4067	9.6093	.9135	9.9607	.4452	9.6486	2.2460	0.3514	66° 00′
10	.4094	6121	.9124	9602	.4487	6520	2.2286	3480	50
20	.4120	6149	.9112	9596	.4522	6553	2.2113	3447	40
30	.4147	6177	.9100	9590	.4557	6587	2.1943	3413	30
40	.4173	6205	.9088	9584	.4592	6620	2.1775	3380	20
50	.4200	6232	.9075	9579	.4628	6654	2.1609	3346	10
25° 00′	.4226	9.6259	.9063	9.9573	.4663	9.6687	2.1445	0.3313	65° 00′
10	.4253	6286	.9051	9567	.4699	6720	2.1283	3280	50
20	.4279	6313	.9038	9561	.4734	6752	2.1123	3248	40
30	.4305	6340	.9026	9555	.4770	6785	2.0965	3215	30
40	.4331	6366	.9013	9549	.4806	6817	2.0809	3183	20
50	.4358	6392	.9001	9543	.4841	6850	2.0655	3150	10
26° 00′	.4384	9.6418	.8988	9.9537	.4877	9.6882	2.0503	0.3118	64° 00′
10	.4410	6444	.8975	9530	.4913	6914	2.0353	3086	50
20	.4436	6470	.8962	9524	.4950	6946	2.0204	3054	40
30	.4462	6495	.8949	9518	.4986	6977	2.0057	3023	30′
40	.4488	6521	.8936	9512	.5022	7009	1.9912	2991	20
50	.4514	6546	.8923	9505	.5059	7040	1.9768	2960	10
27° 00′	.4540	9.6570	.8910	9.9499	.5095	9.7072	1.9626	0.2928	63° 00′
	Nat.	Log.	Nat.	Log.	Nat.	Log.	Nat.	Log.	
Angles	Cosines		Sines		Cotangents		Tangents		Angles

TABLE VIII.—TRIGONOMETRIC FUNCTIONS—*Continued*

Angles	Sines Nat.	Log.	Cosines Nat.	Log.	Tangents Nat.	Log.	Cotangents Nat.	Log.	Angles
27° 00′	.4540	9.6570	.8910	9.9499	.5095	9.7072	1.9626	0.2928	63° 00′
10	.4566	6595	.8897	9492	.5132	7103	1.9486	2897	50
20	.4592	6620	.8884	9486	.5169	7134	1.9347	2866	40
30	.4617	6644	.8870	9479	.5206	7165	1.9210	2835	30
40	.4643	6668	.8857	9473	.5243	7196	1.9074	2804	20
50	.4669	6692	.8843	9466	.5280	7226	1.8940	2774	10
28° 00′	.4695	9.6716	.8829	9.9459	.5317	9.7257	1.8807	0.2743	62° 00′
10	.4720	6740	.8816	9453	.5354	7287	1.8676	2713	50
20	.4746	6763	.8802	9446	.5392	7317	1.8546	2683	40
30	.4772	6787	.8788	9439	.5430	7348	1.8418	2652	30
40	.4797	6810	.8774	9432	.5467	7378	1.8291	2622	20
50	.4823	6833	.8760	9425	.5505	7408	1.8165	2592	10
29° 00′	.4848	9.6856	.8746	9.9418	.5543	9.7438	1.8040	0.2562	61° 00′
10	.4874	6878	.8732	9411	.5581	7467	1.7917	2533	50
20	.4899	6901	.8718	9404	.5619	7497	1.7796	2503	40
30	.4924	6923	.8704	9397	.5658	7526	1.7675	2474	30
40	.4950	6946	.8689	0300	.5606	7556	1.7556	2444	20
50	.4975	6968	.8675	9383	.5735	7585	1.7437	2415	10
30° 00′	.5000	9.6990	.8660	9.9375	.5774	9.7614	1.7321	0.2386	60° 00′
10	.5025	7012	.8646	9368	.5812	7644	1.7205	2356	50
20	.5050	7033	.8631	9361	.5851	7673	1.7090	2327	40
30	.5075	7055	.8616	9353	.5890	7701	1.6977	2299	30
40	.5100	7076	.8601	9346	.5930	7730	1.6864	2270	20
50	.5125	7097	.8587	9338	.5969	7759	1.6753	2241	10
31° 00′	.5150	9.7118	.8572	9.9331	.6009	9.7788	1.6643	0.2212	59° 00′
10	.5175	7139	.8557	9323	.6048	7816	1.6534	2184	50
20	.5200	7160	.8542	9315	.6088	7845	1.6426	2155	40
30	.5225	7181	.8526	9308	.6128	7873	1.6319	2127	30
40	.5250	7201	.8511	9300	.6168	7902	1.6212	2098	20
50	.5275	7222	.8496	9292	.6208	7930	1.6107	2070	10
32° 00′	.5299	9.7242	.8480	9.9284	.6249	9.7958	1.6003	0.2042	58° 00′
10	.5324	7262	.8465	9276	.6289	7986	1.5900	2014	50
20	.5348	7282	.8450	9268	.6330	8014	1.5798	1986	40
30	.5373	7302	.8434	9260	.6371	8042	1.5697	1958	30
40	.5398	7322	.8418	9252	.6412	8070	1.5597	1930	20
50	.5422	7342	.8403	9244	.6453	8097	1.5497	1903	10
33° 00′	.5446	9.7361	.8387	9.9236	.6494	9.8125	1.5399	0.1875	57° 00′
10	.5471	7380	.8371	9228	6536	8153	1.5301	1847	50
20	.5495	7400	.8355	9219	.6577	8180	1.5204	1820	40
30	.5519	7419	.8339	9211	.6619	8208	1.5108	1792	30
40	.5544	7438	.8323	9203	.6661	8235	1.5013	1765	20
50	.5568	7457	.8307	9194	.6703	8263	1.4919	1737	10
34° 00′	.5592	9.7476	.8290	9.9186	.6745	9.8290	1.4826	0.1710	56° 00′
10	.5616	7494	.8274	9177	.6787	8317	1.4733	1683	50
20	.5640	7513	.8258	9169	.6830	8344	1.4641	1656	40
30	.5664	7531	.8241	9160	.6873	8371	1.4550	1629	30
40	.5688	7550	.8225	9151	.6916	8398	1.4460	1602	20
50	.5712	7568	.8208	9142	.6959	8425	1.4370	1575	10
35° 00′	.5736	9.7586	.8192	9.9134	.7002	9.8452	1.4281	0.1548	55° 00′
10	.5760	7604	.8175	9125	.7046	8479	1.4193	1521	50
20	.5783	7622	.8158	9116	.7089	8506	1.4106	1494	40
30	.5807	7640	.8141	9107	.7133	8533	1.4019	1467	30
40	.5831	7657	.8124	9098	.7177	8559	1.3934	1441	20
50	.5854	7675	.8107	9089	.7221	8586	1.3848	1414	10
36° 00′	.5878	9.7692	.8090	9.9080	.7265	9.8613	1.3764	0.1387	54° 00′
	Nat.	Log.	Nat.	Log.	Nat.	Log.	Nat.	Log.	
Angles	Cosines		Sines		Cotangents		Tangents		Angles

TABLE VIII.—TRIGONOMETRIC FUNCTIONS—*Continued*

Angles	Sines		Cosines		Tangents		Cotangents		Angles
	Nat.	Log.	Nat.	Log.	Nat.	Log.	Nat.	Log.	
36° 00'	.5878	9.7692	.8090	9.9080	.7265	9.8613	1.3764	0.1387	54° 00'
10	.5901	7710	.8073	9070	.7310	8639	1.3680	1361	50
20	.5925	7727	.8056	9061	.7355	8666	1.3597	1334	40
30	.5948	7744	.8039	9052	.7400	8692	1.3514	1308	30
40	.5972	7761	.8021	9042	.7445	8718	1.3432	1282	20
50	.5995	7778	.8004	9033	.7490	8745	1.3351	1255	10
37° 00'	.6018	9.7795	.7986	9.9023	.7536	9.8771	1.3270	0.1229	53° 00'
10	.6041	7811	.7969	9014	.7581	8797	1.3190	1203	50
20	.6065	7828	.7951	9004	.7627	8824	1.3111	1176	40
30	.6088	7844	.7934	8995	.7673	8850	1.3032	1150	30
40	.6111	7861	.7916	8985	.7720	8876	1.2954	1124	20
50	.6134	7877	.7898	8975	.7766	8902	1.2876	1098	10
38° 00'	.6157	9.7893	.7880	9.8965	.7813	9.8928	1.2799	0.1072	52° 00'
10	.6180	7910	.7862	8955	.7860	8954	1.2723	1046	50
20	.6202	7926	.7844	8945	.7907	8980	1.2647	1020	40
30	.6225	7941	.7826	8935	.7954	9006	1.2572	0994	30
40	.6248	7957	.7808	8925	.8002	9032	1.2497	0968	20
50	.6271	7973	.7790	8915	.8050	9058	1.2423	0942	10
39° 00'	.6293	9.7989	.7771	9.8905	.8098	9.9084	1.2349	0.0916	51° 00'
10	.6316	8004	.7753	8895	.8146	9110	1.2276	0890	50
20	.6338	8020	.7735	8884	.8195	9135	1.2203	0865	40
30	.6361	8035	.7716	8874	.8243	9161	1.2131	0839	30
40	.6383	8050	.7698	8864	.8292	9187	1.2059	0813	20
50	.6406	8066	.7679	8853	.8342	9212	1.1988	0788	10
40° 00'	.6428	9.8081	.7660	9.8843	.8391	9.9238	1.1918	0.0762	50° 00'
10	.6450	8096	.7642	8832	.8441	9264	1.1847	0736	50
20	.6472	8111	.7623	8821	.8491	9289	1.1778	0711	40
30	.6494	8125	.7604	8810	.8541	9315	1.1708	0685	30
40	.6517	8140	.7585	8800	.8591	9341	1.1640	0659	20
50	.6539	8155	.7566	8789	.8642	9366	1.1571	0634	10
41° 00'	.6561	9.8169	.7547	9.8778	.8693	9.9392	1.1504	0.0608	49° 00'
10	.6583	8184	.7528	8767	.8744	9417	1.1436	0583	50
20	.6604	8198	.7509	8756	.8796	9443	1.1369	0557	40
30	.6626	8213	.7490	8745	.8847	9468	1.1303	0532	30
40	.6648	8227	.7470	8733	.8899	9494	1.1237	0506	20
50	.6670	8241	.7451	8722	.8952	9519	1.1171	0481	10
42° 00'	.6691	9.8255	.7431	9.8711	.9004	9.9544	1.1106	0.0456	48° 00'
10	.6713	8269	.7412	8699	.9057	9570	1.1041	0430	50
20	.6734	8283	.7392	8688	.9110	9595	1.0977	0405	40
30	.6756	8297	.7373	8676	.9163	9621	1.0913	0379	30
40	.6777	8311	.7353	8665	.9217	9646	1.C850	0354	20
50	.6799	8324	.7333	8653	.9271	9671	1.0786	0329	10
43° 00'	.6820	9.8338	.7314	9.8641	.9325	9.9697	1.0724	0.0303	47° 00'
10	.6841	8351	.7294	8629	.9380	9722	1.C661	0278	50
20	.6862	8365	.7274	8618	.9435	9747	1.0599	0253	40
30	.6884	8378	.7254	8606	.9490	9772	1.0538	0228	30
40	.6905	8391	.7234	8594	.9545	9798	1.0477	0202	20
50	.6926	8405	.7214	8582	.9601	9823	1.0416	0177	10
44° 00'	.6947	9.8418	.7193	9.8569	.9657	9.9848	1.0355	0.0152	46° 00'
10	.6967	8431	.7173	8557	.9713	9874	1.0295	0126	50
20	.6988	8444	.7153	8545	.9770	9899	1.0235	0101	40
30	.7009	8457	.7133	8532	.9827	9924	1.0176	0076	30
40	.7030	8469	.7112	8520	.9884	9949	1.0117	0051	20
50	.7050	8482	.7092	8507	.9942	9975	1.0058	0025	10
45° 00'	.7071	9.8495	.7071	9.8495	1.0000	0.0000	1.0000	0.0000	45° 00'
	Nat.	Log.	Nat.	Log.	Nat.	Log.	Nat.	Log.	
Angles	Cosines		Sines		Cotangents		Tangents		Angles

ANSWERS

Pages 14, 15. Art. 8

3. $V = \frac{4}{3}\pi r^3$, $V = \frac{1}{6}\pi d^3$. **4.** $T = 2\pi rh + 2\pi r^2$.

5. $A = \frac{1}{2}d^2$, $d = \sqrt{2A}$.

6. $W = k\dfrac{bd^2}{l}$, $b = \dfrac{lW}{kd^2}$, $d = \sqrt{\dfrac{lW}{kb}}$, $l = \dfrac{kbd^2}{W}$.

8. $S = \sqrt[3]{36\pi V^2}$. **9.** $H = \dfrac{EI}{746}$ **10.** $R = k\dfrac{l}{d^2}$.

11. $x = \pm\sqrt{25 - y^2}$, $y = \pm\sqrt{25 - x^2}$.

12. $0, \frac{1}{2}\sqrt{2}, -\frac{1}{2}\sqrt{3}, 1, \frac{1}{2}\sqrt{3}, \frac{1}{2}\sqrt{2}$.

13. $-4, 44, -12$. **14.** $2, 1.6778, \bar{2}.0792$.

15. $1, \sqrt{10}, 7$.

16. $3x^2y - 4xy^2 - 2y^3, -3x^2y + 4xy^2 + 2y^3, -3x^2y - 4xy^2 + 2y^3$.

17. $3^x, 3^{x+y}$.

19. $x = \sin^{-1}y$, $x = \log_2 y$.

Pages 17, 18, 19. Art. 9

1. $10\Delta x$, 20, 20, no. **2.** 2 sq. in., $\Delta A = 2$, no.

3. 4.5, 0.0802. **4.** $A = x^2$, 13. **5.** $A = \pi r^2$, 32.201.

6. 0.015, 0.00025, 0.00004. **7.** 0.00021, 0.0001.

8. 0.2168. **9.** 0.00005. **12.** -0.249.

13. Average rate in miles per hour for distance m miles. Average rate in miles per hour for distance Δm miles.

14. 80, 65.6, 64.16, 64.016, 64.

15. 1330, 133; 7, 7; 0.331, 3.31; 0.030301, 3.0301; 0.003003001, 3.003001; 3; 3.

Pages 28, 29. Art. 14

1. 64, yes. **2.** 3, yes. **3.** 3, 48, 0, 12.

4. $\pm 3, \pm\frac{1}{3}\sqrt{6}, \pm 10\sqrt{10}$. **5.** $12, 4\sqrt{3}, -4\sqrt{3}$.

417

Page 33.   Art. 17

1. $x - y + 1 = 0.$ **2.** $2x - y + 11 = 0.$
3. $2x + y - 8 = 0.$ **4.** $x + 3y + 7 = 0.$
5. $4x - 5y + 29 = 0.$ **6.** $x - y + 1 = 0.$
7. $3x + \sqrt{3}y + \sqrt{3} + 6 = 0.$ **8.** $x - \sqrt{3}y - 2\sqrt{3} - 4 = 0.$
9. $4, -\frac{1}{4}.$ **10.** $2, 2x - y + 1 = 0, x + 2y - 7 = 0.$
11. $12x - y - 13 = 0, x + 12y - 134 = 0.$

Pages 41, 42.   Art. 26

1. $6x.$ **2.** $20x^3.$ **3.** $\frac{28}{3}x^{\frac{2}{3}}.$ **4.** $\frac{2}{3}ax^{-\frac{1}{3}}.$
5. $\frac{9}{16}x^{-\frac{1}{4}}.$ **6.** $2x^{-\frac{1}{2}}.$ **7.** $x^{-\frac{2}{3}}.$ **8.** $\frac{3}{5}x^{-\frac{2}{5}}.$
9. $-2x^{-\frac{5}{3}}.$ **10.** $-\frac{8}{3}x^{-\frac{1}{3}}.$ **11.** $-\frac{5}{2}\frac{1}{\sqrt{x}}.$ **12.** $\frac{5}{8}x^{-\frac{1}{8}}.$
13. $gt.$ **14.** $\frac{12}{5}t^{-\frac{2}{5}}.$ **15.** $\frac{3}{4}\sqrt[4]{t}.$ **16.** $4x^3 + 6x.$
17. $6x - 2.$ **18.** $3x^2 - \frac{3}{2}\sqrt{x} + 3.$ **19.** $\frac{3}{2}\sqrt{x} + \frac{1}{2}x^{-\frac{2}{3}}.$
20. $\frac{5}{2}x^{\frac{3}{2}} + 9x^{-4}.$ **21.** $6(2x + 1)^2.$ **22.** $24x(3x^2 + 2)^3 - 2.$
23. $\dfrac{1}{\sqrt{2x + 3}} - 3.$ **24.** $\dfrac{4x - 7}{2\sqrt{2x^2 - 7x}}.$ **25.** $\dfrac{2x + 7}{3\sqrt[3]{(x^2 + 7x - 2)^2}}.$
26. $-\dfrac{2}{x^3}.$ **27.** $-\dfrac{3}{x^4}.$ **28.** $-\dfrac{3}{x^3}.$ **29.** $-\dfrac{2}{(x + 1)^2}.$
30. $-\dfrac{1}{2\sqrt{(x + 1)^3}}.$ **31.** $-\dfrac{20x}{(x^2 - 1)^3}.$ **32.** $\dfrac{2}{(x + 1)^2}.$
33. $-\dfrac{5}{(x - 3)^2}.$ **34.** $\dfrac{1 - x^2}{(x^2 + 1)^2}.$ **35.** $21x^6 - 24x^5 + 12x^3.$
36. $\dfrac{1}{2\sqrt{x + 1}} - \dfrac{1}{2\sqrt{x - 1}}.$ **37.** $\dfrac{9x^2 + 14x - 3}{2\sqrt{3x^3 + 7x^2 - 3x + 2}}.$
38. $\dfrac{2ax + b}{2\sqrt{ax^2 + bx + c}} - \dfrac{1}{2\sqrt{x + d}}.$ **39.** $\dfrac{4x^4 + 10x}{\sqrt[3]{x^3 + 5}}.$
40. $-\dfrac{2x}{(x - 1)^3}.$ **41.** $\dfrac{1}{(x + 1)\sqrt{x^2 - 1}}.$ **42.** $-\dfrac{a^2}{\sqrt{(x^2 - a^2)^3}}.$
43. $\frac{1}{2}(t + 1)^{-\frac{1}{2}} + \frac{2}{3}(2t - 3)^{-\frac{2}{3}}.$ **44.** $\frac{1}{2}t^{-\frac{1}{2}} - t^{-\frac{3}{2}} + 12t^3.$
45. $5x^4 - 3x^2 + 2x - 2.$
46. $(x + a)^{n-1}(x - b)^{m-1}[x(m + n) + am - bn].$
47. $(x + 1)^4(2x - 1)^2(16x + 1).$
48. $\dfrac{2 - 4x}{(x - 1)^3}.$ **49.** $\dfrac{nt^{n-1}}{(1 + t)^{n+1}}$ **50.** $\dfrac{2t}{(t^2 + 1)\sqrt{t^4 - 1}}.$
51. $0, 3, 12.$ **52.** $0, 3, 12; 0, 3, 12.$
53. $1:4, 1:8, 1:16.$

54. $x - y - 6 = 0$, $x + y + 6 = 0$, $29x - y - 38 = 0$,
$$x + 29y - 582 = 0.$$

55. At point whose abscissas are $\dfrac{-4 \pm \sqrt{13}}{3}$.

56. $y - y_1 = \dfrac{x_1{}^2 - 1}{x_1{}^2} (x - x_1)$, $y - y_1 = \dfrac{x_1{}^2}{1 - x_1{}^2} (x - x_1)$.

57. $(-1, -6)$, $7x + y + 13 = 0$. **58.** 1.0025025.

Pages 44, 45. Art. 27

1. $-\dfrac{x^2}{y^2}$. **2.** $\dfrac{3x^2 + 1}{3y^2 + 1}$. **3.** $-\dfrac{b^2x}{a^2y}$.

4. $-\dfrac{p}{v}$, $-\dfrac{v}{p}$. **5.** $\dfrac{8xy^2 - 4x^3}{3y^2 - 8x^2y}$, $\dfrac{3y^2 - 8x^2y}{8xy^2 - 4x^3}$.

6. $-\sqrt[3]{\dfrac{y}{x}}$, $-\sqrt[3]{\dfrac{x}{y}}$. **7.** $-\sqrt{\dfrac{x}{y}}$. **8.** $-\dfrac{x + \sqrt{x^2 - y^2}}{y}$.

9. $\dfrac{av - 2ab - pv^3}{v^3(v - b)}$, $\dfrac{v^3(v - b)}{av - 2ab - pv^3}$.

10. $-\tfrac{2}{21}\sqrt{21}$, $\tfrac{2}{21}\sqrt{21}$. **12.** $3x + 4y - 25 = 0$, $4x - 3y = 0$.

13. $x - 6y + 17 = 0$, $6x + y - 9 = 0$.

14. $8x + 5\sqrt{5}y - 36 = 0$, $25x - 8\sqrt{5}y - 18 = 0$.

15. $x\sqrt{y_1} + y\sqrt{x_1} - \sqrt{ax_1y_1} = 0$,
$$x\sqrt{x_1} - y\sqrt{y_1} - x_1\sqrt{x_1} + y_1\sqrt{y_1} = 0.$$

Page 48. Art. 30

1. 5, −3. **2.** 0, 0. **3.** ±5, ±5. **4.** ±4, ±8.

5. $\tfrac{1}{2}(2 \pm \sqrt{3})$, 1. **6.** 0, 0. **7.** 0, 2; 0. **8.** −2, 1, 3; 6.

9. No finite intercepts.

10. $\pm n\pi$, where $n = 0, 1, 2, 3, \cdots$; 0.

11. $\pm(2n + 1)\tfrac{1}{2}\pi$, 1. **12.** 0, $\pm n\pi$.

Page 49. Art. 31

1. All have centers of symmetry.

2. 4, 2, infinite, 0, 6.

3. $(2, -4)$, $(-2, -5)$, $(-4, 2)$, $(6, 8)$, $(x, -y)$;
$(-2, 4)$, $(2, 5)$, $(4, -2)$, $(-6, -8)$, $(-x, y)$;
$(-2, -4)$, $(2, -5)$, $(4, 2)$, $(-6, 8)$, $(-x, -y)$.

Page 50.   Art. 32

1. No symmetry.   **2.** x-axis, y-axis, origin.
3. x-axis, y-axis, origin.   **4.** x-axis, y-axis, or'gin.
5. x-axis.   **6.** Origin.   **7.** y-axis.
8. x-axis, y-axis, origin.   **9.** None.   **10.** Origin.
11. x-axis.   **12.** x-axis, y-axis, origin.
13. None.   **14.** Origin.

Page 58.   Art. 37

3. In 2nd and 4th quadrants, 1st and 3rd quadrants, 2nd and 4th quadrants, 1st and 3rd quadrants.   When $x = 0$.

4. Rising for all values of x.

5. Rising for $x > -2$, falling for $x < -2$.

6. Rising for $x > 0$, falling for no values of x.

7. Rising for $x > 0$, falling for $x < 0$.

8. Rising for all values of x except $x = 0$, falling for no values of x.

9. Rising for no values of x, falling for all values of x except $x = 0$.

10. Rising for $x > \sqrt{3}$ and $x < -\sqrt{3}$,

falling for $-\sqrt{3} < x < \sqrt{3}$.

11. Rising for $x < \frac{1}{3}(1 - \sqrt{7})$ and $x > \frac{1}{3}(1 + \sqrt{7})$, falling for $\frac{1}{3}(1 - \sqrt{7}) < x < \frac{1}{3}(1 + \sqrt{7})$.

12. Rising for $x > 1$ and $x < \frac{1}{3}$, falling for $\frac{1}{3} < x < 1$.

13. Rising for $-1 < x < 1$, falling for $x < -1$ and $x > 1$.

14. Rising for $-1 < x < 1$, falling for $x < -1$ and $x > 1$.

15. Rising for $x > 2$ and $x < -1$, falling for $-1 < x < 2$.

16. Rising for $x > -2$, falling for $x < -2$.

17. Rising for $x > 1$ and $-1 < x < 0$, falling for $x < -1$ and $0 < x < 1$.

18. 278, 19, 3, -2.   **19.** $\dfrac{2 \pm \sqrt{22}}{3}$, for no values.

Page 61.   Art. 38

1. Min. at $(0, 0)$.   **2.** Min. at $(2, 1)$.
3. Max. at $(3, 13)$.   **4.** Max. at $(0, 2)$, Min. at $(0, -2)$.
5. Max. at $x = \frac{2}{3}(1 - \sqrt{13})$, Min. at $x = \frac{2}{3}(1 + \sqrt{13})$.
6. Min. at $(16, -16)$.
7. Max. at $(0, 36)$, Min. at $(4\frac{2}{3}, -14\frac{22}{27})$.   **8.** Min. at $(3, -27)$
9. $(4\frac{1}{2}, 4\frac{1}{16})$.   **10.** $\dfrac{v^2 \sin^2 \alpha}{2g}$, $\dfrac{v^2 \sin 2\alpha}{g}$.

Pages 63, 64. Art. 39

1. Upward for $x > 0$, downward for $x < 0$, inflection (0, 0)
2. Upward for all values of x.
3. Upward for $x > 0$, downward for $x < 0$, inflection (0, 0).
4. Upward for $x < 0$, downward for $x > 0$, inflection (0, 0).
5. Upward for $x < -1$ and $x > 1$, downward for $-1 < x < 1$, inflection $(-1, -5)$ and $(1, -5)$.
6. Upward for $x > 1$, downward for $x < 1$, inflection (1, 6).
7. Upward for $x < 0$ and $x > \frac{2}{3}$, downward for $0 < x < \frac{2}{3}$, inflection $(0, -1)$ and $(\frac{2}{3}, -1\frac{16}{27})$.
8. Upward for $x > \frac{4}{3}$, downward for $x < \frac{4}{3}$, inflection $(\frac{4}{3}, -\frac{11}{27})$.
9. Upward for $x < -\frac{1}{3}\sqrt{3}$ and $x > \frac{1}{3}\sqrt{3}$, downward for $-\frac{1}{3}\sqrt{3} < x < \frac{1}{3}\sqrt{3}$, inflection $(-\frac{1}{3}\sqrt{3}, 39\frac{4}{9})$ and $(\frac{1}{3}\sqrt{3}, 39\frac{4}{9})$.
10. Upward for $x < \frac{1}{3}(4 - \sqrt{19})$ and $x > \frac{1}{3}(4 + \sqrt{19})$, downward for $\frac{1}{3}(4 - \sqrt{19}) < x < \frac{1}{3}(4 + \sqrt{19})$, inflection at $x = \frac{1}{3}(4 \pm \sqrt{19})$.
11. -2, Max. at $x = 1 - \frac{1}{3}\sqrt{6}$, Min. at $x = 1 + \frac{1}{3}\sqrt{6}$.
12. 0 and 2, 20 in. a sec.   **13.** None, 1, 2.

Page 68. Art. 41

1. Min. at (1, 4).   **2.** No Max. nor Min. point.
3. No Max. nor Min. point.   **4.** No cusp Max. nor Min. point.
5. Max. at $(0, a)$, Min. at $(0, -a)$.

Pages 75–81. Art. 45

1. 25 sq. in.   **2.** $640   **3.** 2 and 3.

4. 3 in.   **5.** $3\frac{1}{3}$ in.   **6.** Dia. = Alt. = $\sqrt{\dfrac{231}{\pi}}$ = 4.190 in.

7. Edge of bottom = 6.96 ft., height = 3.48 ft.

9. $u = v = \frac{1}{2}c$.   **10.** $\dfrac{mq}{np} = \dfrac{v^n}{u^m}$.

12. Side of cross section = 1 ft., length = 2 ft., vol. = 2 cu. ft.
13. 2.887 mi. from P. **14.** Breadth = $\frac{2}{3}a\sqrt{3}$, depth = $\frac{2}{3}a\sqrt{6}$.
16. Breadth = a, depth = $a\sqrt{3}$.   **18.** $\frac{3}{4}n$.   **19.** $\frac{2}{3}n$.
20. $25\sqrt{2}$ ft.   **21.** $\frac{1}{2}a\sqrt{2}$.
22. 9 mi. an hr., $\frac{3}{2}a$ mi. an hr.
23. 12.6 mi. an hr., $1190.55, $1250, $1229.17.
24. 24.49 ft.   **25.** 16.97 ft.   **26.** $7\frac{1}{2}$ amperes.
30. 225 ft. in soft rock, 125 ft. in hard rock, $2600.

Pages 88, 89.   Art. 51

1. 60 mi., 1 mi., 88 ft.   **2.** 0.2454 cu. ft., 14.726 cu. ft.

7. −0.15, 0.25.   **8.** −0.0943, 0.0943.   **9.** $(6x + 2)dx$.

10. $(3x^2 + 4)dx$.   **11.** $(4x^3 − 9x^2 + 4x)dx$.

12. $\dfrac{9x\,dx}{16y}$.   **13.** $\dfrac{x\,dx}{\sqrt{x^2 + 4}}$.   **14.** $-\sqrt[3]{\dfrac{y}{x}}\,dx$.

15. $-\sqrt{\dfrac{y}{x}}\,dx$.   **16.** $-\dfrac{x\,dx}{(x^2 + 5)^{\frac{3}{2}}}$.   **17.** $gt\,dt$, 64.

Pages 96–100.   Art. 56

1. 12t ft. per sec., 12 ft. per sec., 60 ft. per sec., 120 ft. per sec.

2. 104 ft. per sec., 32 ft. per sec.²   **3.** $3\frac{1}{8}$.

4. 2000 ft. per sec., 62,500 ft., 1680 ft. per sec.

5. 0.7800.   **6.** 9.142 mi. per hr., 6.997 mi. per hr.

7. 0.499 Deg. per sec., 0.498 Deg. per sec.   **8.** −27.82 in. per sec.

9. 0 ft. per sec., 2.49 ft. per sec., $5\frac{1}{3}$ ft. per sec.

10. $\dfrac{k^2 a^{\frac{2}{3}}}{3\sqrt[3]{x^4 y}}$.   **11.** Decreasing 2.256 lb. per sec.

13. $\frac{1}{2}\pi$ sq. in. per min.   **14.** 100π sq. ft. per sec.

15. 0.0013392 cu. in. per Deg.   **16.** $2\sqrt{3}$ ft. per min.

17. 67.42 ft. per sec., 95.34 ft. per sec.   **19.** 4 mi. per hr.

20. 4.42 mi. per hr., 57.7 ft.   **21.** 25.98 ft.

22. 60 ft. per sec.   **23.** 4.472 ft. per sec.

24. 1.59 in. per sec.

Pages 105, 106.   Art. 62

25. $y = 2x^2 + C$.   **26.** $y = −x^3 + C$.

27. $y = −5x^2 + C$.   **28.** $y = \frac{1}{150}x^3 + C$.

29. $y = \frac{1}{3}(x^2 − 3)^3 + C$.   **30.** $y = \frac{1}{900}x^9 + C$.

31. $s = −16t^2 + C$.   **32.** $s = \frac{1}{2}at^2 + C$.

33. $s = 0.002t^3 + C$.   **34.** $v = −3t^{-1} + C$.

35. $v = 8t^{\frac{1}{2}} + C$.   **36.** $p = -\dfrac{k}{1.41v^{1.41}} + C$.

37. $y = \frac{4}{3}x^3 + C$.   **38.** $y = \frac{1}{2}(x^2 + 6)^2 + C$.

39. $y = −\frac{1}{2}x^{-2} + C$.   **40.** $y = 0.003x^5 + C$.

41. $s = −2t^{-5} + C$.   **42.** $s = \frac{3}{2}t^{\frac{2}{3}} + C$.

43. $v = 2t^{-2} + C$.   **44.** $v = −\frac{1}{60}t^{0.6} + C$.

45. $p = -\dfrac{2}{1.41v^{1.41}} + C$.   **46.** $y = −0.75x^{-6} + C$.

47. $y = \frac{1}{3}(x^3 + 5)^3 + C$.   **48.** $y = (x^3 + 2x^2)^4 + C$.

Pages 109, 110. Art. 63

1. $x - 2y = 0$.   **2.** $x = \frac{1}{2}t^3$.   **3.** $3x^2 - 2y = 0$.

4. $x^3 - 3y + 2 = 0$.   **5.** $2x^{\frac{3}{2}} - 3y + 12 - 4\sqrt{2} = 0$.

6. $\frac{32}{3}\sqrt{2}$ sq. units.   **7** $\frac{28}{3}\sqrt{6}$ sq. units.

8. 100 sq. units.   **9.** 64 sq. units.   **10.** $20\frac{1}{4}$ sq. units.

11. $25\frac{3}{5}$ sq. units.   **12.** $3\sqrt{2}$ sq. units.

Pages 113–116. Art. 66

1. $\frac{1}{20}(4 + 5x^2)^2 + C$.   **2.** $\frac{1}{2}x^6 - \frac{8}{5}x^5 + C$.

3. $\frac{6}{5}t^5 - \frac{5}{4}t^4 + t^3 + C$.   **4.** $\frac{1}{3}x^3 - x + C$.

5. $\frac{1}{15}(x^3 + 1)^{\frac{5}{2}} + C$.   **6.** $\frac{4}{3}x^{\frac{3}{2}} - 6x^{\frac{1}{2}} + C$.

7. $\frac{1}{5}x^5 + \frac{2}{3}x^3 + x + C$.   **8.** $\frac{1}{6}(x^2 + 1)^3 + C$.

9. $\frac{2}{3}x^{\frac{3}{2}} + \frac{6}{5}x^{\frac{5}{3}} + C$.   **10.** $\frac{1}{2}x^2 + \frac{24}{13}x^{\frac{13}{6}} + \frac{10}{7}x^{\frac{7}{5}} + C$.

11. $\frac{2}{7}x^{\frac{7}{2}} + \frac{2}{3}a^2x^{\frac{3}{2}} + C$.   **12.** $\frac{3}{4}a^2x^{\frac{4}{3}} - \frac{3}{10}x^{\frac{10}{3}} + C$.

13. $\frac{1}{4}(x^2 + 3x)^4 + C$.   **14.** $\frac{1}{32}(x^4 + 4x)^8 + C$.

15. $\frac{8}{3}(x^2 + 3x + 2)^{\frac{3}{2}} + C$.   **16.** $\frac{2}{3}(ax^2 + bx + o)^{\frac{3}{2}} + C$.

17. $\frac{3}{5}x^{\frac{5}{3}} + \frac{1}{4}ax^{-4} + C$.   **18.** $2\sqrt{x + 1} + C$.

19. $-\sqrt{1 - 2t} + C$.   **20.** $\dfrac{1}{2x(x - 2)} + C$.

21. $y = -\frac{1}{8}(1 - x^2)^4 + C$.   **22.** $y = \frac{2}{9}(x^3 - 2)^3 + C$.

23. $y = \frac{1}{8}x^8(2x + 1)^4 + C$.   **24.** $v = \frac{3}{2}t^4 + \dfrac{3}{t} + C$.

25. $y = 0.02x^3 - 0.01x^4 + C$.   **26.** $y = \dfrac{1}{8(9 - 4x^2)} + C$.

27. $y = c^{\frac{3}{2}}x - 2cx^{\frac{3}{2}} + \frac{3}{2}c^{\frac{1}{2}}x^2 - \frac{2}{5}x^{\frac{5}{2}} + C$.

28. $s = \frac{2}{15}\sqrt{5t^3 + 7} + C$.   **29.** $1\frac{1}{3}$ sq. units.

30. $2\frac{2}{3}$ sq. units.   **31.** $\frac{256}{5}\sqrt{2}$ sq. units.

32. 128.   **33.** 336 ft.   **34.** 1104 ft.

36. $s = \frac{1}{24}t^3$, $2\frac{2}{3}$ ft.   **37.** 12.59 sec., 2.38 sec., 0.70 sec.

38. 50.95.   **39.** $kx^2 + 2kx - 2y - 3k + 8 = 0$.

40. 1832 ft. per sec.   **41.** 309.4, 108 sec.

42. 7.99 min.

Pages 124–127. Art. 71

1. $3\cos 3x$.   **2.** $-6\sin 6x$.   **3.** $\cos^2 x - \sin^2 x$

4. $-5\cos^4 x \sin x$.   **5.** $n\sin^{n-1} x \cos x$.

6. $2\sin x \cos^2 x - \sin^3 x$.   **7.** $2\cos 3x \cos 2x - 3\sin 2x \sin 3x$.

8. $2 \cos 3x \sin x \cos x - 3 \sin^2 x \sin 3x$.

9. $\frac{1}{2} \cos 5x \cos \frac{1}{2}x - 5 \sin \frac{1}{2}x \sin 5x$.

10. $\dfrac{3 \cos 3x}{2\sqrt{\sin 3x}}$.   **11.** $-2a \cos \theta \sin \theta$.   **12.** $\dfrac{\sin \theta}{2\sqrt{1 - \cos \theta}}$.

13. $\sec^2 x$.   **14.** $2 \sin x \sec^3 x$.   **15.** $-\csc^2 x$.

16. $\dfrac{2 \sin x}{(1 + \cos x)^2}$.   **17.** $a(1 - \cos \theta)$.   **18.** $x \cos x + \sin x$.

19. $x(x \cos x + 2 \sin x)$.   **20.** $x^2(3 \cos x - x \sin x)$.

21. $2(x + 1) \cos (x^2 + 2x - 3)$.   **22.** $(3 - 4x) \sin (2x^2 - 3x)$.

23. $2x \sin 2(x^2 - 3)$.   **24.** $\frac{4}{3} \sin^3 x \cos x + 6x$.

25. $\sin^2 x \cos x(3 \cos^2 x - 2 \sin^2 x)$.   **26.** $\dfrac{\sin 2x(1 - 3 \cos^2 x)}{\sqrt{\cos 2x}}$.

27. $2a(\cos 2\theta - \sin 2\theta)$.   **28.** $3 \cos 3x - 12 \sin^2 x \cos x$.

29. $\tan \theta \sec \theta(1 - 2 \sin \theta \cos^2 \theta - \sin \theta)$.

30. $\frac{1}{2} \tan \theta(3 \cos^2 \theta + 1)\sqrt{\sec \theta}$ **31.** $\dfrac{1}{1 + \cos x}$.

32. $a(2 \cos \theta - \theta \sin \theta)$.   **33.** $-\cos 3x + C$.

34. $\sin 2x + C$.   **35.** $-\frac{1}{2} \cos 2x + C$.   **36** $\frac{1}{4} \sin 4x + C$.

37. $\sin(2x + 1) + C$.   **38.** $-\frac{1}{3} \cos(3x + 2) + C$

39. $-\frac{1}{5} \cos(5x - 16) + C$.   **40.** $\frac{1}{2} \sin^2 x + C$.

41. $-\frac{1}{3} \cos^3 x + C$. **42.** $\dfrac{\sin^{n+1} x}{n + 1} + C$.   **43.** $-\dfrac{\cos^{n+1} x}{n + 1} + C$.

44. $\frac{1}{4} \sin^4(x + 2) + C$.   **45.** $-\frac{1}{6} \cos^3(2x - 1) + C$.

46. $\frac{1}{4} \sin^4 x - \frac{1}{3} \sin^3 x + C$.   **47.** $\dfrac{\sin \theta}{1 - \cos \theta} = \cot \frac{1}{2}\theta$.

48. 2 sq. units.   **49.** $\frac{1}{2}\sqrt{2}$, -0.4161.

50. 1, 0, indeterminate.

51. Max. at $x = (4n + 1)\frac{1}{2}\pi$, Min. at $x = (4n + 3)\frac{1}{2}\pi$, inflection at $x = n\pi$.

52. $y = \sin x$.   **53.** $45°$, 53.3 mi.

55. $\rho = 3a$, $\theta = 120°$.

Pages 130, 131.   Art. 73

1. $2 \sec^2 2x$.   **2.** $2 \sec^2 x \tan x$.   **3.** $-3 \csc 3x \cot 3x$.

4. $15 \tan^2 5x \sec^2 5x$.   **5.** $-mnq \cot^{n-1} qx \csc^2 qx$.

6. $\dfrac{3}{1 - \sin 3\theta}$.   **7.** $\tan^4 \theta$.   **8.** $\frac{1}{2} \tan x(3 \cos^2 x + 1)\sqrt{\sec x}$.

9. $\sec 2x(2 \tan x \tan 2x + \sec^2 x)$.   **10.** $8 \sec^5 x - 3 \sec x$.

11. $\dfrac{8 \sec^2 x}{(\tan x + 3)^2}$.   **12.** $\dfrac{3 \sec 3x(\tan 3x - 1)}{(\tan 3x + 1)^2}$.

13. $\dfrac{1}{\sqrt{a^2 - x^2}}$.

14. $-\dfrac{1}{\sqrt{a^2 - x^2}}$.

15. $\dfrac{\sin x}{\sqrt{1 - x^2}} + \cos x \sin^{-1} x$.

16. $\dfrac{1}{1 + x^2}$.

17. $\dfrac{1}{\sqrt{a^2 - x^2}}$.

18. $-\dfrac{2x + 2}{(x^2 + 2x)\sqrt{(x^2 + 2x)^2 - 1}}$.

19. $\dfrac{3a}{a^2 + x^2}$.

20. $\sqrt{a^2 - x^2}$.

21. $\frac{1}{2}$.

22. $\dfrac{\cos x + \sin x}{\sqrt{1 + \sin 2x}}$.

23. $\dfrac{2}{1 + x^2}$.

24. $-\sqrt{\dfrac{x}{2a - x}}$.

29. $-y \cot x$.

30. $\dfrac{y + 2x + 2x^3}{(1 + x^2)(2y - \tan^{-1} x)}$.

31. $\dfrac{y \cos x + \cos y - y}{x \sin y - \sin x + x}$.

32. $\dfrac{y(1 - x^2 - y^2)}{x(1 + x^2 + y^2)}$.

33. $1 + 2 \csc(x - y)$.

34. $\dfrac{\sin(x - y) + y \cos x}{\sin(x - y) - \sin x}$.

35. $-2 \sin 2x,\ -4 \cos 2x$.

Pages 139–141. Art. 80

1. $\dfrac{2}{x}$.

2. $\dfrac{3}{x}$.

3. $\dfrac{n}{x}$.

4. $\dfrac{2x + 3}{x^2 + 3x}$.

5. $\dfrac{6x^2 + 1}{2x^3 + x}$.

6. $\dfrac{3x^2 + 7}{x^3 + 7x}$.

7. $-\dfrac{1}{x}$.

8. $-\dfrac{3x + 2}{3x^2 + x}$.

9. $\dfrac{1}{x^2 - 1}$.

10. $\dfrac{1}{\sqrt{x^2 - a^2}}$.

11. $\cot x$.

12. $\tan x$.

13. $\sec x$.

14. $\dfrac{4x}{\sin 2(x^2 + a^2)}$.

15. $(2x + 3) \cot(x^2 + 3x)$.

16. $\dfrac{1}{x \log x}$.

17. $\dfrac{1}{2t(1 - t)}$.

18. $\dfrac{2x(7 + x^2)}{1 - x^4}$.

19. $\dfrac{8}{3 + 5 \sin 2x}$.

20. $\sec ax$.

21. $M \cdot \dfrac{2}{x}$.

22. $-\dfrac{2M}{x}$.

23. $M \cdot \dfrac{3}{1 + 3x}$.

24. $M \cdot \dfrac{1 - t^2}{t^3 + t}$.

25. $M \cdot \dfrac{2 \log_{10} x}{x}$.

26. $\dfrac{3 \log_b e}{x}$.

27. $M \cot x$.

28. $-M \cdot \dfrac{2x^2 + 10x + 25}{(2x + 5)(x^2 + 5x)}$.

29. $2e^{2x}$.

30. $6xe^{3x^2 + 4}$.

31. $2a^{2x} \log a$.

32. $2 \log 10 \cdot 10^{2x + 3}$

33. $-\dfrac{xe^{\sqrt{1-x^2}}}{\sqrt{1-x^2}}.$

34. $\sec^2 x \cdot a^{\tan x} \log a.$

35. $-bae^{-at}.$

36. $-\dfrac{RI}{L} e^{-\frac{Rt}{L}}.$

37. $e^{x+e^x}.$

38. $\frac{1}{2}(e^x - e^{-x}).$

39. $e^x\left(\log x + \dfrac{1}{x}\right).$

40. $xe^{3x}(3x + 2).$

41. $x^x(1 + \log x).$

42. $\dfrac{1}{x}\sqrt[x]{\sin x}\left(\cot x - \dfrac{1}{x}\log \sin x\right).$

43. $e^x(\sin x + \cos x).$

44. $e^{-x}(\cos x - \sin x).$

45. $10^{2x+3}(1 + 2x \log 10).$

46. $\dfrac{1 - 2x - x^2}{1 - x^2}.$

47. $-\frac{1}{3}e^{-\frac{1}{3}t}(6 \sin 2t + \cos 2t).$

48. $e^{-x^2}(3 - 4x - 6x^2).$

49. $2(x^2 + 1)^{2x+3}\left[\dfrac{2x^2 + 3x}{x^2 + 1} + \log(x^2 + 1)\right].$

50. $2x(1 + 2 \log x).$

51. $x^{\sin x}\left(\dfrac{\sin x}{x} + \cos x \log x\right).$

52. $\csc x.$ **53.** $-\dfrac{2 \sin x}{e^x}.$ **54.** $e^x(x^2 + 2x + bx + b + c).$

55. $-\dfrac{2xe^{-x^2}(2 + x^2)}{(1 + x^2)^2}.$

56. $e^x\left(\dfrac{1}{\sqrt{1-x^2}} + \sin^{-1} x\right).$

57. $-\dfrac{2}{e^x + e^{-x}}.$ **58.** $\dfrac{2}{e^x + e^{-x}}.$ **59.** $5^x x^4(x \log 5 + 5)$

60. $\sec^2 x \cdot a^{\tan x \sec^2 x} \log a(3 \tan^2 x + 1).$ **61.** $-\tan y.$

62. $\dfrac{x + y - 1}{x + y + 1}.$ **63.** $\dfrac{e^{x-y} - 1}{e^{x-y} + 1}.$ **64.** $-e^{x-y}.$

65. $\dfrac{am\, x^{m-1}}{e^{ny}(ny + 1)}.$ **66.** $\dfrac{a^2}{x^2} - \dfrac{y}{x}.$ **67.** $1,\ 7.389.$

68. $0.4343,\ 0.0434.$ **69.** $(1, \log 2),$ or $(1, 0.6931).$

70. No Max. point. Min. point at $x = \frac{1}{2}.$

72. Points of Infl. at $x = \pm\frac{1}{2}\sqrt{2}.$ **73.** $(2e^{\frac{3}{2}}, 3e^{-\frac{3}{2}}).$

74. Max. point at $x = 2.$ Min. point at $x = 0.$

Page 144.   Art. 82

1. $2,\ 2y.$ **2.** $3 \log 10,\ 3y \log 10.$

3. $9x^2 - 2x,\ y(9x^2 - 2x).$

4. $\dfrac{\sin x}{x} + \cos x \log x,\ y\left(\dfrac{\sin x}{x} + \cos x \log x\right).$

5. $\dfrac{n}{x} + \log n,\ y\left(\dfrac{n}{x} + \log n\right).$

6. $\dfrac{13x + 19}{3(x + 1)(2x + 5)}, \dfrac{y(13x + 19)}{3(x + 1)(2x + 5)}.$

7. $\dfrac{2x}{1 - x^4}, \dfrac{2xy}{1 - x^4}.$

8. $\dfrac{2x(6x^2 - 1)}{3x^2 - 2}, \dfrac{2xy(6x^2 - 1)}{3x^2 - 2}.$

9. $\dfrac{1}{2\sqrt{x}} (2 + \log x), \dfrac{y}{2\sqrt{x}} (2 + \log x).$

10. $\dfrac{2t(2t + 3)}{t^2 + 1} + 2 \log(t^2 + 1), 2s \left[\dfrac{2t^2 + 3t}{t^2 + 1} + \log(t^2 + 1) \right].$

11. $\dfrac{1}{u}\dfrac{du}{dx} + \dfrac{1}{v}\dfrac{dv}{dx}, v\dfrac{du}{dx} + u\dfrac{dv}{dx}.$

12. $\dfrac{1}{u}\dfrac{du}{dx} + \dfrac{1}{v}\dfrac{dv}{dx} + \dfrac{1}{w}\dfrac{dw}{dx}, vw\dfrac{du}{dx} + uw\dfrac{dv}{dx} + uv\dfrac{dw}{dx}.$

13. $\dfrac{y(1 - x)}{x(y - 1)}.$ **14.** $\dfrac{y^2(\log x - 1)}{x^2(\log y - 1)}.$

16. (1) Equal. (2) Opposite in sign. (3) Ratio = $\log_{10} e$.
(4) Ratio = $-\cot^2 x$. **17.** 0.4, 40.

Pages 149–151. Art. 84

1. $\frac{1}{2}e^{2x} + C.$ **2.** $\dfrac{a^{3x}}{3 \log a} + C.$ **3.** $\frac{1}{2}e^{x^2} + C.$

4. $\log(x - 1) + C.$ **5.** $3 \log x + C.$ **6.** $x + \log x + C.$

7. $\log \sin x + C.$ **8.** $\frac{1}{2}x^2 - 2x + \log x + C.$

9. $x - 4e^{-x} + C.$ **10.** $\frac{1}{2}(e^{2x+1} + x^2) + C.$

11. 2.303 sq. units. **12.** 6.693 sq. units.

13. $y = e^{\frac{1}{2}x^2}.$ **15.** $0.8248q_0, 0.9996\ q_0.$ **16.** $N = 100e^{0.3t}.$

17. $L = 10e^{0.00001T}$, 990 degrees. **18.** 0.00265.

19. $s = \dfrac{m}{k} (1 - e^{-kt}).$ **20.** $i = 100e^{-0.02x}.$

21. $p = 30e^{-0.00004h}$, 20.11.

Pages 161, 162. Art. 90

9. First and second. First and third.

10. First and third. First and second. First and fourth.

11. Same as Ex. 9.

12. First and third. First and second. First and fourth.

13. Revolves curve about x-axis.

16. Determine regions from lines $x = \pm a$ and $y = \pm a$ instead of $x = \pm 1$ and $y = \pm 1$.

17. $0.0000082, p = 0.0000082t^{3.439}.$ **18.** $c = 5028, pv^{1.37} = 5028.$

Page 178.   Art. 99

2. 2π.   Curve rising when x is in third and fourth quadrants, and falling when x is in first and second quadrants.

3. π.   **6.** $2\pi, \frac{1}{2}; 2\pi, 1; 2\pi, 2; 2\pi, \frac{3}{2}$.

7. $4\pi, 1; 2\pi, 1; \pi, 1; \frac{4}{3}\pi, 1$.   **8.** 2π.

9. Not periodic.

Pages 184, 185.   Art. 103

1. $-6\sin 2t, 6\cos 2t$.   **2.** $-8\omega \sin \omega t, 8\omega \cos \omega t$.

3. $\frac{3}{2}\cos \frac{1}{2}t, -\frac{1}{4}y$.   **4.** $\frac{4}{3}\cos(\frac{1}{3}t + \frac{1}{4}\pi), -\frac{1}{9}y$.

5. $9\cos 3t - 12\sin 3t, -9y$.

6. $-A\omega \sin \omega t + B\omega \cos \omega t, -\omega^2 x$.

7. In first quadrant, -4π and $4\sqrt{3}\,\pi$ ft. per sec.   In second quadrant, -4π and $-4\sqrt{3}\,\pi$ ft. per sec.

8. $y = 18\sin\frac{1}{4}\pi t$.   **9.** $y = 8\sin(t\cdot120° + 55°), 3, \frac{1}{3}$.

10. (1) 3.34, 0.299; (2) 16, $\frac{1}{16}$.   **12.** $\frac{1}{4}\pi, \frac{1}{2}\pi$, or 1 sec., 2 sec.

13. $\frac{1}{2}\pi$. 0.

Pages 196, 197.   Art. 113

1. $2\sqrt{2}$.   **2.** $\dfrac{(1 + 9x^4)^{\frac{3}{2}}}{6x}$, 145.5.

3. $\dfrac{2}{(1 + 4x^2)^{\frac{3}{2}}}, \frac{1}{2}(1 + 4x^2)^{\frac{3}{2}}$.   **4.** $\dfrac{p^2}{(y^2 + p^2)^{\frac{3}{2}}}, \dfrac{(y^2 + p^2)^{\frac{3}{2}}}{p^2}$.

5. $\dfrac{2a^2}{(x^2 + y^2)^{\frac{3}{2}}}, \dfrac{(x^2 + y^2)^{\frac{3}{2}}}{2a^2}$.

6. $\dfrac{2a}{(4a^2x^2 + 4abx + b^2 + 1)^{\frac{3}{2}}}, \dfrac{(4a^2x^2 + 4abx + b^2 + 1)^{\frac{3}{2}}}{2a}$.

7. $\dfrac{1}{y^2}, y^2$.   **8.** $\dfrac{a}{y^2}, \dfrac{y^2}{a}$.

9. $\dfrac{y}{(1 + \cos^2 x)^{\frac{3}{2}}}, \dfrac{(1 + \cos^2 x)^{\frac{3}{2}}}{y}$.

10. $\dfrac{y}{(1 + \sin^2 x)^{\frac{3}{2}}}, \dfrac{(1 + \sin^2 x)^{\frac{3}{2}}}{y}$.   **11.** $\dfrac{1}{a}, a$.

12. $\dfrac{y(\log b)^2}{[1 + y^2(\log b)^2]^{\frac{3}{2}}}, \dfrac{[1 + y^2(\log b)^2]^{\frac{3}{2}}}{y(\log b)^2}$.

13. $\dfrac{a^4b^4}{(b^4x^2 + a^4y^2)^{\frac{3}{2}}}, \dfrac{(b^4x^2 + a^4y^2)^{\frac{3}{2}}}{a^4b^4}.$ **14.** Same as Ex. 13.

15. $1\frac{4}{5}, 8\frac{1}{3}.$ **16.** $R = \infty$ at point of inflection.   **17.** $4a.$

Pages 199, 200.   Art. 114

1. 16.492, 4.123, 16, 1.   **2.** 4.123, 1.031, -4, $-\frac{1}{4}$.

3. 3.29, 3.51, 2.25, 2.56.   **4.** $a, a.$ **5** 4.02, 36.22.

6. $x^2 - y^2 = C.$ **7.** $y^n = Cx.$

Pages 208, 209.   Art. 118

1. $\frac{1}{2}x^2 + 3x + \log(x - 3).$ **2.** $\frac{4}{9}(1 + \frac{3}{2}x)^{\frac{3}{2}}.$ **3.** $-\frac{1}{6}(3 - x^3)^2.$

4. $-\sqrt{4x - x^2}.$ **5.** $\frac{1}{3}x^3 - x^2 + 2x.$ **6.** $\frac{1}{15}\tan^{-1}\frac{3}{5}x.$

7. $\frac{1}{30}\log\dfrac{3x - 5}{3x + 5}.$ **8.** $\frac{1}{3}\sin^{-1}\frac{3}{5}x.$

9. $\frac{1}{3}\log(3x + \sqrt{9x^2} + 25).$ **10.** $\frac{1}{15}\sec^{-1}\frac{3}{5}x.$

11. $\frac{1}{3}\sin^{-1}\dfrac{9x - 5}{5}$ or $\frac{2}{3}\sin^{-1}\sqrt{\dfrac{9x}{10}}.$ **12.** $\frac{1}{9}\sqrt{9x^2 - 25}.$

13. $\frac{1}{18}\log(9x^2 - 25).$ **14.** $\tan^{-1}(x - 2).$

15. $\frac{1}{6}\log\dfrac{x + 5}{x - 1}.$ **16.** $\log(x - 2 + \sqrt{x^2 - 4x + 5}).$

17. $\sin^{-1}\dfrac{x + 2}{3}.$ **18.** $\frac{1}{2}\log(x^2 - 4x + 5).$ **19.** $\sqrt{x^2 - 4x + 5}.$

20. $x + 2\log(x^2 - 4x + 5) - \tan^{-1}(x - 2).$

21. $\dfrac{2}{\sqrt{7}}\tan^{-1}\dfrac{4x + 3}{\sqrt{7}}.$ **22.** $\dfrac{1}{2\sqrt{13}}\log\dfrac{3x + 1 + \sqrt{13}}{3x + 1 - \sqrt{13}}.$

23. $-\log(4 - 2x - 3x^2).$ **24.** $\frac{1}{6}x^2 - \frac{1}{9}x + \frac{1}{27}\log(3x + 1).$

25. $\frac{2}{3}(1 + e^x)^{\frac{3}{2}}.$ **26.** $\frac{1}{4}(\log x)^4.$

27. $\frac{1}{2}(\tan^{-1} x)^2.$ **28.** $\frac{3}{2}\log(x^2 - 9).$

29. $\frac{5}{3}\log(x + 3) + \frac{4}{3}\log(x - 3).$

30. $\frac{3}{2}\log(x^2 + 9) - \frac{1}{3}\tan^{-1}\dfrac{x}{3}$

31. $\sin^{-1}(\tan x).$ **32.** $\frac{1}{3}\log(4 + 3\sin x).$

33. $\frac{1}{3}\log(1 + \tan 3x).$ **34.** $-\frac{1}{15}\log(3\cos 5x - 5).$

35. $-\sqrt{4x - x^2} + 2\sin^{-1}\dfrac{x - 2}{2}.$ **36.** $\frac{1}{2}\log(e^{2x} + 3).$

37. $\frac{1}{2}\log(e^{2u} + 2u).$

1. $\dfrac{a^{5x}}{5 \log a}$

2. $\frac{1}{3}e^{x^3}$.

3. $-e^{\cos x}$.

4. $e^{\tan x}$.

5. $\frac{1}{2}e^{\tan(2x + 4)}$.

6. $\frac{1}{3}e^{\sin 3x}$.

7. $\frac{1}{2}e^{x^2 + 6x - 2}$.

8. $3e^{\tan \frac{1}{3}x}$.

9. $-\frac{1}{3}e^{\cot 3x}$.

10. $\dfrac{a^{bx + c}}{b \log a}$

11. $\frac{1}{2}e^{2x} - 2e^x + x$.   12. $\frac{1}{4}(e^x - 1)^4$.

13. $-\dfrac{1}{2e^{x^2}}$.

14. $2(e^{\frac{x}{2}} - e^{-\frac{x}{2}})$.   15. $2e^{\sqrt{x-2}}$.   16. $u - \log(e^u + 1)$.

1. $-\frac{1}{6}\cos(6x + 2)$.   2. $\frac{1}{2}\sin(2x - 1)$.

3. $-\frac{1}{3}\log\cos 3\theta$.   4. $\frac{1}{5}\log\sin 5\theta$.

5. $\frac{1}{2}\log(\sec 2\theta + \tan 2\theta)$ or $\frac{1}{2}\log\tan(\theta + \frac{1}{4}\pi)$.

6. $\frac{1}{4}\log(\csc 4\theta - \cot 4\theta)$ or $\frac{1}{4}\log\tan 2\theta$.

7. $\frac{1}{2}\tan(2x - 1)$.   8. $-\frac{1}{3}\cot(3x + 2)$.   9. $\frac{1}{3}\sec 3x$.

10. $-\frac{1}{4}\csc 4\theta$.   11. $\tan u - u$.   12. $-\cot u - u$.

13. $6x + 8\cos x - \sin 2x$.   14. $\frac{1}{2}x + \frac{1}{4}\sin 2x$.

15. $\frac{2}{3}(\sin x)^{\frac{3}{2}}$.   16. $\frac{1}{3}\sec^3 x$.   17. $\frac{1}{2}\log(3 + \sin^2 x)$.

18. $-\frac{1}{9}\cos^3 3x$.   19. $-\frac{1}{5}\cot^5 x - \frac{1}{7}\cot^7 x$.

20. $\frac{1}{5}\cos^5 x - \frac{1}{3}\cos^3 x$.   21. $\frac{1}{3}\sin^3 x - \frac{2}{5}\sin^5 x + \frac{1}{7}\sin^7 x$.

22. $\frac{1}{4}\sin^4 x - \frac{1}{6}\sin^6 x$.   23. $-\frac{1}{3}\cos^3 x + \frac{2}{5}\cos^5 x - \frac{1}{7}\cos^7 x$.

24. $-\cos x + \frac{1}{3}\cos^3 x$.   25. $-\cos\theta + \frac{2}{3}\cos^3\theta - \frac{1}{5}\cos^5\theta$.

26. $\sin\theta - \frac{1}{3}\sin^3\theta$.   27. $\frac{2}{3}(\sin x)^{\frac{3}{2}} - \frac{2}{7}(\sin x)^{\frac{7}{2}}$.

28. $2\sqrt{\sin\theta} - \frac{2}{5}(\sin\theta)^{\frac{5}{2}}$.   30. $\frac{3}{8}x - \frac{1}{4}\sin 2x + \frac{1}{32}\sin 4x$.

31. $\frac{3}{8}x + \frac{1}{4}\sin 2x + \frac{1}{32}\sin 4x$.   32. $\frac{1}{16}x - \frac{1}{64}\sin 4x - \frac{1}{48}\sin^3 2x$.

33. $\frac{1}{16}x - \frac{1}{64}\sin 4x + \frac{1}{48}\sin^3 2x$.

1. $-\frac{2}{147}(4 + 7x)\sqrt{2 - 7x}$.   2. $\frac{3}{5}\sqrt[3]{(1 + x)^5} - \frac{3}{2}\sqrt[3]{(1 + x)^2}$.

3. $\frac{3}{5}x^{\frac{5}{3}} - \frac{3}{4}x^{\frac{4}{3}} + x - \frac{3}{2}x^{\frac{2}{3}} + 3x^{\frac{1}{3}} - 3\log(x^{\frac{1}{3}} + 1)$.

4. $4x^{\frac{1}{2}} - 8x^{\frac{1}{4}} + 8\log(x^{\frac{1}{4}} + 1)$.

5. $x + \frac{4}{3}x^{\frac{3}{4}} + 6x^{\frac{1}{2}} - 4x^{\frac{1}{4}} - 6\log(x^{\frac{1}{2}} + 1) + 4\tan^{-1}x^{\frac{1}{4}}$.

6. $\dfrac{1}{\sqrt{b}}\log\dfrac{\sqrt{ax + b} - \sqrt{b}}{\sqrt{ax + b} + \sqrt{b}}$ if $b > 0$, $\dfrac{2}{\sqrt{-b}}\tan^{-1}\sqrt{\dfrac{ax + b}{-b}}$

if $b < 0$.

7. $-\dfrac{1}{\sqrt{7}} \log\left(\dfrac{\sqrt{x^2 - 3x + 7} + \sqrt{7}}{x} - \dfrac{3\sqrt{7}}{14} \right)$

9. $a \log \dfrac{\sqrt{a^2 + x^2} - a}{x} + \sqrt{a^2 + x^2}$

$$= \sqrt{a^2 + x^2} - a \log \dfrac{a + \sqrt{a^2 + x^2}}{x}$$

10. $\dfrac{1}{2a} \cos^{-1} \dfrac{a}{x} - \dfrac{\sqrt{x^2 - a^2}}{2x^2}.$ **11.** $\log(x + \sqrt{x^2 - a^2}).$

12. $\sqrt{x^2 - a^2} - a \cos^{-1} \dfrac{a}{x}.$

13. $\dfrac{1}{a} \log \dfrac{a - \sqrt{a^2 - x^2}}{x} = \dfrac{1}{a} \log \dfrac{x}{a + \sqrt{a^2 - x^2}}.$

14. $\dfrac{1}{a} \log \dfrac{\sqrt{a^2 + x^2} - a}{x} = \dfrac{1}{a} \log \dfrac{x}{a + \sqrt{a^2 + x^2}}.$

15. $x - 3 - 12\sqrt[3]{x - 3} + 24 \tan^{-1} \dfrac{\sqrt[3]{x - 3}}{2}.$ **16.** $2 \tan^{-1} \sqrt{e^x}.$

17. $-2 \log(1 - \sqrt{x}) - 2\sqrt{x}.$ **18.** $2 \log(\sqrt{x + 2} + 1).$

Page 219. Art. 122

1. $e^x(x^2 - 2x + 2).$ **2.** $x(\log x - 1).$ **3.** $\tfrac{1}{2}x^2(\log x - \tfrac{1}{2}).$
4. $\sin x - x \cos x.$ **5.** $x \sin x + \cos x.$
6. $2x \cos x + (x^2 - 2) \sin x.$ **7.** $\tfrac{1}{3}x^3(\log x - \tfrac{1}{3}).$
8. $\tfrac{1}{2}e^x(\sin x - \cos x).$ **9.** $\tfrac{1}{2}e^x(\sin x + \cos x).$
10. $\dfrac{e^{ax}(n \sin nx + a \cos nx)}{a^2 + n^2}.$ **11.** $-\tfrac{1}{17}e^{-x}(\sin 4x + 4 \cos 4x).$
12. $x \sin^{-1} x + \sqrt{1 - x^2}.$ **13.** $x \cos^{-1} x - \sqrt{1 - x^2}.$
14. $x \tan^{-1} x - \tfrac{1}{2} \log(1 + x^2).$ **15.** $\tfrac{1}{4} \sin 2x - \tfrac{1}{2}x \cos 2x.$
16. $\tfrac{1}{4}(\cos 2x + 2x \sin 2x - 2x^2 \cos 2x).$
17. $\tfrac{1}{8}(\cos 2x + 2x \sin 2x - 2x^2 \cos 2x).$
18. $-\tfrac{2}{65}e^{-0.5t}(\sin 4t + 8 \cos 4t).$
19. $\tfrac{5}{829}e^{-0.4t}(25 \sin 5t - 2 \cos 5t).$

Page 223. Art. 125

1. $\log(x - 3) + \dfrac{2}{x - 3}.$ **2.** $\dfrac{9 - 4x}{2(x - 2)^2}.$

3. $\tan^{-1} x - \dfrac{2}{x^2 + 1} - 3 \displaystyle\int \dfrac{dx}{(x^2 + 1)^2}.$

4. $3 \log(x - 1) - \dfrac{1}{x - 1} - \dfrac{1}{(x - 1)^2}.$

5. $\frac{1}{2}\log(x^2 + 1) + \dfrac{1}{2(x^2 + 1)}.$

6. $\frac{1}{2}\log(x^2 + 1) + 2\tan^{-1}x + \dfrac{1}{2(x^2 + 1)}.$

7. $\frac{3}{2}x^2 + 4x + 9\log(x - 1) - \dfrac{7}{x - 1}.$

Page 226.   Art. 126

1. $\log(x - 2) + 2\log(x - 3).$ **2.** $3\log(x + 2) + 2\log(x - 1).$

3. $\frac{1}{2}\log x + \frac{5}{2}\log(x + 2) + \log(x - 2).$

4. $\frac{1}{5}\log(x + 2) + \frac{2}{5}\log(x^2 + 1) - \frac{8}{5}\tan^{-1}x.$

5. $-\frac{1}{2}\log(x + 1) + \frac{1}{4}\log(x^2 + 2x + 3) + \dfrac{1}{\sqrt{2}}\tan^{-1}\dfrac{x + 1}{\sqrt{2}}.$

6. $\frac{1}{2}\log(x + 1) + \frac{1}{6}\log(x - 1) - \frac{1}{3}\log(x^2 + x + 1).$

7. $\frac{1}{2}x^2 + \frac{1}{3}\log(x + 1) - \frac{1}{6}\log(x^2 - x + 1) - \dfrac{1}{\sqrt{3}}\tan^{-1}\dfrac{2x - 1}{\sqrt{3}}.$

Page 229.   Art. 127

1. $-\frac{1}{4}\log(x + 1) - \dfrac{1}{2(x + 1)} + \frac{1}{4}\log(x - 1).$

2. $-\dfrac{1}{3x} - \dfrac{1}{3\sqrt{3}}\tan^{-1}\dfrac{x}{\sqrt{3}}.$

3. $-3\log(x + 1) - \dfrac{1}{x + 1} + \frac{3}{2}\log(x^2 + x + 1) - \dfrac{1}{\sqrt{3}}\tan^{-1}\dfrac{2x + 1}{\sqrt{3}}.$

4. $-\frac{1}{2}\log(x - 1) - \dfrac{1}{4(x - 1)} + \frac{1}{4}\log(x^2 + 1)$

$$+ \frac{1}{4}\tan^{-1}x - \dfrac{1}{4(x^2 + 1)}.$$

Pages 233, 234.   Art. 130

1. $-\frac{2}{135}(2 - 9x)\sqrt{(1 + 3x)^3}.$ **2.** $\frac{1}{16}[3 - 4x - 3\log(3 - 4x)].$

3. $\frac{2}{405}(200 - 60x + 27x^2)\sqrt{3x + 5}.$ **4.** $\dfrac{2}{\sqrt{a}}\tan^{-1}\sqrt{\dfrac{x - a}{a}}.$

5. $-\frac{1}{21}(3x^2 + 6x + 10)\sqrt{(5 - 2x)^3}.$

6. $\frac{1}{4}\left(2x\sqrt{3 - 4x^2} + 3\sin^{-1}\dfrac{2x}{\sqrt{3}}\right).$

7. $\frac{1}{4}\log(2x^2 + 3x + 1) + \frac{1}{4}\log\dfrac{2x + 1}{2x + 2}.$

8. $-\sqrt{1-x^2} - 2 \sin^{-1}\sqrt{\dfrac{1-x}{2}}.$

9. $-\dfrac{5}{3}\sqrt{3-2x^2} - \dfrac{1}{2}\sqrt{2}\,\sin^{-1}\dfrac{2x}{\sqrt{6}}.$

10. $\dfrac{1}{8}x(2x^2-5a^2)\sqrt{x^2-a^2} + \dfrac{3}{8}a^4\log(x+\sqrt{x^2-a^2}).$

11. $\log(2x+5+2\sqrt{x^2+5x+6}).$ **12.** $\sin^{-1}(2x-5).$

13. $-\sqrt{-x^2+6x-5} + 3\sin^{-1}\dfrac{x-3}{2}.$ **14.** $\dfrac{1}{\sqrt{5}}\tan^{-1}\dfrac{3x-2}{\sqrt{5}}.$

15. $\dfrac{1}{4}\log(2x^2+3x+1) + \dfrac{5}{4}\log\dfrac{2x+1}{2x+2}.$

16. $\dfrac{1}{\sqrt{6}}\sin^{-1}\dfrac{5x-12}{x}.$

17. $\dfrac{1}{2}x\sqrt{x^2+a^2} - \dfrac{1}{2}a^2\log(x+\sqrt{x^2+a^2}).$

18. $\dfrac{1}{2}x\sqrt{x^2-a^2} + \dfrac{1}{2}a^2\log(x+\sqrt{x^2-a^2}).$ **19.** $-\dfrac{\sqrt{x^2+a^2}}{a^2x}.$

20. $-\dfrac{\sqrt{a^2-x^2}}{2a^2x^2} + \dfrac{1}{2a^3}\log\dfrac{x}{a+\sqrt{a^2-x^2}}.$

21. $\dfrac{1}{12}\log\dfrac{3x-2}{3x+2}$ or $\dfrac{1}{12}\log\dfrac{2-3x}{2+3x}.$

22. $\dfrac{1}{12}\tan^{-1}\dfrac{4x}{3}.$ **23.** $\dfrac{1}{2a^2}\tan^{-1}\dfrac{x^2}{a^2}.$

24. $\dfrac{1}{6a^3}\log\dfrac{x^3-a^3}{x^3+a^3}$ or $\dfrac{1}{6a^3}\log\dfrac{a^3-x^3}{a^3+x^3}.$

25. $3\sin^{-1}\dfrac{1}{2}x - \dfrac{1}{2}x\sqrt{4-x^2}.$ **26.** $\dfrac{2}{\sqrt{7}}\tan^{-1}\left(\dfrac{1}{\sqrt{7}}\tan\dfrac{1}{2}\theta\right).$

27. $\dfrac{1}{\sqrt{21}}\log\dfrac{2\tan\frac{1}{2}\theta+5-\sqrt{21}}{2\tan\frac{1}{2}\theta+5+\sqrt{21}}.$ **28.** $\tan(\tfrac{1}{4}\pi+\tfrac{1}{2}\theta).$

29. $\dfrac{9}{10}(1+x)^{\frac{2}{3}}(2x-3).$ **30.** $\dfrac{1}{4}\log(x^4+9) + \dfrac{1}{6}\tan^{-1}\tfrac{1}{3}x^2.$

31. $\sec x.$ **32.** $-\dfrac{2}{3}\cos^3 x.$ **33.** $\dfrac{2}{3}\sqrt{\sin^3 x}.$

34. $-\dfrac{1}{6}\sin\theta\cos^5\theta + \dfrac{1}{24}\sin\theta\cos^3\theta + \dfrac{1}{16}\sin\theta\cos\theta + \dfrac{1}{16}\theta.$

35. $\dfrac{2}{45}(\sin\theta)^{\frac{5}{2}}(5\cos^2\theta+4).$ **36.** $-\dfrac{1}{15}\cos^3\theta(3\sin^2\theta+2).$

37. $\dfrac{1}{6}\tan^6\theta.$ **38.** $-\dfrac{1}{3}\cot^3\theta - \dfrac{1}{5}\cot^5\theta.$

39. $-\csc\theta - \sin\theta.$ **40.** $\tan\theta - \cot\theta.$

41. $-e^{-x}(x^2+2x+2).$ **42.** $x\tan x - \dfrac{1}{2}x^2 + \log\cos x.$

43. $\dfrac{1}{3}[x^3\sin^{-1}x + \dfrac{1}{3}(x^2+2)\sqrt{1-x^2}].$

44. $2x\sin 2x - (2x^2-1)\cos 2x.$

45. $\dfrac{5}{52}e^{0.4x}(5\sin 2x + \cos 2x).$

46. $-\frac{1}{34}e^{-3x}(3 \sin 5x + 5 \cos 5x)$.

47. $-\frac{2}{37}e^{-0.5x}(\sin 3x + 6 \cos 3x)$.

48. $-\frac{10}{409}e^{-0.3x}(3 \sin 2x + 20 \cos 2x)$.

49. $-\dfrac{5e^{-0.2t}(\sin \omega t + 5\omega \cos \omega t)}{1 + 25\omega^2}$.

50. $\frac{3}{4}x^4(\log x - \frac{1}{4})$.

Pages 242, 243.   Art. 135

1. $60\frac{2}{3}$.   **2.** $-\frac{1}{2}\sqrt{2}$.   **3.** $38\frac{2}{5}$.   **4.** 2.3026.

5. 0.1115.   **6.** 0.1168.   **7.** 0.4142.   **8.** 0.8591.

9. π.   **10.** 1.792.   **11.** 16.63 sq. units.

12. 12.47 sq. units.   **13.** 2.824 sq. units.   **14.** πr^2.

15. 24π sq. units.   **16.** 12.88 sq. units.   **17.** $10\frac{2}{3}$ sq. units.

18. $18\frac{3}{4}$ sq. units.   **19.** 59 sq. units.   **20.** $5\frac{1}{3}$ sq. units.

Page 245.   Art. 136

1. 5.1416 sq. units.   **2.** 9π sq. units.   **3.** $\frac{3}{2}a^2\pi$.

4. 2π sq. units.   **5.** $\frac{4}{3}a^2\pi^3$.

Pages 249, 250.   Art. 139

1. 14 sq. units, $17\frac{1}{2}$ sq. units, $21\frac{1}{3}$ sq. units, 34.4%, 18%.

2. 35 sq. units.   **3.** 1.954 sq. units.

Pages 255–257.   Art. 144

1. 13.88.   **2.** $14\frac{2}{3}$.   **3.** 12.   **4.** 3 sq. units.

5. 2.8345 sq. units.   **6.** 36 sq. units.   **7.** 9 sq. units.

8. 10.75 sq. units.   **9.** 14.15 sq. units.   **10.** $5\frac{1}{3}$ sq. units.

12. 0.4142 sq. units.   **13.** $16g$.

Page 263.   Art. 146

1. 12π.   **2.** 5.916.   **4.** 58.76 ft., 13.58 ft.   **5.** $6a$.

6. 1,026 ft.

Page 267.   Art. 149

1. $2\pi a$.   **2.** $2\pi a$.

3. $a[\pi\sqrt{4\pi^2 + 1} + \frac{1}{2} \log(2\pi + \sqrt{4\pi^2 + 1})]$ or $21.257a$.

Pages 273, 274.   Art. 152

1. 135.35 sq. ft.   **2.** 223.6 sq. ft.   **3.** 91.34 sq. ft.

4. 400π sq. ft.   **5.** 85.3 sq. units.   **6.** 60.95 sq. units.

7. $\frac{1}{5}^2\pi a^2$.   **8.** 5593.7 sq. ft.

Pages 282, 283.   Art. 155

1. 523.6 cu. units.   **2.** 64π cu. in.   **3.** $\frac{1}{2}\pi^2$ cu. units.

4. 128π cu. units, $\frac{64}{5}\pi$ cu. units.   **5.** $\frac{1}{4}\pi a^3 (e^2 - e^{-2} + 4)$.

6. $\frac{64}{5}\pi$ cu. units.   **7.** $5\pi^2 a^3$.

8. $2\pi^2 a^2 b$.   **9.** $\frac{4}{3}\pi ab^2$.   **10.** 1,876.6 cu. in.

Pages 289, 290.   Art. 157

1. 1,152 cu. in.   **2.** 1,995.3 cu. in.   **3.** 159.6 gal.

4. 173.6 cu. in.   **5.** 565.5 cu. in.   **6.** 9,216 cu. in.

Pages 295, 296.   Art. 160

1. $y,\ x,\ ydx,\ xdy,\ ydx + xdy$.

2. $a \cos(ax + by),\ b \cos(ax + by),\ a \cos(ax + by)dx,$
$b \cos(ax + by)dy,\ (adx + bdy) \cos(ax + by)$.

3. $6x + 4y,\ 4x + 4y$.

4. $3x^2 y^2 - 2y^4 + 6xy^3,\ 2x^3 y - 8xy^3 + 9x^2 y^2$.

5. $e^x \sin y,\ e^x \cos y$.   **6.** $-e^y \sin x,\ e^y \cos x$.

7. $\log y \cdot x^{\log y - 1},\ \dfrac{1}{y} \cdot \log x \cdot x^{\log y}$.   **8.** $\dfrac{e^x}{e^x + e^y},\ \dfrac{e^y}{e^x + e^y}$

Page 299.   Art. 162

1. $\frac{2}{3}\pi rh,\ \frac{1}{3}\pi r^2$.   **2.** $\dfrac{1}{R},\ -\dfrac{E}{R^2}$.

3. $\sec \theta,\ x \sec \theta \tan \theta$.

4. Decreasing 163 lb. per sq. ft. per min.

5. Increasing $1,600\pi$ cu. in. per sec.

Pages 307, 308.   Art. 166

1. $x^2 + z^2 = 32,\ y^2 + z^2 = 27,\ x^2 + y^2 = 20,\ x^2 + y^2 = 36$.

3. $-\frac{4}{11}\sqrt{11},\ -\frac{3}{11}\sqrt{11},\ \frac{6}{11}\sqrt{11}$.   **7.** 1.732.

Page 313.   Art. 167

1. $\frac{1}{3}x^3 + C_1 x + C_2$.   **2.** $\frac{1}{2}C_1 x^2 + C_2 x + C_3$.

3. $e^x + \frac{1}{2}C_1 x^2 + C_2 x + C_3$.   **4.** $\frac{1}{20}x^5 + \frac{1}{6}x^3 + C_1 x + C_2$.

5. 4.   **6.** $x^3 - x - 2y + 4 = 0$.   **7.** $\dfrac{W}{48EI}(3l^2 x^2 - 2x^4)$.

Page 315.   Art. 168

1. 32.   **2.** $\frac{7}{15}$.   **3.** $\frac{3}{4}\pi a^2$.   **4.** $\frac{1}{4}\pi a^2$.

5. 0.   **6.** $\frac{1}{8}(e^8 - 6e^4 + 8e^2 - 3)$.

Page 321.   Art. 170

1. 16π sq. units   2. $\frac{64}{3}\sqrt{2}$ sq. units.   3. 7.135 sq. units.
4. 16 sq. units.   5. $85\frac{1}{3}$ sq. units.   6. 19.635 sq. units.
7. 37.70 sq. units.   8. 62.83 sq. units.   9. 7.55 sq. units.

Page 325.   Art. 171

1. 36π sq. units.   2. 200 sq. units.   3. $2(\pi - 2)a^2$.

Page 328.   Art. 172

1. 2,000 cu. units.   2. $\frac{1}{6}abc$.   3. 234.57 cu. units.   4. $\frac{4}{35}\pi a^3$.

Pages 334, 335.   Art. 175

1. $(2\frac{2}{5}, 0)$.   2. $\left(\dfrac{4r}{3\pi}, 0\right)$.   3. $\left(\dfrac{3a\sqrt{3}}{2\pi}, 0\right)$.
4. $\left(\dfrac{4a}{3\pi}, \dfrac{4b}{3\pi}\right)$.   5. $(\pi a, \frac{5}{6}a)$.   6. $\frac{2}{3}h$.   7. $\frac{3}{4}h$.

Pages 336, 337.   Art. 176

1. $\bar{x} = \bar{y} = 7.766$.
2. On axis $4\frac{1}{4}$ in. from left base of cylinder.
3. $\bar{x} = \frac{7}{8}$, $\bar{y} = 1\frac{7}{8}$.   4. 2.718 in.
5. $3\frac{9}{19}$ in. from larger base.

Page 339.   Art. 177

1. 1,100.7 sq. in., 953.2 cu. in.   2. 6.75 cu. ft.
3. $5\pi^2 a^3$.   4. $288\pi^2$ cu. in.

Pages 344–346.   Art. 180

1. (a) $\frac{1}{12}Mh^2$, (b) $\frac{1}{3}M(b^2 + h^2)$, (c) $\frac{1}{12}M(b^2 + h^2)$.
3. $\frac{1}{36}bh^3$.   4. $\frac{1}{4}\pi ab^3$, $\frac{1}{4}\pi a^3 b$, $\frac{1}{4}\pi ab(a^2 + b^2)$.
6. 19.64.   7. $1,400\pi$.   8. 12.61.
9. (a) $\frac{1}{2}Mr^2$, (b) $\frac{1}{12}M(4h^2 + 3r^2)$.

Page 350.   Art. 182

1. 33,000 lb.   2. 1,125 lb.   3. $136,533\frac{1}{3}$ lb.   4. 93,659 lb.

Page 352.   Art. 183

1. $\dfrac{\pi D^2}{2a}\sqrt{\dfrac{H}{2g}}$.   2. 24 min. 17.2 sec.

Page 358.   Art. 188

1. 25 ft.-lb.   **2.** 20 ft.-lb.   **3.** 50,010 ft.-lb.
4. 38,430 ft.-lb.   **5.** 26,507,000 ft.-lb.
6. 2,912,000π ft.-lb.   **7.** 2,663 ft.-lb.

8. $\displaystyle\int_{v_1}^{v_2}\left(\frac{C}{v-b}-\frac{a}{v^2}\right)dv.$

Pages 368, 369.   Art. 195

1. $x-\dfrac{x^3}{3!}+\dfrac{x^5}{5!}-\dfrac{x^7}{7!}+\cdots,\ 0.47943,\ 0.84147.$

2. $1+x+\dfrac{x^2}{2!}+\dfrac{x^3}{3!}+\dfrac{x^4}{4!}+\cdots,\ 2.71828\ +.$

3. $13+60(x-4)+30(x-4)^2+4(x-4)^3.$

4. $\sin a+(x-a)\cos a-\dfrac{(x-a)^2}{2!}\sin a-\dfrac{(x-a)^3}{3!}\cos a+\cdots$

5. $1+x+\dfrac{x^2}{2!}-\dfrac{3x^4}{4!}-\dfrac{8x^5}{5!}-\cdots.$ **8.** 0.7468.

Pages 374, 375.   Art. 196

1. 0.   **2.** 0.   **3.** 0.   **4.** 3.   **5.** 1.   **6.** 2.

7. 0.   **8.** 1.   **9.** e^2.   **10.** a.   **11.** $e^{\frac{4}{\pi}}$.   **12.** -1.

13. 1.   **14.** $-\frac{1}{2}$.   **15.** e^2.   **16.** a.

INDEX

Numbers refer to pages.